Project
Economy

THE IRWIN SERIES IN MANAGEMENT

Consulting Editor JOHN F. MEE, *Indiana University*

PROJECT
ECONOMY

by EDWIN SCOTT ROSCOE

PROFESSOR OF INDUSTRIAL ENGINEERING
THE PENNSYLVANIA STATE UNIVERSITY

RICHARD D. IRWIN, INC.
HOMEWOOD, ILLINOIS · 1960

First Printing, February, 1961
Second Printing, February, 1963

Library of Congress Catalogue Card No. 61–8017

PRINTED IN THE UNITED STATES OF AMERICA

Preface

MANY persons engaged in the applied sciences are called upon to analyze the economic prospects of their projects. Managers must rely on economic studies that relate to important projects under consideration. In the engineering professions, the analytical procedure is commonly known as *engineering economy*. Many of the principles, however, are applicable to transactions in business and personal affairs, transactions that would not be classed as engineering.

The primary objective of this book is to present the important principles of engineering economy with sufficient exposition and argument to provide thorough understanding. The principles are those of time value of money, investment, required return (interest) on investment, cost, income, profit, financing, and the weighing of intangibles. Techniques for handling typical types of problems are included; but the book does not attempt to cover specialized practices in various fields of engineering and enterprise. The essential contributions of market research, business forecasting, and allied activities are emphasized. Recent developments in operations research are also described, although its advanced mathematical techniques are considered beyond the scope of this book.

This book is designed as a text suitable for a term's study. It is also useful for reference. Although the work is oriented to readers with some background in engineering in general, professional competence in that area is not essential. Proficiency in the practical use of algebra is important. Calculus is useful for a limited number of the problems. The reader should be familiar with the preparation of charts and graphs. The slide rule is a great time saver; and with few exceptions, its accuracy is sufficient for the economy studies.

Most of the practice problems at the ends of the chapters are entirely hypothetical. Problem data are not to be used for practical references because cost factors are too fluid and varied among industries. Many of these problems are extracted or adapted from state professional examinations; and the sources are indicated in parentheses following such problems (e.g., PE Pa.—meaning *pro-*

fessional examination, Pennsylvania). In some problems, situations have been introduced that have not been covered specifically in the text. The objective is to stimulate thinking and application of principles rather than the memorizing of procedures or formulas.

E. S. ROSCOE

THE PENNSYLVANIA STATE UNIVERSITY
November, 1960

Table of Contents

vii

CHAPTER 1

Introduction

PERSONS engaged in the applied sciences or devoted to product or process design, construction, manufacture, and professional services are naturally concerned with the physical aspects of their activities. They may not be so aware of the essential economic factors in the realization of their projects. If they do appreciate economic necessity, they may not understand the techniques of economic appraisal. Economy analysis is the subject of this book.

The realization of any material project depends on three essentials:

1. The project must respond to a human need or desire.
2. It must satisfy the demand.
3. It must be economically justified. (Will it pay?)

The cleverest mouse trap can not be made available to the public unless it can be produced and distributed at a profit. A marvelous development in automation would be impractical without adequate market for its output and a return attractive to investors. A superhighway should be justified by savings to the public in transportation costs. Cost is a factor even in the erection of a beautiful memorial that yields no tangible return. National defense projects compete with alternatives on an economic basis. There are financial limitations in all projects, public or private.

Phases of Project Realization

From inception to successful outcome, the realization of a material project includes three basic types of activity, all of which involve economic factors. These activities are:

1. Initial planning and development.
2. Providing means for execution of plans.
3. Operation.

1

Initial planning starts with preliminary investigation or intensive research, from which prospects for development are derived. Actual invention may be a result; but, in the general case, this stage of the problem is one of decision as to the basic characteristics of the project (or alternatives) that are to be developed. It may be tentatively decided, for example, that a certain type and size of building is to be erected at a certain site. Then follows the completion of plans as to product, process, or structure, including final designs or specifications.

The means for execution include provisions for financing, human organization, and construction or purchase. Upon completion of this phase, the project is ready to operate or perform its service. Operation or utilization of the project is the final phase. This includes activities such as manufacture, distribution, transportation, and public services, or any activity associated with the project's objectives.

The stages mentioned have been classified broadly. All of them involve considerations of cost, returns, and profit or other benefits measurable in money. Economic appraisals are essential criteria for decisions at the various stages leading to project realization. Economy studies may be preliminary or intermediate, and they may apply only to individual details of the program. These preliminary and intermediate appraisals are guides to subsequent actions. More research and changes in the development program may be required. A final over-all appraisal is the economic criterion for completion of the project. Succeeding appraisals may take place during operations to determine whether the program should be continued or changed.

Role of Management

Any project that involves organized effort requires management of some sort to provide impetus, means, and coordination of effort. Management functions include establishing basic objectives, planning, financing, organizing, direction, and control. These activities affect all stages of project realization. They involve costs to be included in economic appraisals. The manager or management group makes the decisions to pursue the project, to change its character, or to abandon it at any stage of its progress. Economic appraisals are essential criteria for these decisions.

Personal Enterprises

This book is concerned principally with enterprises, public or private, that require organized effort and management. It must be recognized, however, that many of the principles to be discussed also apply to the private affairs of individuals. Economic appraisals affect many personal projects—a situation appreciated by anyone who makes and spends or invests money. The purchase and sale of securities and physical properties are examples. These applications to personal affairs will be apparent in subsequent chapters.

ECONOMIC APPRAISAL

Economic Criteria

Economic criteria that are derived from economy studies and that influence management decisions may be classed as *tangible* and *intangible.* Tangibles are factors that can be readily measured in *quantitative* terms, as in money. Intangibles are *qualitative*, not readily measurable in money or similarly exact terms. Although tangible criteria are essential considerations, intangibles influence decisions even in the most advanced types of management. Intangibles include personnel problems, ethical considerations, competitors' reactions, and future risks regarding costs, prices, and market conditions. There are many possible intangibles that contribute to success or failure, depending on the character of the project and the individuals or group concerned.

The objective of most economy studies is to obtain and analyze quantitative data that are significant for decision making. What are the estimated costs and potentials for return and profit? Intangibles are usually considered separately by decision makers; but the person responsible for the economy study may then invite attention to the intangibles. Among the developments in scientific management are techniques for conversion of intangible factors into quantitative values that can be combined with tangibles. If there is a known risk, for example, what is the numerical probability of success or failure, and how does that affect the potential return required to justify the venture? In most of the economy problems with which we shall be concerned, the values of one or more tangible factors are affected by intangible considerations.

Almost all business or professional decisions are choices among alternatives—to act or not to act; to change a program or to leave it as is; to select a definite product or procedure from several feasible proposals; or to decide on details of specifications. The basic problem of the analyst is to obtain data and derive economic criteria that will be most significant for comparison of the alternatives. The early chapters of this book will be devoted to the basic principles of economic evaluation and comparison. In subsequent chapters, these principles of analysis will be applied to several types of practical projects, in addition to those required to demonstrate the principles.

Engineering Economy

Engineering economy (or economics) is a term commonly applied to the techniques of economic analysis relating to engineering projects. As previously stated, studies of this kind are not necessarily restricted to projects associated with engineering. The principles can apply to many problems in business, construction, manufacture, and personal affairs. Engineering economy, however, is not an isolated technical field of study. It is assisted by or makes use of other professional specialties. Let us consider the relationship of several of these specialties to engineering economy.

The *science of economics* is devoted primarily to widespread conditions affecting the acquisition and distribution of wealth. Of particular interest in engineering economy studies are the predictions of economists regarding trends in business, markets, prices, costs, purchasing power, and the like. Such predictions are of vital importance to projects that depend on the future. A long look ahead is required for a public works, a building, a new plant, an important new product, or long-life equipment. Unfortunately, economics is not an exact science, and expert economists frequently differ in their conclusions. Nevertheless, principles of economics and the predictions of experts in that field are essential contributions to engineering economy studies.

Market research is concerned with public needs and demands, competition, distribution, public reactions to product and service offerings, relations between prices, volume, and quality, and similar market conditions. Much of this activity is dependent on principles of economic science and statistical analysis. The conclusions of market research relating to selling prices and volume of output are particularly important in economy studies.

Accounting is the accumulation, recording, and analysis of financial data relating to any public or private enterprise. Simple accounting techniques are mentioned in early recorded history. In enterprises of substantial size, it is now a complex professional specialty. Accounting deals principally with transactions that have taken place. But in computing depreciation, overhead allocations, and budgetary control, accounting involves forecasted events. Certain common accounting practices are followed in engineering economy studies. Economy studies, however, aim to predict future results, including evaluation of intangibles. Its techniques may, on occasion, deviate considerably from accounting procedures.

Operations research is a term that became popular during World War II to cover techniques applied to studies of military strategy and tactics. It now broadly applies to any scientific mathematical investigation of operating problems in business, industry, and government. Actually, operations research is not a new practice. It dates back more than half a century to the pioneering work of Frederick W. Taylor, Frank Gilbreth, and others in the field of industrial engineering. Scientific motion and time study, for example, is a form of operations research.

Operations research often employs principles of engineering economy. Conversely, studies that may be called engineering economic analysis may employ methods of operations research. No exact separation of the two types of activity is necessary. For example, operations research may be applied in a commercial enterprise to analyze economic factors so as to determine the most favorable of several alternatives. In that case, its objectives are exactly the same as the aims of engineering economy study; and the techniques employed may be the same. Operations research is a broad subject, however. Its methods can be used to assist decision making in almost any large organized activity—in military planning, for example. And, its most notable contributions in recent years have dealt with conversion of intangible factors into quantitative criteria.

Some techniques of operations research are relatively new and complex. Specialties in higher mathematics may be required, and electronic computers may be necessary. Among these techniques are procedures known as linear programming, game theory, queueing theory, graphical risk analysis, and communications theory. *Linear programming* is a procedure for determining the most favorable "product mix" (combination of products and schedules) or utilization of materials and facilities. *Game theory* is used to determine the best of alternatives in competitive situations. *Queueing theory* determines the best compromise of waiting time for pending orders and the efficient utilization of men and equipment. *Risk analysis* is concerned with quantitative measures of risk and applies risk probability to selection among alternatives. *Communications theory* deals with facilities and methods of transmitting information that contribute to organized activities. Some of these procedures will be mentioned in succeeding chapters, but exposition of such techniques is beyond the scope of this book. Those interested should refer to the bibliography (Appendix G) and to current literature.

COST, INCOME, AND PROFIT

Profit in the broad sense is any form of compensation including intangible benefits such as status, power, or satisfaction from unselfish efforts. Profit in the financial sense is the surplus of income over total cost of operations—the basic objective of commercial enterprise. Nonprofit organizations, however, must be concerned with cost and income, both of which determine profit in the profit-making enterprise. It may be possible to evaluate intangible benefits or disadvantages in terms of money. For example, how much profit in money would be required to compensate for the unusual effort and worry demanded of a certain project? In the subject of engineering economy, however, we are mostly concerned with tangible cost, income, and profit, although conclusions may be modified by intangible considerations.

Cost

The early chapters of this book are concerned with the characteristics of cost. To the layman, cost is the cash expenditure for a product or service. In the technical sense, cost is broader and more complex than simple expenditure. It can be difficult to measure and predict. Cost is affected by current conditions, age, and time. There are apportionments of cost among products, orders, and activities of an enterprise. Cost is associated with the evaluation of existing properties or assets, in the sense that the owner is deprived of equivalent money that would otherwise be available for other uses. Some intangibles can be rated approximately in terms of money (cost or profit). A specialty of accounting is the determination of cost that can be attributed to individual products, orders, and activities of an enterprise—a practice known as *cost accounting*. Engineering economy is concerned with *prediction* of cost.

Cost may be analyzed in several ways, each of which yields important economic criteria. Cost may be evaluated or classified as to:

1. Time (*time value of money*)—a principle that also applies to items of income and profit.
2. Duration of benefit—
   a) Long term (two or more years), the cost being classified as *capital* or *investment*.
   b) Short term or current, the item being classified as *operating cost*.
3. Internal relationship—
   a) *Direct labor*, labor cost that can be identified directly with an individual product or order.
   b) *Direct material*, material cost that can be identified directly with an individual product or order.
   c) *Overhead* (burden or expense), costs which can not be conveniently classified as direct.
4. Variability with relation to some independent variable among the economic factors (e.g., volume of output, rate of operations, income, or investment)—
   a) Fixed costs, those which do not change with the independent variable.
   b) Variable costs, costs which do change in some manner with said independent variable.

   This variability also applies to investment, income, and profit elements. The independent variable mentioned above is most often the rate of operations of the enterprise or project under consideration.

Predictions of cost, income, and profit are affected by precision of estimates, future uncertainties, risk, and other intangibles that contribute to decisions by management. The following chapter deals with time value of money, a matter of particular importance in many economy studies.

PROBLEMS

1.1.   Make a list of the sciences and professional specialties that may contribute to economy studies in general, omitting those that are peculiar to a particular type of enterprise. Then explain briefly, from your present knowlege, the manner in which each of the items listed may influence the study.

1.2. Assume that one of the following *personal* projects is under consideration. Make a list of all the factors that you would consider in making a decision. Identify by T the items that are tangible as to economy (measurable in dollars), and by I the intangible factors (not measurable in dollars).

a) Purchase of a new home.

b) Purchase of a new automobile if you don't have one now.

c) Purchase of a new automobile to replace an old one.

d) Purchase of a automatic washing machine to replace an old non-automatic machine.

e) Purchase of a new combination refrigerator-freezer to replace an old but usable refrigerator.

f) The selection of a job (from several offers) upon graduation.

1.3. Assume that one of the following industrial projects is under consideration. The project has now advanced to the stage of a concrete proposal, or alternative proposals, that merit economic appraisal before it is decided to proceed further. You are to make an appropriate *economy* study. As the first step in your program, you should make a comprehensive list, in logical sequence, of the various items that you will have to investigate as to economy. At this point, details are unknown so that the minor items must be grouped—"cost of property maintenance," for example.

a) An apartment house.

b) An interurban-highway bridge.

c) A new detergent manufactured for national distribution.

d) A new boiler for a steam plant.

e) A new 10,000 KVA turbogenerator for a power station.

f) A large automobile service station that will include rest and food facilities.

g) A new vacuum cleaner manufactured for national distribution.

h) A new paper-making process to be installed in existing plant.

i) A new textile fabric (required processes are spinning, weaving, dyeing, and finishing, plus minor operations).

j) Any substantial project concerning an industry with which you are familiar.

In making the study, you must consider the history of the project to date and the outcome from ultimate operations to estimate the economic feasibility. Make an outline of your plan for the study as suggested above.

CHAPTER 2

Time Value of Money

THE time value of money is important in the economic analysis of any project that has extended life. The concept applies to public works, business enterprises, and private affairs, and to any property or transaction that can be measured in money.

Time as a factor in value is a basic human concept. A child appreciates it. To him, "the bird in the hand is worth two in the bush." One may wait for an advantage or gain expecting to be compensated for the waiting. A demand for immediate result may involve acceptance of less than would be obtainable at a later date. Consider the following example.

A young man received a legacy from a deceased uncle. The uncle was not confident of his nephew's ability to manage a small fortune at that time, and the will specified that a trust fund be established sufficient to release to the nephew $20,000 at the end of ten years. The young man, a recent college graduate, had a good opportunity to go into business. But he required capital. A prosperous friend offered to lend $14,000, without periodic interest but covered by a note for $20,000 payable in ten years when the legacy became due. The young man's wife commented: "A friend, indeed! He wants to make $6,000 for lending you $14,000." Actually the offer was a generous one. The friend could have done better for himself by investing in industrial bonds, high-grade stock, or a mortgage.

U.S. Savings Bonds are a familiar example. A $100 bond can be purchased for $75. In somewhat less than eight years, it can be redeemed at face value (1960).

The qualitative effect of time on value is apparent to almost anyone. *Quantitative* determination of time value involves some concepts that may be difficult for the layman. And the principles can apply to items of cost, income, and profit.

INTEREST

Return on Investment

Investment means to tie up funds for an extended period in some
kind of project—a savings account, a loan, a machine, or a business.
Investment is capital that is put to work. Burying money in the
ground or in a vault is not investment in a business sense. Capital is
an asset that should not remain idle.

Invested capital is expected to earn a return to compensate for
its deferment of use for other benefits. This is an ancient concept.
Consider the Parable of the Talents in the New Testament (Mat-
thew 25:15–30). The master entrusted three servants with eight
talents—five talents (a large sum) to one, two talents to a second,
and one talent to the third. Upon return from long absence, the
master demanded an accounting. The first two servants proudly
reported that they had doubled the amounts committed to their
charge. They were highly praised for their diligence. The third man
said he knew the master to be a hard and exacting man. Consequently, he buried the money safely and now returned the original
sum intact. This servant was condemned for slothfulness.

Interest is commonly thought of as compensation for a loan. In
the more general sense, as in engineering economy, it is the return or
rate of return on any form of investment. As a rate of return it is
expressed as a percentage or a decimal. This rate applied to the
investment is the return in dollars. The interest rate is sometimes
designated *yield*. Various usages will be mentioned in later chapters.

Interest as a factor in time value of money need not be confined
to actual investment. We can assume a hypothetical investment to
support a future cost, or a similar investment that would be equivalent to future items of income and profit. In short, the concept of
interest applies to the time value of any financial event.

Simple and Compound Interest

Simple interest is the periodic return on a fixed investment at a
fixed rate. The *principal* (the amount on which interest is based)
does not change with time, and the interest earned remains idle or is
consumed for current uses. This happens when the holder of a 4%
$1,000 bond cashes his annual $40 coupons (interest) and does not
invest the proceeds. The same idea could be paralleled in a business

in which profits are withdrawn completely and are currently consumed by those who receive the profits. In these cases, time does not affect the amount of investment. Time is simply a factor in the relationship between fixed investment and periodic earnings.

Compound interest is the situation in which the periodic interest is added to the previous investment, or is otherwise invested, so that the total amount invested increases with time. This takes place in the savings bank account when the depositor does not withdraw interest, and in the trust fund which builds up with accumulated earnings. This condition is paralleled in a business in which profits are retained as capital for future operations and expansion.

The compounding of interest is assumed in all conventional time-value-of-money calculations. It is the basis for the formulas to be discussed presently and the interest tables of Appendix B. Many handbooks for engineering, business, and mathematics contain compound interest tables.

Some readers may question the validity of compound interest for evaluating financial events in general with respect to time. Is it reasonable to assume that earnings will be invested and at the same rate of interest? Of course, the earnings from any venture may be variously disposed of. In the time value calculations of engineering economy, however, the assumption of investment and accumulation of earnings is usually hypothetical. It is important to consider that any financial event (income or outgo) has its equivalent in an amount of capital that could be invested with its accumulating earnings. Invested capital is the yardstick for time value, whether or not an investment enhanced by earnings is actually involved.

Compounding Frequency

In most of the problems dealing with time value, it is assumed that interest or returns from investment are received and added to the investment *annually.* On the other hand, the interval mentioned can be much more frequent (rarely less frequent) than the annual. Some banks compute interest monthly on savings deposits. Most industrial bonds pay semiannual interest. Most home mortgages are settled by monthly payments. The capital turnover (reuse of capital) in various businesses ranges from less than one to many times a year. Unless otherwise specified or apparent in the problem, however, the annual period can be reasonably assumed.

The effects of compounding frequency on time value will be demonstrated in the following pages. The frequency will be designated *t* in "times per year" in certain of the formulas.

FUTURE WORTH

Let us consider the effect of compound interest on the *future worth* of a single investment. Naturally the result is affected by the elapsed time, the interest rate, and the interest payment periods (the frequency of interest payment and assumed investment of interest). The following notation will be used in the immediate formulas and those to follow:

N = elasped time in years
t = compounding frequency (number of times per year at which interest is paid and invested)
n = elapsed time in terms of interest payment periods = Nt
I = *nominal* interest rate, always specified on an annual basis
i = interest rate per payment period = I/t
P = dollar amount of initial investment
F = future worth (dollar amount of investment enhanced by accumulated earnings)

In most problems, time is expressed in years (N) and the interest rate is the nominal value (I). When interest payment and investment periods are not annual, it is essential that N and I be converted to n and i respectively as indicated above. In most engineering or business estimates, the annual basis is assumed—*i.e.,* $N = n$ and $I = i$. In *continuous* compounding, a mathematical concept, t becomes infinite. Although interest rates are usually expressed as percentages, they are decimals in the formulas.

The future worth of investment as it increases with time, period by period, develops as follows:

Period	Formula
1	$F_1 = P(1 + i)$
2	$F_2 = [P(1 + i)](1 + i) = P(1 + i)^2$
3	$F_3 = [P(1 + i)^2](1 + i) = P(1 + i)^3$
.	.
.	.
.	.
n	$F_n = P(1 + i)^n$

Compound Amount Factor

The factor $(1 + i)^n$, which is familiar to most high school students, appears in all compound interest formulas and interest tables

(Appendix B). The tables should always be used when practicable, but they do have limits in values of i and n. It is usually safe to interpolate between table values, but extrapolations beyond the limits of i and n are not reliable. In such problems, the factor can be computed by log-log slide rule, logarithms, or binomial series. Large values of n can be managed by combining smaller values, as will be demonstrated.

The slide rule is accurate enough for most time value estimates, but the simple scales are cumbersome for large values of n. The log-log scales are suitable for a large range of i and n values.

Logarithms (Appendix C) are useful for some problems, but the four-place tables are not accurate enough for combinations in which i is small and n is large.

The binomial series is the basis for the tables. It can be used for any value of i or n. The series may be written as follows:

$$(1 + i)^n = 1 + in + k_1 i(n - 1)/2 + k_2 i(n - 2)/3 \cdots$$
$$k_x i(n - x)/(x + 1)$$

in which $k_1 = in$, $k_2 = k_1 i(n - 1)/2$, $k_3 = k_2 i(n - 2)/3$, etc. This series converges rapidly when the factor k_1 is small. Note that, as the formula is written, each calculation furnishes a basis for the next. Calculation can be continued until the added amount is small enough to neglect.

To illustrate the use of the series, assume a *nominal* interest rate of 6%, with interest paid monthly for 10 years. Then $i = .005$ and $n = 120$, beyond the range of most interest tables. Using the series formula:

$$
\begin{aligned}
& & & 1.0000 \\
ni = k_1 &= (.005)(120) & &= .6000 \\
k_2 &= (.6000)(119)(.005)/2 & &= .1785 \\
k_3 &= (.1785)(118)(.005)/3 & &= .0351 \\
k_4 &= (.0351)(117)(.005)/4 & &= .0051 \\
k_5 &= (.0051)(116)(.005)/5 & &= \underline{.0006} \\
\text{Total} &= (1.005)^{120} & &= 1.8193
\end{aligned}
$$

The fourth decimal place is approximate but would be changed little, if any, by additional calculations. For practical use in economy studies, four significant digits or less are usually adequate.

For large values of n (beyond the interest tables), the following relationship should be recognized:

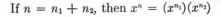
$$\text{If } n = n_1 + n_2, \text{ then } x^n = (x^{n_1})(x^{n_2})$$

To illustrate this, assume the conditions of the previous problem. Let $n_1 = 100$ and $n_2 = 20$. Making use of Table B-1 in Appendix B:

$$(1.005)^{120} = (1.005)^{100}(1.005)^{20} = (1.647)(1.105) = 1.8199$$

The slight difference in this result compared with the former is due to the limitations of the interest tables. The same result with sufficient adequacy can be obtained by some log-log slide rules, five-place logarithms, or by the following continuous-compounding approximation.

Although *continuous compounding* is a purely mathematical concept, it does have practical applications where the turnover of capital is frequent or for situations in which the periodic interest is small and the number of periods is large. The formula is derived by substituting for i and n in terms of t, I, and N as follows:

$$(1 + i)^n = (1 + I/t)^{tN}$$

$$(1 + I/t)^{tN} = 1 + \frac{tNI}{t} + \frac{tN(tN - 1)I^2}{(1)(2)t^2} + \frac{tN(tN - 1)(tN - 2)I^3}{(1)(2)(3)t^3} \text{ etc.}$$

Then, as $t \to \infty$:

$$(1 + I/t)^{tN} \to 1 + NI + \frac{(NI)^2}{2} + \frac{(NI)^3}{3} + \frac{(NI)^4}{4} \text{ etc.}$$

which is a rapidly converging series equivalent to e^{IN}, in which the factor e is the base of natural logarithms (2.718). For practical use (small i and large n), the formula may be written:

$$(1 + i)^n \to e^{in} \text{ or } e^{IN}, \text{ in which } in = IN.$$

Applying this as an approximation to the previous example:

$$(1 + .005)^{120} = (2.718)^{.600} = 1.822$$

This computation requires one setting of the runner on the log-log slide rule. Table B-4 in Appendix B provides for values up to $in = 4.00$. The approximation is a very good one for interest rates that are lower than $1\frac{1}{2}\%$.

The effect of compounding frequency is shown in the following table. The initial investment is $1,000, time is 10 years, and the nominal interest rates are 4% and 10%.

t	I @ 4%	I @ 10%
0	$1,400	$2,000
½	1,469	2,488
1	1,480	2,594
2	1,486	2,653
3	1,489	2,685
12	1,491	2,707
∞	1,492	2,718

Effective Interest Rates

Interest payment periods do not always coincide with the dates of other financial events, as assumed in the formulas. It is possible to adjust the interest rate (i) to agree with the investment period. This adjusted value is known as the *effective* interest rate, usually stated on an annual basis. This effective interest rate is of particular importance in some cases because the *nominal* rate can be quite misleading.

Let the length of the investment interval over the interest payment period be represented by a factor (t'); i' is the effective interest rate. Then:

$$(1 + i)^{t'} = 1 + i'$$

and

$$i' = (1 + i)^{t'} - 1$$

effective Interest Rate

As an example, assume that a 5% industrial bond pays interest semiannually. The nominal rate is 5%. What is the effective (actual) annual rate?

$$i = .025 \text{ and } t' = 2$$

then

$$i' = (1 + .025)^2 - 1 = 1.0506 - 1 = 5.06\%$$

It is possible that a financial event may be anticipated at intervals greater than a year, and in such problems it may be useful to employ an interest rate that is effective for that time interval. Assume that such an event is scheduled every two years. Funds are invested for this purpose. The nominal interest rate is 4%, but in bonds that pay semiannually. Then $i = .02$ and $t' = 4$. (There are four interest periods during the two-year interval.) The effective biennial rate (i') is:

$$i' = (1.02)^4 - 1 = 8.24\%$$

Future Worth of a Uniform Series

A program may call for a succession of financial events to take place at intervals for a substantial period of time, and it may be necessary to estimate the future worth of the accumulated amount at some specified future date. The general case is simple. Determine the future worth of each individual event (treated as investment) based on the date of its inception and the specified future date. Then total the individual future worths to arrive at the grand total. This process of multiple calculations and summation is necessary when the financial events are irregular in amount and timing.

Often the financial events are expected to be *uniform in amount and timing*—for example, a savings program calling for fixed monthly payments, or deposits in a sinking fund. In these cases, the forementioned future worth summation can be accomplished by a single calculation using a device known as the *sinking fund formula*. In the development of this formula, two symbols will be used in addition to the previous notation:

D = periodic amount (of payment into fund, for example)
S = total amount at the end of n time periods

Consider the future worths of the individual events, assuming that each occurs at the *end* of a time period (from 1 to n).

$$F_1 = D(1 + i)^{n-1}$$
$$F_2 = D(1 + i)^{n-2}$$
$$F_3 = D(1 + i)^{n-3}$$
$$\cdot \quad \cdot$$
$$\cdot \quad \cdot$$
$$\cdot \quad \cdot$$
$$F_n = D(1 + i)^o = D$$
$$S = \Sigma F = D[(1 + i)^{n-1} + (1 + i)^{n-2} + (1 + i)^{n-3} \cdots \cdots + (1 + i)^o]$$

This series can be simplified by multiplying and dividing each term within the brackets by the factor $[(1 + i) - 1]$. All the resulting products in the numerator will then cancel out except the first and the last, so that the series reduces to:

$S = D \left(sfaf \right)$

end of
Period payments
$$S = D \left[\frac{(1 + i)^n - 1}{i} \right]$$

The bracketed factor (*sinking fund factor*) is evaluated in Table B-2 in Appendix B.

It is often useful to determine the periodic amount (D) that will accumulate to a future worth (S). Then:

$$D = S \left[\frac{i}{(1 + i)^n - 1} \right], \qquad D = \frac{S}{Sff}$$

using a reciprocal of the sinking fund factor. To illustrate this last situation, assume that a young father desires to insure his son's education by investing in a trust fund at the end of each year an amount sufficient to accumulate \$8,000 in 18 years. The trust fund earns $4\frac{1}{2}\%$. To determine the annual requirement:

$$D = (8{,}000) \left[\frac{.045}{(1.045)^{18} - 1} \right]$$
$$D = 8{,}000/26.86 = \$298$$

The bracketed factor (reciprocal) is selected from Table B-2 in Appendix B, and the result is rounded to the nearest dollar.

Now let us consider situations in which the financial event is scheduled for the _beginning_ of each time period. In this case:

$$F_1 = D(1 + i)^n$$
$$F_2 = D(1 + i)^{n-1}$$
$$F_3 = D(1 + i)^{n-2}$$

$$\cdot \qquad \cdot$$
$$\cdot \qquad \cdot$$

$$F_n = D(1 + i)$$

Compare this series with that for events scheduled at the ends of the time periods. The exponent of F_1 is greater by one period, and the final item (D) of the previous series is now omitted. In other words, we add a time period and subtract a payment, with the following result:

$$S = D \left[\frac{(1 + i)^{n+1} - 1}{i} - 1 \right] \qquad \text{Beginning of Period Payment}$$

When using the tables to determine the bracketed factor, it is only necessary to increase the value of n by one and subtract one from the factor given in the tables.

To demonstrate the condition just described, assume that the father in the previous example wished to contribute to the trust fund at the beginning of each time period. Then:

$$D = (8{,}000) \div \left[\frac{(1.045)^{19} - 1}{.045} - 1 \right]$$
$$D = 8{,}000/28.06 = \$285$$

PRESENT WORTH

The *present worth* of a future event is a concept that must be grasped by the student of engineering economy. It has many applications in the appraisals of costs, income items, and profit. In the introduction to this chapter, we cited the case of the man who inherited $20,000 payable in ten years and was offered $14,000 for a note to cover the future $20,000. In that example, $14,000 was the present worth of the $20,000. Similarly, $75 is the initial present worth of a $100 Savings Bond. That present worth becomes greater as the age of the bond approaches its terminal date. Present worth is always less than future worth, a relationship that depends on the time difference and the earning power of comparable investment.

Consider the future worth formula that was previously developed for a single financial event:

$$F = P(1 + i)^n = Pf$$

in which f is the compound interest factor. The present worth may be designated P, and the formula for P becomes:

$$P = F/(1 + i)^n = F/f$$

Referring now to the inheritance case previously cited, what rate of return (interest) would the man's friend expect to realize from his loan? In this case:

$$14,000 = 20,000/f$$
$$f = 20,000/14,000 = 1.421$$

Now refer to Table B–1 in Appendix B for $(1 + i)^n$. In the line for $n = 10$, it will be seen that the above value of f lies between interest rates $3\frac{1}{2}\%$ and 4%. By interpolation, the unknown interest rate (i) is 3.57%.

Present Worth of a Uniform Series

As in the future worth applications, there are many problems that involve a dated succession of future events. When the events are irregular in amounts and timing, the present worth of each individual item can be computed by the above formula and the sum of these is the present worth of the entire series. When the anticipated events are uniform in amounts and at regular intervals, the present worth determination can be shortened by use of a formula that accomplishes the summation directly. The derivation of this formula is similar to that demonstrated for future worth. Let the present worth of the series be designated R, which is the sum of the detail present worths (P). If the periodic events (D) take place at the ends of each period:

$$P_1 = D/(1 + i)$$
$$P_2 = D/(1 + i)^2$$
$$P_3 = D/(1 + i)^3$$
.   .
.   .
.   .
$$P_n = D/(1 + i)^n$$

and the summation may be written as follows:

$$R = \Sigma P = D[(1 + i)^{-1} + (1 + i)^{-2} + (1 + i)^{-3} \cdots \cdots + (1 + i)^{-n}]$$

If the series is multiplied and divided by the factor $[(1 + i) - 1]$, all the terms within the brackets will cancel out except the first and the last; and the simplified result is:

end of

$R = D(Aff)$ $\qquad R = D\left[\dfrac{1 - (1 + i)^{-n}}{i}\right]$ or $D\left[\dfrac{(1 + i)^n - 1}{i(1 + i)^n}\right]$ *Period*

The formula is written both ways in various interest tables. It is often designated the "annuity" or "endowment" formula because of the fixed periodic amount (D) that is provided for. The *annuity fund factor*, used above, is evaluated in Table B–3 in Appendix B.

To illustrate the annuity application, assume that a retirement fund of $30,000 has accumulated. At this time, the plan is to withdraw at the end of each year an amount that will exhaust the fund in 15 years. The invested fund is earning 4%. What is the annual amount?

$Crf = \dfrac{1}{Aff}$

$$D = R \div \left[\frac{(1 + i)^n - 1}{i(1 + i)^n}\right] = 30,000 \div \left[\frac{(1.04)^{15} - 1}{.04(1.04)^{15}}\right]$$
$$D = 30,000/11.12 = \$2,680 \text{ per year}$$

The reciprocal of the above factor, to be used as a multiplier, is often designated *annuity factor* or *capital recovery factor*.

As in the future worth series, more often perhaps, it is necessary to provide for periodic events at the *beginning* of each period. Then:

$$P_1 = D/(1 + i)^o = D$$
$$P_2 = D/(1 + i)$$
$$P_3 = D/(1 + i)^2$$
.   .
.   .
.   .
$$P_n = D/(1 + i)^{n-1}$$

Comparing this with the result obtained for events at the ends of the time periods, it will be seen that we have, in effect, added an amount D and subtracted a period. The sum may then be written:

$$R = D\left[\frac{(1+i)^{n-1}-1}{i(1+i)^{n-1}}+1\right]$$ *Beginning of Period*

Assume now that the person with the retirement fund wished to provide for cash at the beginning of each year. The annual amount then becomes:

$$D = 30,000 \div \left[\frac{(1.04)^{14}-1}{.04(1.04)^{14}}+1\right]$$
$$D = 30,000/11.56 = \$2,586 \text{ per year}$$

Perpetual Endowment

A perpetual endowment is one that is designed to yield a fixed periodic amount for an endless period of time. In other words, n of the present worth formula is infinite. The formula is solvable algebraically in the form:

$$R = D\left[\frac{1-(1+i)^{-n}}{i}\right]$$

When $n = \infty$, the $(1+i)^{-n}$ becomes zero, so that:

$$R = D/i \text{ or } D = Ri$$

The formula for D is obvious. D is the periodic earnings of an amount R at an interest rate i for an indefinite time.

A simple example of perpetual endowment is a scholarship fund that is intended to be permanent. Assume that such a fund is desired to establish a scholarship of $500 per year. The trust fund earns $4\frac{1}{2}\%$ interest. The required endowment is:

$$R = 500/.045 = \$11,111$$

An inspection of Table B–3 in Appendix B that would be used for an endowment of n years will show that the factor approaches $1/i$ as n becomes very great, and the reciprocal values (for solving D) approach i. This makes it practical to assume perpetual endowment rather than a finite n in many long-term programs so that the present worth can be computed without tables. The error in this assumption may be less than that of other estimates in the study. The perpetual endowment is often designated *capitalized cost*, meaning the capital that would be required to sustain indefinitely a uniform periodic cost.

MIXED PROGRAMS

There are many possible combinations and irregularities in the sequence of financial events that are to be evaluated. There may be items of cost and items of income or profit. If the endowment concept is appropriate, cost or outgo would be positive, and offsetting income or profit would be negative. If we are considering the future result of profit accumulation and investment, the cost items would be negative. The plus or minus sign, therefore, depends on the character of the problem.

A problem of time value may cover any desired length of time (the *study period*) starting and ending at any specified dates. An intermediate date may be the basing point for either the present worth or the future worth concept, as will be shown presently in an example. In other words, any dated financial event has a time value either before or after the date of the event. These time values are said to be equivalent. The present worth of a uniform series, for example, is equal to the present worth of the future worth of the same series, as inspection of the R and S formulas will show:

$$R = S/(1 + i)^n$$

Heretofore, we have considered either isolated financial events or a uniform series of regularly spaced events. A practical program may include both types of situations. The character of a series in spacing of events and interest rates may change. The elapsed time for a uniform series may be only a portion of the total study period. In any case, the present worth or future worth of the over-all program is simply the sum of its parts.

To illustrate the application of both present and future worths in a changing program, consider another retirement plan. The plan is to provide an income of $3,000 at the beginning of each year from ages 65 to 80 (15 years of benefit). The individual's present age is 25. He desires to make a fixed annual contribution to the retirement fund at the end of each year until age 55 is reached. For the next 10 years, he is to be relieved of that obligation. The earning rate of the fund is predicted to be 4%. What is the required annual payment into the fund?

This problem must be solved in reverse order of timing. The questions to be answered are as follows: How much is needed by the 65th year to support the $3,000 income for 15 years? How much is needed by the 55th year to establish the 65-year sum? And what annual amount is necessary to build up the 55-year requirement? The first two portions of the problem are present worth concepts. The last portion involves future worth of an annual payment. Calculations follow:

$$R_{65} = (3,000) \left[\frac{(1.04)^{14} - 1}{.04(1.04)^{14}} + 1 \right]$$

$$R_{65} = (3,000)(11.56) = 34,680$$

$$P_{55} = 34,680/(1.04)^{10} = 34,680/1.480 = 23,430$$

$$D = 23,430 \div \left[\frac{(1.04)^{30} - 1}{.04} \right]$$

$$D = 23,430/56.08 = \$418 \text{ per year}$$

SUMMARY

The concept of compound interest applies in engineering economy to the time value of transactions or conditions that can be measured in money. Items so evaluated may include investments, costs, income, and profits. The assumption is that items of income or outgo are equivalent in value to investment, the earnings from which are similarly invested.

Future worth is the value of one or more financial events at some date after their occurrence. Future worth always exceeds the amount of the initial value or the sum of the individual events, due to the fact that investment would be enhanced by accumulated earnings.

Present worth is the value of one or more financial events at some date (e.g., the present) prior to their anticipated occurrence. Present worth is always less than the anticipated amount at time of occurrence or the sum of the individual events. As an appraisal device, present worth answers the question: how much would one accept now in exchange for future prospects?

Time value calculations require specifications of time, interest rate on real or hypothetical investment, and frequency of compounding (receipt and investment of earnings). In practical problems, the stated interest rate and the compounding are to be assumed annual unless otherwise specified or implied. Interest rates (i) and time periods (n) in the formulas, however, must agree with the frequency of interest payment and compounding, or time-adjusted values must be substituted (e.g., *effective* interest rates).

The formulas developed in this chapter, and summarized in Appendix A, are the basic tools of time value computations. The conditions that the formulas represent, their derivations, and algebraic relationships should be thoroughly understood by persons engaged in economy studies. The compound interest factors evaluated in the tables of Appendix B are also included in the various handbooks on engineering and business. Methods of calculation have been suggested in this chapter for values of interest and time beyond the range of available tables.

PROBLEMS*

2.1. How many years would be required for the following investments (principals) to increase to the stated amounts at the specified *nominal* interest rates and interest payment periods?

Principal	Interest Rate	Interest Paid:	Future Worth
$1,000	4 %	annually	$2,000
500	6	semiannually	750
2,000	3½	semiannually	2,250
150	4½	quarterly	300
1,700	6½	monthly	2,500

2.2. Determine the *effective* interest rates for the specified time intervals at the given nominal rates and interest payment periods.

Nominal Rate	Interest Paid:	Effective Rate for:
6%	bimonthly	1 year
8	quarterly	1 year
4	annually	3 years
7	monthly	1 year
3	monthly	1 year

2.3. Determine the *nominal* and *effective* interest rates required to accumulate the following future worths under the stated conditions.

Principal	Years	Interest Paid:	Future Worth
$10,000	10	annually	$20,000
1,200	20	quarterly	5,000
2,500	16	semiannually	5,000
75	8	monthly	100
1	100	semiannually	50

2.4. Statistical records of a population indicate an annual increase of 3% based on each preceding year. If this rate of growth is maintained uniformly, how long will it take for the population to:

---

* NOTE: In all problems that involve time value, in this chapter and those to follow, it is to be assumed that the interest rates mentioned are nominal and that interest payments are annual, unless otherwise specified or dictated by conditions.

a) Increase 20%.
b) Increase 50%.
c) Double in size.

2.5.   In 1800, the population of the United States was approximately 5,300,000. By 1960, it was approximately 180,000,000. If the annual growth were at a uniform percentage of each preceding year's population, what was the effective annual rate of increase based on continuous compounding?

2.6.   A grandfather wishes to provide for the college education of a new grandchild by a gift of money that is to be held in a trust account until the child is 18 years old. The nominal interest rate on the trust fund is 4½%, but interest is paid semiannually and is accumulated in the fund.
   a) How much will the trust fund amount to in 18 years if the initial deposit is $2,500?
   b) If it is estimated that $8,000 would be required for the college education, how much would the donor have to contribute to the fund at the beginning?

2.7.   Federal Savings Bonds have been sold to buyers at 75% of face value (i.e., a $100 bond would be purchased for $75). These bonds do not provide for periodic interest payments, but the interest that is earned accumulates in the value of the bond. In 1960, the interest rate was such that a bond could be redeemed in 7.75 years at the face value. Interest is credited to the value of a bond every six months. Under the stated conditions, what are the nominal and effective interest rates.

2.8.   An aged eccentric has provided a clause in his will that sets up a trust fund for his alma mater in the amount of $100,000 at the time of his death. But the will stipulates that the beneficiary is not to receive the proceeds from this fund until 100 years after the death. The bank administering the fund computes interest semiannually and the nominal interest rate is expected to be 3½%. If this interest rate is maintained for the 100 years, how much will the beneficiary receive when the fund is finally released? Compute the answer two ways: (*a*) based on the interest tables, and (*b*) by the continuous compounding approximation. Why is the latter result somewhat larger than the former?

2.9.   A savings account was started by parents for a young son. When the boy was 5 years old, the parents were killed in an accident and the savings account ($2,500) was forgotten. When the boy had become a man of 30 years, the old account came to his attention. By that time it had grown to what amount? The interest rate has averaged 3% and accounts have been balanced monthly (monthly compounding).

2.10.   What will be the ultimate worth of a fund that is accumulated from periodic deposits as specified below? Rates given are nominal, but paid at the frequency of the deposits. Deposits are made at the ends of the stated periods.

Periodic Deposit	Frequency	Years	Interest Rate
$ 600	annual	20	5½%
250	semiannual	25	4½
150	quarterly	20	6
25	monthly	2	8
75	monthly	20	4
1,000	biennial	20	4½

2.11. Solve Problem 2.10 based on deposits at the beginnings of periods.

2.12. Determine the periodic payments into a fund necessary to accumulate the following amounts under the stated conditions. Interest rates are nominal, but paid at the frequency of the deposits. Payments are at the ends of periods.

Future Amount	Years	Interest Rate	Periods
$12,000	10	15%	annual
20,000	20	8	quarterly
5,000	18	6	monthly
50,000	20	4	annual
50,000	20	4	monthly

2.13. Solve the above problem based on payments at the beginnings of periods.

2.14. How long will it take to accumulate the following stated amounts by accumulating the periodic deposits to a fund? Interest rates are nominal, but interest is paid at the frequency of the deposits. Deposits are at the ends of the periods.

Payments	Frequency	Interest Rate	Final Amount
$ 650.00	annual	8%	$13,000
1,500.00	semiannual	7	20,000
130.00	quarterly	6	2,500
43.33	monthly	6	2,500
10.00	weekly	6	2,500

2.15. Solve the above problem based on deposits at the beginnings of periods.

2.16. A young couple looks forward to building their own home. They do not wish to attempt this until they have $5,000. (They can get a mortgage to cover the additional requirement.) The couple plans to save $400 a year for this purpose. The homeowners' loan association with whom the savings are to be deposited pays a nominal interest rate of 4% on a quarterly basis. The savings will also be deposited quarterly. How long will it take to accumulate the needed $5,000?

2.17. A municipal bond issue of $20,000,000 is to mature in 20 years. A sinking fund is to be established to retire the bonds at the end of the 20 years. The fund is to be invested in safe securities that are expected to average 4% at the nominal rate, but the interest is expected *semiannually*. What is the *annual* deposit that would be required?

2.18. A young man wishes to save money for a new car that will cost $2,600. His plan is to deposit $60 monthly in a savings account that maintains a nominal interest rate of 3%. Accounts are balanced and interest is computed on a monthly basis; but the end-of-month interest applies only to the balance at the *beginning* of each month. How long will it take to accumulate the needed $2,600 beginning with the first deposit? (Note that the last deposit will earn no interest.)

2.19. A well-known savings plan calls for the monthly purchase of a Federal Savings Bond. The purchase price of such a bond is 75% of the face value (the value on the basis of which the accumulating interest is computed). Assume that a $50 bond is purchased monthly, and that the prevailing *nominal* interest rate is 3¾% computed semiannually. (Actually the interest rate on the Type E Bonds in 1960 changed from 2½% to 4% when the age of a bond reached 1½ years.) Based on a uniform interest rate, what will be the value of the savings in 20 years beginning with the first purchase? No interest will accumulate on the bonds purchased during the last 6 months.

2.20. Determine the present worths of the following future amounts under the stated conditions. Interest rates given are nominal, but interest is computed at the periods mentioned. The present worth applies to the current date, bearing in mind that interest will not be earned on a fraction of the normal interest payment period.

Future Amount	Date	Interest Paid	Rate
$ 2,000	Jan. 1, 1970	1st of Jan. each year	4½%
5,000	July 1, 1980	1st of Jan. and July	6½
5,000	July 1, 1980	1st of Jan. and July	10
10,000	May 1, 1975	1st of each month	8
20,000	Oct. 15, 1985	15th of each month	4

2.21. A long-term expansion program is being planned for a hospital. The program calls for expenditure for construction amounting to $300,000 2 years from now, $200,000 more in 5 years, and another $200,000 in 10 years. The trustees propose to raise the funds now by subscription. What is the necessary amount? Assume that the amount subscribed is paid at once, that the funds will be invested at once, and that the investments will average 5% nominal interest paid semiannually.

2.22. In a certain cemetery, it costs $15 a year for the seasonal planting and maintenance of a grave plot. The cemetery association is now soliciting from the plot owners single deposits to cover *perpetual* care. These deposits are to be managed by the trust department of a bank. The average earnings on trust accounts have been 3½% per year. How much for each plot should be charged for perpetual care?

2.23. A manufacturer is considering an improved process for making his product. It is estimated that the saving in annual cost would be $15,-000. How much could the manufacturer afford to invest for this purpose? Assume that capital similarly invested would be expected to earn 22% and that the life of the venture would be at least 10 years.

2.24. A man has willed to a university $30,000 as a scholarship fund. The will specifies a semiannual scholarship of $800. The fund is to be deposited in a trust account that is expected to earn income at the nominal rate of 4½%, but the interest is paid semiannually. How long will it be before the fund is exhausted? Assume that the last $800 may be supplied in part by university cash if the fund remaining in the trust account is insufficient.

2.25. In the campaign for hospital funds mentioned in Problem 2.21, donations are being solicited for individual rooms. The directors have advised that $50,000 will permanently endow a single room for patients. It is subsequently found that the average cost for such a room (depreciation and maintenance) amounts to $2,200 per year. What must be the rate of earnings (interest) on the endowment to take care of the annual cost?

2.26. A child just 6 years old has been willed $15,000. The will specifies that the amount will be kept as a trust fund until the child's 21st birthday; and beginning with that birthday, the money is to be released in quarterly periods in uniform amounts for 10 years. The nominal interest rate is 3½%; but accounts are balanced and interest is added monthly. What is the amount of the quarterly payment to the beneficiary?

2.27. Parents are planning for the education of two children. They wish to establish a savings program to accomplish this. One child will go to college in 10 years, the other in 13 years. It is expected that each student will require $1,000 a semester for 4 years. The money is to be advanced to each student at the beginning of each semester. The savings bank in which the funds are to be deposited pays 3½% (nominal rate) on a semiannual basis. The parents will make the first deposit 6 months from now and will continue every 6 months until the younger child has received his last $1,000. If the parents' periodic contribution is to be a uniform amount, how much is that periodic deposit?

2.28. A steam boiler is purchased on the basis of guaranteed performance. A test indicates that the operating cost will be $300 more per year than guaranteed. If the expected life of the boiler is 20 years and money is worth 6%, what deduction from the purchase price would compensate the purchaser for the extra operating cost? (PE Pa.)

2.29.   With interest at 4% compounded annually, determine:

a) If a down payment of $7,500 was made on a piece of real estate and $1,500 at the end of each of the succeeding 5 years was required, what was the cash price of the property?

b) What payment *10 years hence* is equivalent to a payment of $5,000 5 years hence? (PE Pa.)

2.30.   The prepaid premium of insurance policies covering loss to buildings by fire and storm for a 3-year period is usually 2.5 times the premium for one year of coverage. What rate of interest does a purchaser of this type of insurance receive on the additional present cash investment if he purchases a 3-year policy now rather than three 1-year policies at the beginning of succeeding years? (PE Pa.)

CHAPTER 3

Investment

THE time value of money, discussed in the previous chapter, is dependent on the earning power of invested capital—investment that is actual or equivalent in value to other financial events. In this chapter and the two to follow, we shall be concerned with the character and value of investment.

Investment Characteristics

About the first step in the analysis of economic data is the proper distinction of expenditures or property values either as invested capital or current operating costs. An investment expenditure is one that has long-term benefit (two years or more), with the exception of some items that may be classified as operating cost for accounting convenience. Property represented by investment is said to be capitalized. Investment is capital tied up in a project or enterprise for a sustained period of time.

The necessity for separation of investment from operating cost arises from consideration of profit. Profit over the entire life of a project is simply the excess of receipts over expenditures. For practical reasons, including income tax regulations, profit must be appraised periodically, although the benefit from certain expenditures or properties may continue for years. Consider the following situation.

A man purchased a newly built apartment house and paid $200,-000 for it at the beginning of a fiscal year. During the first year, the income from rentals was $26,000. Expenditures for janitor service, utilities, maintenance, and taxes were $12,000. The total expenditures for the year were $212,000. Would it be reasonable to conclude that the owner *lost* $186,000 during this first year? That conclusion is obviously absurd because the owner still possessed a property worth nearly as much as the initial expenditure. Only a portion of that first cost can be treated as an annual cost. This is done by the

29

process of depreciation, the subject of the next chapter. In other words, an expenditure with long-term benefit can not be charged to one year, but it can be spread over a period of years. It is, therefore, evident that the expenditures and properties with long-term benefit should be separately classified in economic analysis.

The capital invested in any enterprise may be represented by three general classes of assets that are usually grouped accordingly in financial statements:

1. *Fixed assets*—land, buildings, and equipment.
2. *Current assets*—cash, inventory (materials, parts, supplies, work in process, and finished products), money due to come in (accounts receivable), prepaid obligations, and securities owned—values that fluctuate up and down with daily transactions.
3. Other assets including *intangibles* (assets of uncertain value in terms of dollars).

Investment is shared by financial contributors, a matter that will be discussed at length in Chapter 16. The net value of the investment to owners of the enterprise is the value of the above assets less the amounts due creditors and other prior obligations.

First Cost

The initial capital expenditure for any enterprise or individual project may be termed *first cost*. It is the aggregate of costs that precede operation or utilization of project or enterprise. Such costs apply to fixed assets. They may include the costs of research, development, and design of facilities or product to be manufactured. They may also include the costs of business investigations, patents, organization, and financing. Preliminary costs associated with physical properties can be included in their first costs, along with the costs of purchases, construction, installation, and the like. The other first costs mentioned above may be charged to intangible assets, which may or may not be amortized over a period of years.

Theoretically, the cost of any property which has a useful life of two or more years should be classified as investment. Good business practice, however, requires the keeping of records on all investment items, and accounting cost is involved in the record keeping. Also, the life of some properties may be exceedingly uncertain. A twist drill in a machine shop may last for years or it may be used up on a single job. In consequence, minor items (ash trays, small tools, utensils)

may be charged to current operating cost for accounting convenience. The dollar values and anticipated lives required for capitalizing expenditures (classifying them as investment) vary somewhat
with management policy and tax regulations.

In a going enterprise, additional first costs come about with additions and alterations to existing facilities. This adds to investment,
except for the minor expenditures mentioned above. It is also possible to exclude from investment the expenditures for research, design, and promotion if the costs can not be readily identified with
the particular project. But, whether or not such costs are capitalized
in accounting practice, they must be recognized as first costs in the
economy study.

The estimating of first costs is a basic requirement in most economy studies. First costs for manufacture or erection of facilities
include labor, material, and overhead that can be identified with the
project. Items which are purchased—a new machine, for example—
may have a similar basis for their prices. Prices, however, are
mostly controlled by market conditions and trade factors. The problem whether to make or purchase is often a decision factor in project analysis—a problem of choice among alternatives. Of course,
some purchased items are involved in all manufacture or construction by the investor.

There are many factors in first-cost economy relating to the specifications of the product or service in addition to decision as to result
to be accomplished. Usually, the cost starts with certain fixed or
semifixed minimums that include investigation, design work, office
routine, and the like. Other costs can vary considerably with the
specification of details. Unit size is one factor. Five one-horsepower
motors will cost more than one five-horsepower motor, for example.
First cost, however, must always be considered with relation to operating economy. The optimum condition is maximum profit. The
technique of estimating first cost, its economic significance, and decisions among alternatives will be discussed in several chapters.

Investment in Aged Property

Some readers may assume that first cost represents the continuing
amount of investment in a property. Does the owner of a home have
the same amount invested throughout the years of possession, assuming no additions or improvements? Does the owner of a $20,000
machine have $20,000 invested until it reaches the end of its useful

life? The same question applies to some intangible assets such as preliminary development work, organizing expenses, and patents.

Most physical properties decline in value with age. (Land is one exception.) Certainly some provision must be made to account for consumption of capital by aging, wear and tear, and other life limitations. Depreciation, depletion, and amortization, to be discussed in the next chapter, translate investment into operating cost. Other factors also affect the current value of an investment—market conditions, for example. Hence, specific investments are not static in value. The worth of some investments increases with time when earnings are invested, as in time-value-of-money calculations; and in other cases, the amount may decline with depreciation, depletion, amortization, or other causes.

The estimation of an asset's value is more complex than may appear to the layman. The subject deserves coverage in another chapter. From the viewpoint of the investor, the current amount of his investment is the capital tied up in his project or enterprise, capital that would be available, otherwise, for other benefits.

Working Capital

To sustain any project or enterprise that involves operations after it is established requires capital in addition to that represented by long-life properties. This portion of the investment is known as *working capital*. It is characterized by assets that are subject to frequent, perhaps daily, fluctuations in amount—items that were enumerated on page 30. The net amount of working capital at any time is: total *current assets* less the *current liabilities* (amounts currently due creditors). Working capital must be sufficient to provide for adequate inventory, credit to customers (unless business is done on a cash basis), prepayment of certain obligations such as rent and insurance, and cash (in bank or till), or liquid securities to meet financial obligations as they arise. The principal causes of business failure are inept management and lack of capital—related factors. Working capital deficiency is usually the immediate cause because it becomes depleted when the business is under adverse pressure.

Working capital is a continuing need in any operating enterprise, although the amounts needed and available may constantly fluctuate. The average during the year is capital tied up in the enterprise in as real a sense as the funds invested in fixed properties such as land, buildings, and equipment. Inventory must be carried in almost all operating enterprises—finished products, raw materials, parts, work in process, and operating supplies. Receipts for goods and services are seldom timed with expenditures that must be made. The total required depends on the character of the business and operating conditions. The amount available indicates the ability of the organization to meet its financial obligations and therefore reflects its credit standing.

Estimating Working Capital Requirement

To estimate the working capital needed for a new enterprise can be more difficult than the first-cost estimates because of the intangibles involved. The requirement is usually greatest at the beginning of new operations. For example, the designer and manufacturer of a large special machine may require a year or more for preliminary estimates and proposals, completion of design, manufacture, and tryouts. Only when the machine is delivered, installed, and tried by the user will pay be received for the work, unless the customer agrees to make partial payments in advance. In the meantime, the manufacturer will need funds for salaries, wages, materials, and other current expenses. Of course, banks lend money for such projects, but the lending depends on the reputation and prospects of the borrower and must be within limits safe to the lender. Material suppliers may also extend long-term credit.

When the enterprise has become established, the need for working capital may be less because income is supplying funds for expenditures. But funds are still required to meet the fluctuating obligations previously described. As the rate of operations increases, the need for working capital also increases—inventory, credit to customers, wages, and accessory requirements. To simplify the practice problems in this chapter and others, *it is to be assumed that working capital is a fixed amount* unless otherwise specified.

Inventory requirement is one of the most complex problems of management. Inventory control is an advanced specialty in operating economy. The problem of economic lot size is discussed in Chapter 14. Some general considerations will be mentioned at this point.

One common measure for inventory economy is known as *inventory turnover*. It is a gage for utilization of working capital.

$$\text{INVENTORY TURNOVER} = \frac{\text{COST OF GOODS SOLD OR CONSUMED}}{\text{COST OF AVERAGE INVENTORY}}$$

This is usually expressed on an annual basis. It may apply to an entire business, to a sales warehouse, to a particular product, or to a department or division of the organization. It signifies the number of times that portion of working capital is being used during the year. But this figure can be used only as a standard for appraisal that must vary greatly with type of enterprise. The ratio would be small for the manufacturer of large special machines previously mentioned. It could be more than 300 for a fresh fruit and vegetable vendor who purchased his stocks daily and disposed of them within the day. The turnover may be 50 (weekly) for a successful grocery chain store.

The most desirable amount of inventory is that which contributes the greatest profit to the enterprise, bearing in mind that *working capital should earn adequate return* as is expected from other forms of investment. The optimum amount in excess of absolute necessity (such as work in process for goods made to order) is a complex problem replete with intangibles. Excess inventory may be favored by economies in purchase and manufacture. Rising costs and possible shortages may encourage speculation. Finished stocks may be needed for display and demonstration. Stocks available for immediate delivery may promote sales. Moderate surpluses of manufacturing materials and supplies may be needed to guard against contingent shortages that could shut down operations. On the other hand, inventory ties up capital that must earn return, and there are charges for temporary storage including costs of space, handling, insurance, and property taxes. There may be possibilities of changes in demand, specification changes, spoilage, and cost reduction in future production. There may be shortage of capital or more advantageous uses for it elsewhere in the business.

It is evident that no general rule of thumb can be prescribed for estimating working capital needs. Experience or statistical information about the type of enterprise is the usual basis, except for those individual projects that can be subjected to mathematical analysis such as operations research. Management policy may aim at an amount equal to a specified percentage of first cost, income, operating cost, or other criteria. This has been done in many of the practice problems presented in this book. With reference to these problems, a precaution is necessary. The prescribed ratios are illustrative only; they should not be accepted by the reader as customary practice.

One guide to estimating is the financial statements of corporations engaged in comparable activities. Working capital can be compared with fixed assets, total assets, income, cost of goods sold, total operating cost, physical output, and similar criteria. The amount of anticipated income (volume of business) may be the best criterion for a manufacturing, selling, or service business. Periodic operating cost would be better for a public or nonprofit enterprise. Table 3–1 sum-

TABLE 3–1

SUMMARY OF WORKING CAPITAL RATIOS FOR U.S. CORPORATIONS, JULY, 1956 TO JUNE, 1957

Industrial Group	Working Capital Total Assets	Working Capital Total Income
Extractive industry	33.0%	38.1%
Construction	28.2	12.2
Manufacturing	39.9	27.3
Public utilities	6.2	13.6
Trade	44.6	15.1

Data were derived from *Statistics of Income, Corporation Income Tax Returns* for accounting periods ended July, 1956–June, 1957, U.S. Treasury Department, Internal Revenue Service, U.S. Government Printing Office, 1959.

marizes working capital ratios for U.S. corporations during fiscal years ending between July, 1956 and June, 1957, which was a good business year. The figures were derived from the summary of income tax returns published by the U.S. Treasury Department, Internal Revenue Service.

Intangible Assets

Some of the assets of an enterprise that contribute to the worth of investment are classed as *intangible* because the value in dollars can not be reliably determined. The first cost of a patent may be easily accounted for. But the worth of the patent to the business, its useful life, or its market value during legal life, may be quite uncertain. The unamortized organizing expenses of the enterprise may be derived from first cost but do not indicate the true worth of that effort. Good will developed by a reputable concern is clearly an asset but difficult to appraise quantitatively.

Although the worths of preliminary research or investigation, patents, and organizing effort may be classed as intangible the first costs, at least, must be recognized in economy studies of new projects. The costs are parts of the investment, on which returns should be realized. Intangibles may be omitted or listed at nominal values in the financial statements of going concerns. Methods of evaluation will be discussed in Chapter 5.

SUMMARY

Capital investment is a requisite in any form of substantial enterprise. The investment is expected to earn returns—profit in dollars, or other benefits in nonprofit enterprises. Capital expenditures are for properties (assets) that have long-term benefits as distinguished from current operating expenditures or costs. Hence, they must be separately identified in economy studies.

Three classes of assets make up the total of investment. *Fixed assets* are the physical facilities for operations—land, buildings, and equipment. *Working capital* (the difference between *current assets* such as cash, inventories, accounts receivable, prepayments on future obligations, securities, and *current liabilities*) is a constantly fluctuating investment necessary to sustain operations. *Intangible assets* are those of uncertain dollar value (difficult to measure quantitatively). But intangibles may be important factors in the economy study, and their first costs must be included with investment in studies of new projects.

The values of fixed and intangible assets as affected by anticipated life, age, and current conditions are to be considered in detail in following chapters.

PROBLEMS

3.1. Consider one of the following new enterprises. Make a comprehensive list of items that would be classified as, or would contribute to, *first cost*. You may group under single titles items that are alike in character, but the items or groups that are characteristic of the particular enterprise must be definitely identified.

a) An automobile service station with restaurant and rest rooms.
b) A general-purpose machine shop.
c) A cast iron foundry.
d) A dress manufacturing establishment.
e) An office building.
f) A steam power plant.
g) Any other substantial type of industry with which you are familiar.

3.2. With reference to the above problem, make an itemized list of assets that would contribute to working capital. Like items may be grouped under single titles, but the items or groups that characterize the particular enterprise must be definitely identified.

3.3. With reference to the above problem, state the operating or business conditions that will affect the required amount of working capital. State whether each of the conditions listed will increase or decrease the working capital requirement and why.

3.4. With reference to the assets listed in Problem **3.2**, identify those that may be classified as *quick assets,* in the sense that they could be promptly disposed of at the stated (book) value in event of liquidation or forced sale.

3.5. In the operation of the enterprise considered in Problem **3.1**, there may be some expenditures with long-term benefit that would not be capitalized (treated as investment). List at least six such items and explain why you would not include them in investment.

3.6. Assume that you have recently completed a new double house for rental purposes. Up to the beginning of the first lease to tenants, you have incurred the following costs:

Legal fees relating to property	$ 125
Survey of lot	50
Purchase of lot	3,800
Architect's fee	1,250
Construction costs	25,500
Advertising for tenants	15
Interest on mortgage	900
Grading and seeding of grounds	65
Grass mowing	5
Fuel oil for furnaces	15
Fire insurance	40

What is the total amount of your investment in the property?

3.7. Assume that you have just been employed as the manager of a small manufacturing concern. In the past, the accountant has relied on the manager for some of the decisions as to classification of costs. The accountant has accumulated several such items for a few days and now comes to you for decision. The items are:

A set of numbered drills for toolroom	$ 15.00
Two brass ash trays for manager's office	2.30
Paper punch for office records	4.50
Filing cabinet	55.00
Repair of roof (tar and gravel coating)	1,560.00
Purchase of a used lathe	3,500.00
Trucking charge for above	125.00
Installation cost for above	450.00
Case lot of 200-watt fluorescent lamp bulbs	220.00
Reconditioning an old worn-out motor	125.00
An automatic feed added to punch press	1,250.00
Stamping die for a special order (no other use is anticipated)	750.00
Six new milling cutters for production shop	60.00
New battery for truck	25.00

Identify the items that you would capitalize (treat as investment). Assume that the remaining expenditures would be charged to other appropriate accounts. Any of the physical properties that are capitalized must be kept account of individually in the books of the company and will bear property numbers. Explain in a general way your decisions regarding the above items.

3.8.   The proprietor of a small trucking business incurred the following costs prior to and during the first month of operations. Which of these costs can be considered as items of investment? The items are listed at random with regard to timing.

Advertising circulars
Filing supplies and stationery
Filing cabinet
Telephone bill for the month
Telephone installation charge
Gasoline pump and supply tank
Installation of above
Gasoline, 300 gallons
Engine oil, 50 gallons
Grease gun
Grease supply for above
√ Ten-ton truck
Painting name and trade-mark on truck
Tire pump
Kit of small service tools
Truck licenses (for the year)

Operator's license
Insurance for the first quarter
Parking fees during the month
Bond posted (for uninsured liability)
Salary for part-time bookkeeper-secretary
Postage
Money withdrawn from bank for petty cash
Interest paid on loan
Expenditures for meals and accommodations away from home
Bridge and highway tolls
Paid contractor for constructing garage
Paid for land occupied by garage

3.9.   With regard to the above problem, which of the items listed would indicate a need for working capital?

CHAPTER 4

Capital Recovery

N THE previous discussion of investment, the effects of age on the value of fixed assets and certain intangibles were briefly mentioned. First costs do not establish the permanent worth of individual investments. Time and use are prominent factors. In a sense, capital can be consumed in operations. Capital expenditures for long-term assets of limited or uncertain life can be translated into operating cost by procedures known as depreciation, depletion, or amortization. Along with other operating costs, these charges against operations are expected to be recovered by income in the profit-making enterprise—hence the expression *capital recovery*. In the technical accounting sense, these credits to the capital account recover the capital expenditures, whether or not income is realized from operations.

DEPRECIATION

Young Joe Smith had accumulated $5,000 with which he wished to establish his own business. He purchased a truck with that capital and started a trucking enterprise which continued for five years. His surplus of income over out-of-pocket operating expenses averaged about $6,000 per year. Being a poor manager, he allowed this apparent profit to be currently consumed by personal and family demands. At the end of five years, a large estimate for repairs indicated the need for a new truck. The old truck could be traded in on a new one for a net price of $4,000 ($1,000 allowed for the old truck). But Joe had no such resources or credit for borrowing, and he went out of business.

What became of Joe's initial capital? Was the out-of-pocket operating cost a proper basis for assuming profit? Apparently not, as was indicated by the ultimate decline in Joe's fortunes. Before the era of income tax, such errors in the treatment of invested capital were not uncommon among individuals, farmers, and professional people. Even today, some self-employed persons have difficulty with providing for depreciation, although approved practices are included in income tax instructions. Joe should have charged off the truck investment to annual cost, and the periodic amount should have been invested in other assets in order to replace the consumed capital.

Depreciation Concepts

In accounting, depreciation is simply to spread the cost of an investment in a fixed asset over its anticipated life span in some convenient manner. The depreciation amount is periodically deducted from the capital account and added to the cost of operations. The life span is usually expressed in years, and depreciation is usually figured in discrete annual amounts—monthly amounts in some cases. Depreciation can be based on units of production, if the life of the property is so estimated.

To the person engaged in the economic analysis of an important project, accounting records are not as significant as the actual effect of age, use, and conditions on the value of a property. Depreciation is the loss of investment value during a period, and it is continuous, not in discrete annual steps. An automobile depreciates within the first week after its purchase. Value and utility decline with wear (that can not be economically remedied by maintenance), neglect, decay, obsolescence (appearance of improved products), inadequacy (no longer meets requirements), depletion, and disaster. Depletion, such as the exhaustion of a mine, will be discussed later. Maintenance is an operating cost separate from capital recovery. Disaster possibilities should be covered by insurance. The proper depreciation charge is based on an expected life, expected use and operating conditions, and reasonable upkeep.

Whether or not depreciation is based on accounting convenience, business strategy, or consumption of capital, practical estimating in the economy study requires the adoption of a formula that will indicate the amount that should be charged to operations year by year, or per unit of output. There are several commonly accepted methods. All of them require knowledge of initial cost and an assumed life. The salvage, trade-in, or resale value expected at the end of the assumed life may be important. And time value of money is appropriate in some problems.

Anticipated Life

In depreciation of equipment, life in terms of production units is rather uncommon. A tool, such as a stamping die, may be designed to last a certain number of pieces. A product for which special equipment is provided may be planned for a specifically limited quantity. In such cases, the depreciation life may be expressed in terms of output; and the depreciation may be in terms of dollars per piece, per 100 pieces, per pound, per ton, and the like.

The common practice is to state the life in years. For an economy study, this should be a reasonably conservative estimate limited by the term of the project for which the property is intended. There may be additional life for subsequent owners or other uses. Experience and conditions of use guide the estimator. Income tax regulations with regard to depreciation were liberalized in 1962. *Depreciation Guidelines and Rules,* published by the Internal Revenue Service, lists the normal tax lives for many classes of business properties—buildings, machinery, farm animals, etc. The taxpayer will be required to justify deviations from the published schedules and other prescribed depreciation practices.

It is not necessary that the life estimate used in an economy study agree with that prescribed for income tax purposes, although it may be convenient. For business strategy, a short life estimate may be desirable although the property may continue in service long after its first cost has been recovered (written off) by depreciation. This problem will be discussed more fully after depreciation methods have been described.

Salvage Value

Salvage value in depreciation means the amount that can be recovered from disposal of the property at the end of its anticipated life. It can be a considerable percentage of first cost in some cases. Assume a manufacturer makes a precision product which requires general-purpose machines in excellent condition. He plans to use such tools no more than five years, after which they could bring a high price (salvage value) for more ordinary service. A person may make a practice of trading in for a new automobile every two years, and the trade-in value may be as high as 60% of first cost. Such salvage values can not be neglected in computing depreciation.

Salvage values can be negative. An industrial baking oven with much insulation and sheet-metal work may bring less as scrap than removal cost. Removal expenses are proper considerations in salvage value.

Depreciation is often based on zero salvage value because the future worth of the aged property is too uncertain for conservative estimating. The accounting adjustment known as *capital gain* (a taxable profit) ultimately corrects an underestimation of salvage value.

METHODS OF DEPRECIATION

Any reasonable and consistent formula for depreciation may be accepted by accountants and income tax examiners. The analyst engaged in economy study may be concerned with a realistic appraisal which may be different from the accounting records, but a conventional formula would be used in most cases. Let us consider the four most common procedures. The following notation will be used:

F = first cost
n = expected life, or life specified for depreciation purposes
S = salvage value at the end of expected life
D = periodic depreciation (dollars or percentage)
i = interest rate (a decimal) applicable to time value
N = sum of the years = $1 + 2 + 3 \cdots \cdots + n$

Straight-Line Method

Straight line is the term for depreciation that recovers the capital cost in uniform periodic amounts during the expected life. The formula is obvious:

$$D = (F - S)/n$$

D may also be expressed as a percentage of first cost thus:

$$D\% = 100(F - S)/nF$$

This is the simplest and most common method of depreciation. *It should be used in the practice problems in this book unless otherwise specified or conditions indicate another preference.* The most important limitations of the method are that the initial rate of capital recovery may not be rapid enough for good business policy, and the amount of depreciation may not be sufficiently realistic in reflecting the early decline in value of the property.

The straight-line method is invariably used when life is expressed in units of output as previously described.

Declining Balance Method

Declining balance depreciation is the application of a fixed percentage to the periodically diminishing value (the unamortized cost or book value) of the property. In other words, this percentage is applied year after year to the asset's value remaining after deducting the depreciation of previous periods. A 20% rate applying to a first cost of $1,000 for five years results in the following:

Year	Value	Depreciation
0	$1,000.00	..
1	800.00	$200.00
2	640.00	160.00
3	512.00	128.00
4	409.60	102.40
5	327.68	81.92

The percentage could be arbitrarily specified. There are two methods of calculating it. One method aims at a specified salvage value by the nth year. To derive the formula, let

$$x = 1 - D\%/100$$

In the above example, $x = .80$. It is then evident from the demonstration that the unamortized value at the end of the first year is Fx. At the end of the second year, it is Fx^2; and at the end of the third, Fx^3. Hence:

$$S = Fx^n$$
$$x = \sqrt[n]{S/F} = 1 - D\%/100$$
$$D\% = 100 - 100\sqrt[n]{S/F}$$

Income tax regulations have recently provided that a *maximum* percentage *double that of straight line* (without salvage value) can be adopted—$D\% = 200/n$, assuming a life not less than three years. The method can be changed to straight line later to aim at any desired ultimate salvage value. In that case, the salvage value can be zero, which is impossible with a declining balance computation because the depreciation rate can not be 100%.

The advantage of this method of depreciation is the rapid "write-off" in the early life of the asset—better business strategy and more realistic valuation, in most cases. The disadvantages are the more complex calculations and the change in periodic amounts every year.

Sum-of-Digits Method

Sum-of-digits or _sum-of-the-years digits_ is the term applied to a formula that gives results similar to declining balance. The system has the same advantages and disadvantages. The factor N is the sum of the chronologic years, thus:

$$N = 1 + 2 + 3 \cdots \cdots + n = n(n + 1)/2$$

The year-after-year depreciation is:

$$D_1 = n(F - S)/N$$
$$D_2 = (n - 1)(F - S)/N$$
$$D_3 = (n - 2)(F - S)/N$$
$$D_n = (1)(F - S)/N$$

To prove the consistency of the annual amounts, the total depreciation for n years should equal $(F - S)$, which is apparent from the following:

$$\Sigma D = \frac{(F - S)}{N} [n + (n - 1) + (n - 2) \cdots + 1] = \frac{(F - S)N}{N} = (F - S)$$

Sinking Fund Method

A _sinking fund_ is built up by cumulative periodic deposits for an exclusive purpose such as the retirement of a debt. Being reserved for an important objective that _must_ be met, the fund is invested in safe securities during accumulation. No ordinary _reserve for depreciation_ (an accounting device) would be treated as a sinking fund because the capital used in the business usually earns more than it would if invested in the safest of securities. If the depreciating property were vital to the enterprise, the periodic amount of depreciation could be reserved in a sinking fund to safeguard the future; but that is a rare practice.

There are occasions in engineering economy when the analyst may assume a _hypothetical_ sinking fund in connection with depreciation, especially when the project is financed by borrowed money. This is done in engineering estimates of the American Telephone and Telegraph Company, for example. And there are other applications in theoretical economy studies. The practice is known as _sinking fund depreciation._ The formula was developed in Chapter 2.

$$D = (F - S) \left[\frac{i}{(1 + i)^n - 1} \right]$$

Since the periodic deposits are assumed to be invested in a fund, the earnings add to the recovered capital, and the annual amounts are less than required by straight-line depreciation. (The sinking fund deposit factor is always less than $1/n$.) As a measure of decline in the asset's value, sinking fund depreciation is seldom realistic; and business strategy favors more rapid depreciation. For capital recovery over the expected life, however, the logic of sinking fund depreciation is that the amount of depreciation of individual assets should be diverted to new investments within the enterprise to promote growth or preserve its worth.

Other Methods

Special depreciation formulas are sometimes used. If employed for income tax accounting, they must be approved by government authorities. And they must be consistently used; methods can not be changed from year to year. For a certain class of properties, one prominent concern writes off 50% in the first third of the estimated life, 30% in the second third, and 20% in the last third. For certain economy studies, the depreciation for any year can be judged from an estimated drop in value without regard to a long-term pattern, as in the MAPI (Machinery and Allied Products Institute) method of replacement analysis; but that practice would not be acceptable for accounting or income tax purposes.

Comparison of Methods

To illustrate the results of the four depreciation formulas described above, consider a machine that cost $20,000 installed. Estimated life is 12 years, ultimate salvage value $3,000, and interest rate 6%. Two methods of declining balance will be used: (1) the percentage of depreciation is calculated from the specified salvage value, and (2) at double the straight-line percentage *without salvage value* for 8 years, then the straight-line method is used until the specified salvage amount is reached.

		Periodic Depreciation		
Method	*1st Year*	*4th Year*	*8th Year*	*12th Year*
Straight line....................	$1,417	$1,417	$1,417	$1,417
Declining balance (1) @ 14.62%.....	2,924	1,820	967	514
Declining balance (2) @ 16.67%.....	3,333	1,929	930	413
Sum of digits....................	2,615	1,962	1,090	218
Sinking fund....................	1,008	1,008	1,008	1,008

It should be understood that the sum of periodic depreciations, plus interest if a sinking fund is assumed, must be the same regardless of method. The total to be written off during the estimated life is $(F - S)$. If the property continues in service after the original salvage estimate is reached, depreciation can continue based on a lower salvage estimate. When a property is completely written off, no further depreciation can be charged to operations, although service may continue indefinitely.

In view of the above conclusions, why should management tend to favor accelerated depreciation early in the asset's life or by shortening the life estimate? The depreciation charge increases cost, which reduces profit and consequent income tax. Tax savings early in the life of a property have greater *present worth* than tax penalties in later years. Also, income tax rates may be reduced in the future. Another reason is the inflationary trend which makes costs of replacements greater than the capital recovered by ordinary depreciation. Rapid depreciation also guards against unexpected obsolescence or uncertainty in the life estimate.

Disposal of Depreciation

It has been stated that depreciation is deducted from the recorded cost or unamortized cost of a property and charged to operations. Depreciation may go into a *reserve for depreciation*, which is an accounting record for appraisal of investment status and a guide to replacements. In rare cases, depreciation could be deposited in a sinking fund. Except in the sinking fund case, it does not follow that depreciation money is actually used to replace consumption of capital. It should be so used, however, if the worth of the enterprise is to be maintained.

It will occur to the reader that accumulated depreciation on a property may not actually represent the loss of value or consumption of capital that is revealed when the property is disposed of. That situation is taken care of by an accounting device known as *capital gain* or *loss*, previously mentioned. It will be discussed further in connection with book value in the next chapter. The prospect of capital gain encourages rapid depreciation because that form of profit is presently (1960) taxed at a lower rate than other profit in the large successful enterprise.

EXTRACTIVE PROPERTIES AND DEPLETION

Mines, oil wells, gravel pits, timber tracts, and similar properties can become exhausted. These are known as *extractive properties*.

Their depletion is a very real form of capital consumption. The common method of accounting for depletion is equivalent to straight-line depreciation on a units-of-output basis (tons, barrels, etc.). This is known as *cost depletion*.

Usually the most uncertain factor in computing cost depletion is the estimated extent of the deposit. For income tax purposes, it is permissible to reappraise the remaining deposit as a basis for subsequent depletion allowances. But, as in ordinary depreciation, no further depletion charge can be made when the first costs have been written off. Of course, no depletion can be charged when the property is idle. The amount is based strictly on output.

A special method of computing depletion, known as *percentage depletion*, can apply legally (1960) to certain types of extractive property. This is a fixed percentage of the gross income received from the extracted material. The cumulative depletion amounts computed on the percentage basis can exceed the first costs; depletion can continue after the property has been written off. Income tax regulations complicate depletion practice. Various types of leases and mineral rights are additional complexities. It is necessary for the estimator to study the current tax regulations and conditions in his particular industry and location in order to decide on the proper basis for depletion.

Sinking fund depreciation is used for capital recovery in one method of evaluating extractive property (the Hoskold formula) to be described in the next chapter.

AMORTIZATION

Amortization is a term that may apply to capital recovery or to the reduction of debt. In general, it means to reduce an obligation by offsetting charges or payments, which may be according to some prescribed plan such as regular periodic payments. Although the term can be used rather loosely for depreciation, in tax regulations and accounting practice, amortization applies to capital recovery for property or other capital costs without regard to life estimate. It simply means to spread the cost over a convenient number of years, such as in straight-line depreciation without salvage value.

The organizing expenses of a new enterprise are often considered as a permanent asset to be written off only at the end of the venture. Management can elect to amortize that cost over a 60-month period. Tax regulations permit similar amortization of certain physical properties—grain storage and some emergency facilities, in 1960, for example. In general, ordinary depreciation must be employed for capitalized assets such as patents, copyrights, licenses, and the like, all of which have time limits. With the exception of the items mentioned above, all buildings and equipment are subject to depreciation based on expected life.

One unusual application of amortization practice arises in contract settlements that are based on cost. For example, many World War II contracts were terminated before completion, and the contracts provided that the contractors be paid for work done on the undelivered portions of the contracts. If a contractor kept records of the preliminary costs (special tooling and facilities, training of personnel, process development, etc.), those costs could have been amortized over the entire contract and the unamortized portion could have been included in the final settlement. This type of amortization is equivalent to straight-line depreciation based on output.

PROBLEMS

4.1.   A temporary storage building has been erected in a plant area at a cost of $10,000. It is predicted that the building will have to be torn down in 10 years to accommodate plant expansion. The materials would then be worth $800 as scrap or salvage. The dismantling cost is estimated at $1,200. What would be a proper estimate for annual depreciation by the straight-line method?

4.2.   A machine tool cost $32,000 installed. Its life for depreciation purposes is estimated at 15 years, and the salvage value at that time is assumed to be $3,200. Time value estimates require interest at 12%. Compute the depreciation, in dollars, for the first year by the following methods:

   a) Straight line.
   b) Sinking fund.
   c) Declining balance continued to stated salvage value.
   d) Declining balance at maximum rate allowed for tax purposes.
   e) Sum-of-digits.

4.3.   With regard to each of the depreciation methods in the previous problem, consider without computation the depreciation in dollars for the last year (assuming no change in depreciation method during the 15 years).

   a) Would the amount equal, exceed, or be less than the first year's figure?

  b) Would the amount equal, exceed, or be less than that in straight-line computation?

  c) What would be the *average* annual amount for all the methods that aim at the $3,200 salvage value?

4.4. Continue Problem 4.2 by computing depreciation for the years 2, 3, 4, and 5 by the following methods:

  a) Declining balance continued to stated salvage value.

  b) Declining balance at the maximum allowable rate.

  c) Sum-of-digits.

  d) Compute the totals of the amounts written off for 5 years in each case.

4.5. A new machine has just been purchased by a manufacturer for $25,000. Freight and trucking charges were $500, and the installation cost was $250. The machine has an estimated useful life of 12 years, at which time the salvage value is expected to be $5,000. Compute depreciation for the first year by the following methods:

  a) Straight line.

  b) Declining balance to $5,000 in 12 years.

  c) Declining balance at maximum rate allowed for tax purposes.

  d) Sum-of-digits.

4.6. A business building has been erected with the following costs prior to occupancy:

Salaries of superintendent and janitors, 1st month.......$	1,300
Fees for preliminary investigation, survey of site, permits, and legal services...............................	28,000
Cost of land.......................................	350,000
Architect's fee.....................................	40,000
Cost of construction................................	1,500,000
Cost of furnishings.................................	50,000
Advertising for tenants..............................	450
Miscellaneous services during initial period of vacancy after completion of structure.........................	625
Interest on long-term debt...........................	35,000

The estimated life of the building is 40 years without salvage value, furnishings 10 years also without salvage value. Compare the first year's depreciation by four methods. Assume that the earning power of capital is 8% neglecting income tax considerations.

4.7. Compute the depreciation on an automobile—your own car or one in which you are interested. Obtain from the dealer the cost of the new car and the "Blue Book" values of this car, or its equivalent, at the ages of 1, 2, 3, 4, and 5 years. (It should be understood that these are average market values based on average mileage and proper maintenance.) From the values obtained, compute the year-by-year depreciations. Compare the results with depreciations computed by one of the conventional formulas that most nearly approximate the above values.

4.8. The controller of an industrial concern wishes to demonstrate the possible advantages of a method of depreciation that is initially more rapid than the straight-line method now being used. The proposed alternatives are: (1) declining balance at the maximum rate allowable for tax purposes for half the expected life, then straight line for the remainder; and (2) sum-of-digits. These methods are to be compared with straight line in various ways. For the demonstration, the controller has selected a group of equipment representing a first cost of $100,000, expected life 10 years, and no salvage value. The following data are to be computed and tabulated comparatively.

 a) Depreciation (in dollars) for each of the 10 years by the three methods.
 b) Sum of the annual depreciations for each method.
 c) For the two proposed methods, the increase or decrease in depreciation compared with that obtained in straight-line method for each year.
 d) Assume that the results of *c* represent equal decreases or increases in taxable profit and that the income tax would be 52%. On that basis, compute the penalty or saving in tax for each year (Designate the penalty as "−" and the saving as "+").
 e) What is the total penalty or saving by the proposed methods?
 f) Now compute the present worths of the tax savings or penalties for each of the 10 years, and sum the results. Assume an interest rate of 10%.
 g) Compute the annual equivalent of the total present worth for each of the two proposals to indicate a time-valued annual average.
 h) Solely on the basis of previous results, which of the depreciation methods would you prefer?

4.9. Reconsider Problem 4.8. Now assume that the items of equipment depreciated by one of the proposed methods would be equally distributed in age from 0 to 10 years and in first costs, and that replacements of equal first costs would take place at the ends of depreciation lives in each case.

 a) Would there now be a tax advantage in favor of a proposed method? Why?
 b) If the costs of replacements were constantly increasing (as in recent years), would that change your above conclusions?
 c) In addition to the results of the forementioned computations and considerations, what are the comparative advantages and disadvantages of the three methods?
 d) If you were making an economy study that required an estimate of average depreciation for a period of years, which of the above methods would you adopt?

4.10. Review the situation described in Problem 4.8. Management has now decided to adopt declining balance depreciation at double the straight-line rate without salvage value, but only for a portion of the anticipated life of the property in some cases. When the salvage value actually realized is expected to be *less* than would result from declining balance at the end of the asset's life, it is intended to change to straight-line depreciation at an appropriate year. The problem is to specify the age at which depreciation should change to straight line.

a) Based on the present worth advantage of tax savings early in the asset's life, what conditions should characterize the point at which change to straight line should take place? Describe in a general way, without mathematical formulation.

b) Now derive a general formula or mathematical relationship that will meet the above conditions when the anticipated salvage value is zero in n years. (Hint: Let an age of m years be that at which straight-line depreciation will begin. Then the ensuing year's depreciation (D_{m+1}) will be based on the unamortized value of the property at the mth year.)

CHAPTER 5

Valuation

VALUE without modifying adjective or phrase has no precise meaning. Value for what or for whom? An estimate of value, however, can be basically important in an economy study or a simple financial transaction. Consider an elementary situation. A lone traveler in a wilderness loses all his equipment and supplies in a canoe swamped by rapids. He still has a watch that can be bartered for assistance. How much is the watch worth? It has great sentimental value to the traveler because it was given to him by fond parents, now deceased. To the primitive savage whom the man encounters, the watch may seem to be a useless trinket. The man may then meet an itinerant trader whose maximum offer of supplies would be based on the hazards of his business, possible resale value, and bargaining position. Adequate help in this case would probably depend on generosity rather than the intrinsic worth of the watch. It is evident that the value of any property in terms of money or other property depends on conditions and the purpose of evaluation.

Disregarding nonfinancial intangibles such as ethics and emotion, there are three most basic types of evaluation that may be pertinent in economy studies. The values may be classified as:

1. *Book value*—the amount recorded in the accounting records of the enterprise.
2. *Market value*—the price at which the property could be currently bought or sold.
3. *Earning value*—the value of the asset as a contributor to the objectives of the enterprise (cost reduction, income, or profit).

There are modifications and combinations of these basic types, including assessed valuation for tax purposes, replacement cost, replacement cost new less depreciation, going-concern value, and others. It is possible for several types of value to be the same in dollars. For example, a bond may be carried in the books during the first year at its purchase price, a price that may be based on earning power and time value; and the property tax may be based on that value. Ordinarily, the different types of value may be quite different in amounts and significance. As in the case of the traveler's watch, current conditions and purpose affect the results.

BOOK VALUE

Book value is the amount at which an asset is carried in the accounting records of the enterprise. It applies to all assets to which dollar values are attached, including current assets and intangibles. Book values of fixed assets and some intangibles are modified by depreciation, depletion, or amortization. Inventory items and securities may be adjusted for current market conditions. Some intangibles, such as *good will,* may be excluded. Book values depend on accounting practice, business policy, and government regulations.

To a prospective investor, lender of money, or purchaser, book value is not as important as market value and earning potential. Intangibles figure in such transactions. However, the book value of the enterprise as a whole, with its time changes and relationships to operations, is the practical device for appraising financial condition and its growth or decline. It is also a factor in measuring the significance of profit or loss.

Financial Statements

An accounting summary of book values of an enterprise is known as the *balance sheet,* which, in combination with the *profit and loss statement,* indicates the financial status and accomplishment. A condensed balance sheet in rounded figures is shown in Table 5–1.

The values stated in the balance sheet differ in significance according to the accounting practice; and additional details and explanatory notes may be important. Several classes of assets have been previously discussed, but some further comments may be of interest.

Inventories are usually based on cost; but they could be listed at market value if that is lower, for conservative accounting. The cost determination can be complex. Materials may be purchased at variable prices and at times that do not coincide with consumption. Work in process and finished products involve operating costs to be discussed later. The appraisal of inventory in the going concern is a problem for the professional accountant. In the economy study of a

TABLE 5–1

A BALANCE SHEET SHOWING TYPICAL ITEMS IN ROUNDED DOLLARS.

Assets			Liabilities	
Current:			Current liabilities.........$	195,000
Cash...................$		30,000	Long-term debt............	200,000
Inventories.............		350,000	Net worth...............	1,175,000
Receivables.............		40,000	Total. ....$	1,570,000
Prepayments...........		10,000		
Securities..............		25,000		
Total Current.......$		455,000		
Fixed:				
Land...................		45,000		
Buildings..............		400,000		
Equipment.............		650,000		
Total fixed.............$		1,095,000		
Intangibles...............		20,000		
Total Assets.......$		1,570,000		

new project, the analyst would probably include inventory in an over-all estimate of working capital requirement.

Receivables, the amounts due from customers or other debtors, should be adjusted for bad debts that can no longer be considered likely prospects for collection. *Prepayments* are amounts paid in advance on items such as insurance and rent; amounts representing the unconsumed time covered by the payments. *Securities* can be stated at cost or at the current market value.

Fixed assets are subject to depreciation or depletion. Land is usually stated at cost; but accessories, such as roadways, can depreciate, and extractive properties are subject to depletion. All these assets may be listed at first cost, and the accumulated depreciation or depletion can be stated separately as a deduction. If depreciation or depletion is not mentioned, the stated values must be assumed as the depreciated or depleted balances.

Intangibles, if included in the statement, are also subject to depreciation (e.g., patents) or amortization (e.g., organizing expenses). Depreciation or amortization may be included in the stated value or listed separately as described for fixed assets. *Good will* is usually omitted or listed at a low nominal amount such at $1.00. For special purposes, such as in justifying the selling price of a business, good will may be given a very considerable value as will be described later.

Current liabilities include debts that must be retired within the year, accrued tax obligations, amounts due suppliers of goods and services, unpaid dividends and interest, and similar items. *Long-term debt* is an obligation of future years, but the interest due on the principal is a current liability. Other liabilities that can not be classified as above are often listed, such as the accrued obligation for a retirement fund.

Working capital is not separately identified in Table 5–1. It is the difference between current assets and current liabilities. Its significance was discussed at length in Chapter 3.

Net worth is perhaps the most significant of the balance sheet items. It represents the investment of the owners of the enterprise, the net value of the assets after all prior obligations are met. In the statement of a corporation, net worth is a liability of the corporation to the owners; and it is designated *stockholders'* or *shareholders'* equity. The characteristics of ownership will be covered in Chapter 16. Of primary interest at this point is that net worth is a prime factor in judging the adequacy of net profit, and its growth or decline from year to year indicates growth or decline of the enterprise.

Certain ratios of items in financial statements are of particular interest to managers and others financially interested. The relationship between net worth and profit has been mentioned, and this is important in most economy studies as will be indicated in succeeding chapters. The ratio of current assets over current liabilities indicates credit standing, particularly if the assets are restricted to those that can be sold promptly at near the book values (cash, common raw materials, certain finished products, and marketable securities). Goods sold compared with inventories carried is a guide to inventory control. Intelligent appraisal of financial statements is a specialty largely beyond the scope of this book.

Depreciation and Book Value

As previously stated, book values are affected by depreciation, depletion, or amortization. The values of items so treated are the initial costs less the amounts written off (capital recovered). Thus, book value does not necessarily represent the market value of the asset or its actual worth in operating the enterprise. A machine may continue to give useful service long after its depreciated book value becomes zero. On the other hand, it may become prematurely obsolete, inadequate, or worthless in fact, in contrast with a substantial book value. A patent that has years to run may never develop utility. These comments do not necessarily apply to extractive properties which can be reappraised year after year for computing cost depletion. Let us consider the effects of depreciation methods on book values of depreciable assets.

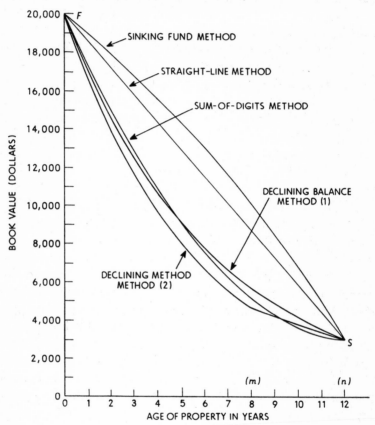

FIG. 5-1.   Depreciated book value of a property, using several methods of depreciation.

Figure 5-1 is a graphic comparison of book values resulting from several methods of depreciation. The equipment evaluated and the essential depreciation factors are those used in the example in the previous chapter (page 45). In addition to the previous notation, the following will be used in the formulas:

m = age of property in years (or other depreciation periods)

ΣD_m = accumulated depreciation at end of m'th year

B_m = book value at end of m'th year = $F - \Sigma D_m$

The book value formulas and applications to the example are as follows: (The book values are figured for an age of 8 years, which is the time at which the second type of declining balance depreciation changes to straight line.)

Straight-line method—

$$D = \$1,417 \text{ per year}$$
$$\Sigma D_m = mD = 8(1,417) = 11,336$$
$$B_m = F - \Sigma D_m = 20,000 - 11,336 = \$8,664$$

Declining balance method (1) for n periods to specified salvage values (S)—

$$D = 14.62\%$$

As indicated in the derivation of the depreciation formula (page 43),

$$B_m = F(1 - D\%/100)^m$$
$$B_8 = (20,000)(.8538)^8 = \$5,646$$

Declining balance method (2) at double straight-line rate—

$$D = 16.67\%$$
$$B_8 = (20,000)(.8333)^8 = \$4,652$$

Sum-of-digits method—Inspection of the depreciation formula (page 44) shows that the annual amounts in *reverse* chronologic order are in proportion to remaining life plus one period $(n - m + 1)$. Then

$$D_m = (n - m + 1)(F - S)/N$$

When $m = n$,

$$D_n = (1)(F - S)/N$$

Figure 5–1 demonstrates that the book value at the end of any year is the ultimate salvage value (S) plus the depreciations that would be taken in the following years. Therefore,

$$B_m = S + \Sigma D_{n-m} = S + [1 + 2 + 3 \cdots\cdots + (n - m)](F - S)/N$$

or,

$$B_m = S + (n - m)(n - m + 1)(F - S)/2N$$

In the example,

$$B_8 = 3,000 + (4)(5)(17,000)/156 = \$5,179$$

Sinking fund method—

$D = \$1,008$ per year

$\Sigma D_m = D \left[\dfrac{(1 + i)^m - 1}{i} \right]$, which includes the accumulated earnings

$B_m = F - \Sigma D_m$

$B_8 = 20,000 - (1,008)(9.8975) = \$10,027$

Summarizing the results obtained in the example by the four methods of depreciation for the age of 8 years (two-thirds the expected life):

Method	Book Value
Straight line	$ 8,664
Declining balance @ 14.62%	5,646
Declining balance @ 16.67%	4,652
Sum-of-digits	5,179
Sinking fund	10,027

It is apparent that an appraisal of stated book values requires knowledge of the depreciation method employed. In general, accelerated depreciation results in book values that are more realistic or conservative. At the end of the depreciation life, however, the results are alike if the same salvage values are used. Book values are zero when first cost is completely written off by depreciation, even when the property has additional useful life or disposal value.

Book Value versus Disposal Value

Whether or not disposal of a physical property takes place early or late compared with expected life, the amount realized would rarely agree with book value. Removal of built-in equipment that is almost new but unexpectedly inadequate may cost more than the scrap can be sold for, although book value may be close to first cost. On the other hand, an old machine tool that has been written off may have considerable worth in the used-machinery market. In 1947, good used cars were often sold for more than new-car prices because deliveries on new cars were so slow. Values of aged property are affected by business conditions and technological changes. The difference between the amount recovered by disposal of a property and its book value is known as capital gain or loss. It is essentially a correction for inevitable disparity in depreciation charges. The same correction applies to other types of assets that are listed in accounting records.

Capital gain is a form of profit because cost would have been reduced by that amount if depreciation were an exact measure of capital consumption. The net annual capital gain—capital gains less capital losses—is subject to income tax at a special rate. When this rate is less than that on ordinary operating profit (25% versus a possible 52% in 1960), rapid depreciation with likelihood of ultimate capital gain is thereby encouraged. Capital gain on a property is not taxable if it applies to trade-in allowance on a replacement. In that case, the recorded investment becomes the net purchase and installation cost plus the old book value. The same principle applies to a residence (when sold at a profit) if it is replaced by another residence within a short time.

The possible tax on capital gain is of significance in economy studies. The effect of the tax is to reduce the recovery value of an aged property that may be pertinent to the study. The analyst must keep up to date on income tax regulations, which may change with every legislative session.

Capital losses may be deducted from capital gains to determine the net result for the year. But, unfortunately, net capital loss can not be treated as an operating cost for tax purposes (as of 1960). To the engineering economist, capital loss is a *sunk cost*. It is "water over the dam." Sunk cost can not be retrieved by failure to take advantage of a profitable venture; and it should not influence decision on a proposed project, with the possible exception of timing. Capital losses may be timed to offset capital gains, for tax strategy.

VALUATIONS BASED ON MARKET CONDITIONS

Market Value

Market value is the price at which a property can be bought or sold. For physical properties and most other assets, it usually differs from book value. It is most likely to be less for properties depreciated by straight-line or less conservative methods.

An estimate of market value (before the transaction takes place) can be highly uncertain if the product is not one that has a stable fixed price market. Supply and demand is a controlling influence that may change greatly in a short time. A special machine may sell at an exorbitant price to a person with an emergency need, and it may be worth no more than scrap when that demand is satisfied. Then there are obvious differences between the price at which the property holder will sell, the price asked, the price bid, and the price that the buyer could be induced to pay. Actual sale may be negotiated at a level between the high and low limits mentioned. Other factors that affect prices will be mentioned in Chapter 7.

In-place Value

In-place value is the purchase price of a property plus the costs of transportation, installation, and preparation for service. For a newly installed item, it is the *first cost*. When the concept is applied to an aged property, the "purchase price" above is the current estimate of market value for an equivalent item, age and condition considered. In-place value is a realistic type of valuation for facilities that already exist and are expected to continue in service.

Salvage Value

Salvage value as a factor in depreciation computation was discussed at length in the previous chapter. In a more general way, the term applies to the amount that may be recovered on a property at *any* time that it may be traded, sold, or scrapped. It is the price paid by the buyer less the cost of removal. Removal cost may include packing and shipping to the buyer. And, if a capital gain is involved, the amount of tax should also be deducted, although salvage value estimates usually neglect it. In the economy study of a new project that involves disposal of existing properties, estimates of salvage values are subject to the uncertainties mentioned in connection with market value. A salvage value can be negative because of removal cost.

Trade-in value, or allowance, is an element of salvage value that neglects removal cost. It is not a market value, although market value may affect it. Equipment or vehicles traded in on replacements are sometimes scrapped by the dealer or manufacturer. The seller's margin of profit on the replacement and the urgency of his need for making the sale are prime factors in trade-in allowance. The effect of capital gain resulting from a trade-in allowance was previously mentioned.

Replacement Cost

Replacement cost is of particular interest in the settlement of damage claims, as in insurance adjustments. It may be equivalent to market or in-place value. But, in some cases, there may be no reliable market information for comparison. Assume that a special structure or machine has been destroyed by fire. Insurance provides for settlement of replacement cost. It may then be necessary to estimate the cost of a new equivalent deducting depreciation based on the age and condition of the old property before destruction. The net cost of a replacement is, of course, modified by the salvage value of the property that is destroyed or replaced for other reasons.

Assessed Value

Taxable property is assessed by government agents as a basis for taxation. Real estate (land and buildings) is always assessed, except the tax exempt. Equipment may be similarly assessed. And in some states, all assets are assessed and taxed.

Policies and practices for property assessment vary greatly among taxing authorities and in different locations. Assessments may be frequent or at rare intervals. They may be based on book value or earning power. For physical fixed property, the most general practice is to estimate market value (for real estate) or in-place value (for installed equipment), and then to make the assessment a fixed percentage of the estimate. The assessment percentage is very low in some locations, which may be offset by a high tax rate. And during the depression of the 1930's, some assessments on real estate were known to exceed the market values. Assessed values in a locality can be very inconsistent if the properties are infrequently assessed.

Good Will at Market Value

Good will may be defined as the intangible worth of an enterprise based on its acquired reputation. Its treatment in the financial statement was previously mentioned.

The most accurate appraisal of good will is to consider it to be the difference between the net worth without good will and the price paid for acquisition of the business (the buyer assuming obligation for outstanding liabilities). In this sense, good will is evaluated at a market price. Good will can be determined in this manner only when a business is offered for sale or sold.

Another basis for good will evaluation is earning power, to be discussed presently.

VALUATIONS BASED ON EARNING POWER

Earning Power

A valuation based on *earning power* is the worth of a property, project, or business based on the profit that it produces. Thus we may say that a conservative, safe bond that earns $400 per year is worth $10,000. Or, possibly, a retail business that realizes a net profit of $100,000 a year is worth $1,200,000. These valuations are not necessarily market values, although professional buyers will consider earning power in price negotiations. On the other hand, a market price may differ considerably from an earning power value as demonstrated in real estate booms, the stock market, and auctions.

Present worth is a common basis for earning power valuations that cover an extended period of time. In general, such an appraisal requires estimates of annual advantage (savings or profit), the duration of that benefit, possible capital expenditures and recoveries, and the rate of return (interest) that should be realized from equivalent investment.

Certain factors in this type of valuation can be exceedingly speculative; others may be quite sure. With a safe bond, one may be assured of the periodic interest payment, the termination date, and the terminal value. But the savings or profit realized from a property, process, or product in a business is subject to the risks of forecasting. The rate of return that would justify an investment in future years is uncertain. The most speculative estimate is usually the duration of the assumed benefit. A patent that is legally good for 17 years may become worthless in a short time because of new developments. And how long may a business enterprise continue to earn its expected profit? Perhaps five years, perhaps 100 years. Nevertheless, management decisions that look into the future must rely on forecasting; and financial appraisal is affected by the time value of money. Uncertainties of the future can be recognized by conservatism in estimates of earning power and time, and by interest rates that reflect risk.

Value of a Business Enterprise

Let us assume that a business has been earning consistently a net profit of $100,000 annually. A conservative estimate of the time that these earnings will continue is 10 years. Experience with this type of business indicates that 10% on investment should be realized. What is the business worth based on earning power?

$$\text{Present worth} = (100,000) \left[\frac{(1.10)^{10} - 1}{.10(1.10)^{10}} \right] = \$614,400$$

To this estimate should be added the present worth of the predicted salvage value of the firm's assets at the end of the 10 years.

Good Will and Earning Power

Good will may be evaluated on the basis of the estimated profit realized because of that asset. Profit estimate may be based on the increase in business resulting from development of clientele and reputation since the beginning, with allowances for changes in investment. The estimates of profit attributable to good will and the duration of that benefit are highly speculative, of course. Hence, the term *intangible* is most appropriate for this asset.

Assume now that the forementioned business is a sales agency with only a small amount of tangible assets. Most of the business volume can be attributed to good will, say $80,000 in this case. Using the same life estimate and interest rate:

$$\text{Good will} = (80,000) \left[\frac{(1.10)^{10} - 1}{.10(1.10)^{10}} \right] = \$491,500$$

Patent Value

In conventional accounting, the book value of a patent is based on its first cost and age, using straight-line depreciation. Actually the patent may be worthless or it may be vital protection for the enterprise. The patent may be earning royalties, others may be interested in buying it, or it may have strategic advantages. Perhaps the annual profit value of the patent can be reasonably estimated, and its life can be assumed. The risk of premature obsolescence (unusually great in patent history) can be taken care of by a high interest rate.

As an example, assume that the earnings attributed to a patent are $8,000 per year, remaining life is 12 years, and expected return on investment is 20%. Then:

$$\text{Patent value} = (8,000) \left[\frac{(1.20)^{12} - 1}{.20(1.20)^{12}} \right] = \$35,510$$

Bond Value

Bond valuation is important to private investors, banks, insurance companies, and treasurers of organizations. Bond prices are subject to market fluctuations. Intelligent appraisal of bonds held or market prices is based on earning power and time value of money. The rate of return demanded by professional buyers largely controls the market prices because bond trading is relatively light among nonprofessional investors.

Student readers may be unfamiliar with the characteristics of bonds, and the following explanation is for their benefit. A bond is, in effect, a promissory note issued by the borrowing institution, and it represents a portion of an extensive borrowing program known as a bond issue. A bond always has a designated par or *face value* stated in round numbers. Except for government bonds, multiples of $1,000 are the most common. With rare exceptions (perpetual bonds), there is always a termination date at which the borrower guarantees to redeem the bond at its face value or some other stipulated amount or condition, such as stock exchange privilege. Furthermore, the borrower guarantees a stipulated interest payment based on face value. Periodic interest in a stated amount of dollars is usually represented by coupons printed in the bond, coupons which may be clipped off and cashed at a bank when due. In Federal Savings Bonds, the interest (compounded) accumulates and is received by the borrower only when he cashes his bond. Ordinary bonds are negotiable (transferable) like currency at any price that may be agreed upon by buyer and seller.

Market prices of bonds may vary considerably from face or redemption values, depending on business conditions and the reputation or prospects of the borrowers. In financial publications, market prices may be reported as follows:

AT&T 2 7/8s 87—high 80 low 78 last 80 (Dec. 7, 1958)

The translation is: American Telephone & Telegraph Co. 2⅞% bonds maturing in 1987 sold at $78 to $80, and the last sales were at $80. Prices are always reported on a $100 face value. This was a depressed bond market. Some later AT&T issues were selling much over par because of advantageous stock exchange privileges.

Professional bond valuation is based on two present worths: (1) that of the periodic interest payments, and (2) that of the stipulated redemption value, usually face value. The formulas will use the following notation:

P = face value
P' = stated redemption value
r = interest rate applied to face value and guaranteed by the borrower
i = rate of return based on purchase price
n = interest periods remaining in the life of the bond
V = value of the bond

The sum of the two present worths mentioned above is the bond value.

$$V = rP \left[\frac{(1 + i)^n - 1}{i(1 + i)^n} \right] + \frac{P'}{(1 + i)^n}$$

Analysis of this formula will show that if $P' = P$ and $r = i$, the bond value will be the face value (P). The most critical factor is the desired rate of return (i) compared with the stipulated interest rate (r).

Assume that a \$5,000 bond is up for sale. It pays 4% (2% every six months) and matures in 10 years. How much would a buyer pay who requires 5% return from such an investment?

$$\text{Present worth of face (redemption) value} = \frac{5,000}{(1.025)^{20}} = \$3,052$$

$$\text{Present worth of periodic interest} = (100) \left[\frac{(1.025)^{20} - 1}{.025(1.025)^{20}} \right] = \underline{1,559}$$

$$\text{Total} = \$4,611$$

The price discount of \$389 is the present worth of the additional 1% yield required of the investment.

A more difficult problem is to determine the yield (i) that would be realized from a bond purchased at a certain price. Referring now to the above example, assume that the bond were offered at \$4,800. What is the yield? It is apparent that the formula does not provide a direct solution for i as a dependent variable. Professional buyers have bond tables to solve this problem, and at least one special slide rule has been devised for the purpose. Without these tools, a cut-and-try solution is necessary. This method will be used in the example.

In general, the bond values for one or more yield rates (i) that seem reasonable should be computed. In the example, a 5% rate gave a value of \$4,611, and a 4% yield would correspond with a par value (\$5,000). Interpolation between the two known values indicates that a rate of 4.51% corresponds with a value of \$4,800. This is close to the exact percentage, as a checking calculation will show. When the result is uncertain, a curve (V versus i) can be plotted for several values of i. The values of i corresponding with various quoted bond values can be found from the graph.

Published market prices do not usually indicate the frequency of interest periods (the nominal interest rate is given) or any special redemption values or exchange privileges. Usually interest is semiannual and redemption value is face value. But the facts must be known if an accurate appraisal of yield is to be accomplished.

Extractive Properties

The *Hoskold formula* is a well-known device for evaluating an extractive property. As in bond valuation, two interest rates are used. One is the required yield on the investment, and the other applies to sinking fund depreciation. In the formula:

R = gross earnings from operations, before deduction for sinking fund
V = value of property
n = estimated life of the mineral deposits
r = rate of return required by owners, before taxes on profit
i = interest rate on sinking fund

Then,

$$R = rV + V \left[\frac{i}{(1 + i)^n - 1} \right]$$
$$V = R / \left[r + \frac{i}{(1 + i)^n - 1} \right]$$

The sinking fund is hypothetical in all probability; and it could be assumed that the equivalent of depreciation or depletion would be invested in new properties that should be expected to earn at the rate demanded from the evaluated property. Then r and i would be equal, and the valuation would become the present worth of annual earnings (R). That is:

$$V = R \left[\frac{(1 + i)^n - 1}{i(1 + i)^n} \right]$$

PROBLEMS

5.1.   Refer to Problem 4.1. Assume that it has become necessary to tear down the storage building in 7 years, to make room for plant expansion, rather than in the 10 years originally estimated.
  a) What is the total amount written off (accumulated depreciation) at the end of 7 years?
  b) What is the capital gain or loss that must be recorded on account of the building's removal?

5.2.   Refer to Problem 4.2.
  a) According to each of the prescribed methods of depreciation, what are the book values in 0, 3, 6, 9, 12, and 15 years?

b) On one sheet of coordinate paper, draw the graphs, book value versus age, for each of the methods.

c) List your order of preference as to method based on:

(1) conservatism as to valuation.

(2) Ease of computation.

5.3. With reference to Problems 4.2 and 5.2, assume that at the end of 9 years the machine is sold for $13,000 f.o.b. purchaser's plant. It cost $800 to remove the machine and deliver it to the purchaser. What is the capital gain or loss in each case?

5.4. A certain manufacturing plant was constructed at a first cost of $6,500,000. A salvage value at the end of a 25-year life was estimated at $150,000. Within $100, what should be the appraisal valuation of this factory at the end of 15 years?

a) By the straight-line method and no interest.

b) By the sinking fund method with interest at 5%. (PE Pa.)

5.5. An asset has a first cost of $13,000, an estimated life of 15 years, and a salvage value of $1,000. For depreciation use the sinking fund method with interest at 5% compounded annually, and find:

a) The annual sinking fund deposit or depreciation charge.

b) The balance in the sinking fund (i.e., the amount accumulated toward depreciation of the asset) at the end of 9 years.

c) If the asset were to be sold for $4,000 at the end of 9 years, what would be the net capital gain or loss? (PE Pa.)

5.6. A shipping firm purchased a freighter for $2,000,000. The expected life of the vessel was 20 years and the salvage value $100,000. In order to safeguard the investment, the company deposited the annual depreciation allowance in an actual sinking fund that was expected to earn $3\frac{1}{2}\%$. Now, after 15 years, a replacement of this vessel is being considered. The company would like to obtain a new ship that will cost $2,500,000. The old vessel can be sold for $500,000.

a) What would be the capital gain or loss from the transaction?

b) How much new capital would the firm have to raise in order to make the purchase of the proposed new vessel?

5.7. A government contract for a special product contained a clause on termination settlement providing for payment to the contractor that would include all costs incurred on any uncompleted (canceled) portion of the order. The order was for 1,200,000 units of product. The contractor kept a record of all special tools and preparation costs, which amounted to $45,000.

The contract was canceled by the government when only 900,000 units of product had been completed. Before final settlement on the contract, salvage of the special equipment had been authorized at a price of $4,500.

The removal cost was $500. How much did the government owe to the contractor for the unamortized cost of preparation and tooling?

5.8.   A financing firm is considering the purchase of a manufacturing plant that is up for sale. The price to be offered depends on a careful appraisal of the assets. In checking the major items of equipment, for example, it was estimated that these could be bought in equal age and condition for $225,000. Transportation from sources of supply would total a probable $9,000; and the installation cost would approximate $7,500. What type of value could realistically apply to these items, and how much in dollars?

5.9.   The annual operating cost for government and municipal services in a small city has been estimated at $3,500,000. In this case, the annual cost is financed entirely by a tax on real estate, the current market value of which has been estimated at $175,000,000. A standard for tax assessment is to be decided upon. It is agreed that, for various reasons, the *assessed* valuations of properties should be considerably less than market value at the time of assessment. Low assessments are easier to defend; but the lower assessments would require a higher tax rate to obtain the same funds. It is now desired to compute the tax rates that would be required for various percentages of market value that could be adopted for assessment purposes. Make the computation for 40%, 50%, 60%, and 70% of market value. (Tax rates are usually expressed in dollars per $1,000 of assessed value, or in mills—for example, $25/$1,000 or 25 mills.)

5.10.   Referring to the situation described in Problem 5.9, assume that you have recently purchased a home in that city for $25,000. Assessments for taxation are now based on 60% of market value. What property tax (in dollars per year) could you expect in this case?

5.11.   A serious fire in a manufacturing plant damaged much of the equipment. One item, a special machine, was reduced to scrap. The scrap value was estimated at $50. The first cost was $45,000. The original life estimate was 20 years, and the salvage value $4,500. The machine was only 8 years old when destroyed; but, in that time, the cost of similar special machines has increased 15%. No market information is available on used equipment of this type. Based on straight-line depreciation, what would you consider a reasonable insurance settlement on this piece of equipment, assuming full insurance coverage?

5.12.   Assume that you own a patent that is 5 years old. It expires in 12 years. You are not using the patent yourself, but licensees are paying royalties averaging $425 per month. One of the licensees now offers to purchase the patent outright for $30,000. Should you accept this offer? You believe that you could realize 15% per year on a similar investment. There is no reason to predict any change in patent royalties.

5.13.   A manufacturer offers an inventor the choice of two contracts for the exclusive right to manufacture and market the inventor's patented article. Plan A calls for an immediate single lump-sum payment of $33,-000. Plan B calls for an annual payment of $1,100 plus a royalty of 55¢ for each unit sold. The remaining life of the patent is 10 years.

Assuming interest compounded annually at 5%, what must be the uniform annual sale of the article to make Plan B as attractive to the inventor as Plan A (disregarding income tax considerations)? (PE N.Y.)

5.14.   A university has been engaged in a publishing business and now wishes to abandon that activity. One of the successful books has provided a net profit of $8,000 per year. This book is expected to sell at this rate for another 5 years at least. A commercial publisher owning the copyright could require a return of 20% annually (before taxes) on the investment. On that basis, what is a reasonable asking price for the copyright?

5.15.   One hundred shares of a certain stock were purchased 12 years ago for $30 per share. The stock paid dividends of $2.00 per share for 8 years, and then $1.50 per share for 4 years. The stock was then sold for $20 per share. What rate of return was made on the investment? (PE N.J.)

5.16.   A retail store is up for sale. The net value of tangible assets has been appraised at $475,000. The firm has been averaging an annual net profit of $85,000 for several years. The business is in a good location and has acquired an enviable reputation. It is estimated that this favorable condition should continue for at least 10 years with good management. Assume that such a business should realize a minimum annual return of 8% on capital invested.

  a) What is a reasonable price for the store?
  b) In a financial statement, based on the above valuation, what should be the amount of *good will?*

5.17.   A highway-construction firm is considering the purchase of new road-making equipment that will cost $15,000. This item is expected to last 12 years with negligible salvage value. It will save a considerable amount of hand labor. Capital for such equipment is considered to be worth 24% in annual return (before income tax). What are the minimum annual savings in labor that would justify the purchase of the equipment?

5.18.   The royalty rate is 15¢ per ton on 15,000,000 net tons of coal. If mining is to start 25 years from now and will require 16 years to mine, calculate the appraised value, to the lessor, of the coal in place, based on interest at 8%. (PE Pa.)

5.19.   What is the value of a perpetual endowment that will provide an institution with an income of $50,000 per year? Invested funds are expected to earn an average of 4% annually.

5.20. The purchase of a certain $5,000 bond is being considered. The bond matures in 25 years and pays 4½% interest (on a semiannual basis). What should be the market price of this bond at the following nominal rates of yield on investment: (a) 4%, (b) 4½%, (c) 5%, (d) 6%?

5.21. The bond of the previous problem is available at a price of $4,500. What yield would be realized in this case? Compute the answer to the nearest .1%.

5.22. In June, 1961, bonds of the XYZ Company were quoted on the New York Stock Exchange as follows:

XYZ 4¼'s 80............last 92

It was known that the interest coupons would be payable on January 1st and July 1st of each year, the last coupon being dated July 1, 1980. What was the yield to be expected from this bond if purchased at the closing price indicated above?

5.23. A man paid $1,100 for a $1,000 bond that pays $40 per year. In 20 years the bond will be redeemed for $1,050. What net rate of interest will the man obtain on his investment? (PE Pa.)

5.24. A syndicate has purchased a mine for $1,000,000, which yields a net income of $100,000 per year (excluding depletion allowance). It is estimated that the mine will produce for 20 years. Part of each year's net income is set aside at 4% so that the original investment will be intact when the mine is exhausted. What annual rate of net income (after depletion allowance) is the syndicate realizing on its investment? (PE Pa.)   6.6 %

5.25. It is estimated that the Deep Gulch Mine, now operating, can be expected to make a net profit, after all taxes are paid, of $150,000 per year for 35 years, at which time it will be exhausted and have no salvage value. What can you afford to pay for the mine now if you wish to have an annual income of 12% on your investment left after you have made an annual deposit into a fund which, at 3% interest, will accumulate to the amount of your investment (return of investment) in 35 years when the mine will be exhausted? (PE Ohio)

5.26. An extensive gravel deposit is up for sale at a price of $160,000. At a feasible rate of extraction, it is estimated that a gross profit of $60,000 per year could be realized before making allowance for depletion and income tax. A person engaged in this business demands a return of 30% on investment (before profit tax). It is also assumed that a sinking fund to protect the investment (or for capital recovery) would average 3½% in earnings. According to the Hoskold formula, how long would the deposit have to last at the anticipated rate of extraction to justify the asking price?

CHAPTER 6

Operating Cost

OPERATING COST, as the term will be used in this book, is the aggregation of current expenditures and apportionments of other costs which can be appropriately charged to current operations, but excluding interest on debt and deductions from profit (e.g., bonuses and income taxes). In general, when an expenditure can not be classed as investment, a financing transaction, a share out of profit, or a disbursement from some special reserve fund, it is an operating cost.

For the purpose of determining profit or loss, operating cost is customarily accumulated for annual periods (fiscal years). But periodic appraisals may be made at frequent intervals, such as monthly. And appraisals may apply to individual orders, products, or activities. In subsequent problems, time periods are assumed to be annual unless otherwise specified or implied. For economy study, operating cost can be time valued; it can be analyzed for variability; and it can be classified and apportioned to activities, products, and orders—an objective of cost accounting.

Cost Accounting

The basic objectives of *cost accounting* are: (1) to determine the cost of individual projects, products, orders, or services rendered by the enterprise; and (2) to determine the cost of internal activities for administrative purposes. The first of these objectives is of particular interest in economy studies. Costs must be predicted for proposed projects, and cost experience of the past is necessary for appraisal of existing operations. Professional accounting is devoted mostly to historical records (records of transactions that have taken place). Budget preparation is partly an accounting process. The engineering economist is concerned mostly with cost prediction, and his methods may not conform with the conventional accounting practices.

71

In the cost analysis of a particular activity, it is relatively easy to identify the costs that are immediately and exclusively associated with it. These costs may be classified as *direct*. When the operation subject to appraisal is part of a larger enterprise and shares facilities and benefits of organization, it must also share costs that can not be classified as direct. These costs that must be appropriately shared may be termed *indirect* because they can not be immediately and exclusively associated with the appraised item. The aggregation of direct costs charged to a particular project, order, product, or service sold to a customer is often known as *prime cost*. It represents immediate out-of-pocket expenditures. The aggregation of indirect costs that must accompany prime cost is known as *overhead, expense,* or *burden*, the apportionment of which is the major problem of cost accounting. In a business enterprise, it must be understood that all operating costs, direct or indirect, must be reflected in the costs of the various products or services sold to customers. And the costs of said products or services must be determined in order to appraise profit accomplishments or potentials.

DIRECT COSTS

Direct Labor

Direct labor is the cost of labor that can be conveniently and exclusively identified with the project, order, product, or service under consideration. In a manufacturing enterprise, it is the labor cost of machine operations and other work performed directly on the product. In construction work and special orders of any kind, it could include engineering and other activities that can be separately identified with the job. In the operation of public utilities and other service enterprises, direct labor is the work performed exclusively for a particular customer service—the wages of a train crew, for example.

Direct labor is usually easy to identify with an order and easy to accumulate from time cards or similar recordings that are a historical record of the workers' time. Estimating direct labor for a new project, however, may require difficult analysis and involves the usual risks of forecasting. Some work that is directly connected with an individual order may be difficult to separate from the miscellaneous responsibilities of the worker, and to time the miscellaneous jobs throughout the day consumes recording time and accounting cost. Such labor may be classed as indirect for accounting convenience.

Direct Material

Direct material is the material which can be conveniently and directly attributed to the product, order, project, or customer service under consideration. It is the raw material and parts that go into a product, including portions that are lost in processing. In a construction job, it could include various supplies that are known to be consumed by the particular job. To be classed with direct material as a part of prime cost are special tools and equipment that can be charged exclusively to the order for work.

Requisitions for material, or other records of amounts consumed, usually identify that which can be charged to the individual work order. Therefore, the determination of direct material cost is comparatively easy in the going enterprise. As in the case of direct labor, there are exceptions. For example, the consumption of anodes and chemicals in electroplating would be difficult to measure for a short run of work. Convenience and economy would dictate the treatment of such materials as indirect costs. This practice applies quite generally to supplies that are accessory to production work. For economy studies of new projects, the estimating of material costs is a problem of analyzing needs and forecasting prices.

INDIRECT COSTS

Overhead

Overhead is the aggregation of all operating costs that can not be conveniently identified as direct labor and direct material. It includes all indirect costs—labor, material, salaries, rent, heat, power, light, transportation, purchased services, insurance, operating taxes, property taxes, depreciation, and other costs that must be spread over the operations of the enterprise. The terms *burden* and *expense* are also used, but with somewhat restricted meanings by certain accounting authorities. (Burden applies to the factory or manufacturing division, and expense to costs of administration and sales.) In the technical sense, *expense* means overhead; it does not include expenditures for capital goods, direct material, or direct labor. For our purposes, we shall adopt the term *overhead*, but the reader should recognize the synonymous expressions.

Overhead costs must be apportioned to all activities that share in their benefits. The total costs of all products and services to be sold must include the total of overhead costs. In the business devoted exclusively to manufacturing and selling, the ideal situation is that the summed-up costs of all product items produced will equal the total direct and indirect costs of operations. The equitable distribution of the overhead costs is often a complex accounting problem. The person engaged in project analysis in a going concern may employ overhead rates supplied by the accountants if the rates seem reasonable; or it may be necessary for him to adjust the existing rates. Conspicuous changes in overhead items must be recognized. And for a proposed new enterprise, the estimator will have to start "from scratch." In ensuing practice problems, *depreciation* identified with a project is usually separated from other overhead charges.

Distribution of Overhead

The simplest and least accurate method of distributing overhead to individual orders is to establish a single fixed rate that is to be applied to all direct labor or direct material involved in such orders. In fact that charge may include profit, a practice that is customary in service industries that charge customers an hourly rate—an automobile service station, for example. The overhead rate can be made applicable to labor hours (as in the case just mentioned), to the cost of direct labor, to the cost or quantity of direct material, or to the prime cost. A *percentage* applies to direct cost; otherwise, the charge is in terms of dollars per hour, per ton, and the like. The following is a cost summary for a situation in which a 220% charge for overhead is based on direct labor cost. A single order is represented.

```
Direct labor.....................................$2,500
Direct material................................    600
Overhead.......................................  5,500
     Total cost................................$8,100
```

In many enterprises, however, the single overhead rate is not accurate enough. Several kinds of production departments or work centers may be employed and in various proportions for different products. In most concerns of substantial size, it is necessary for administrative purposes to separate the cost of manufacturing (factory cost) from the administrative and sales overhead. Other overhead charges, as for special tooling, may deserve identification. The following summary illustrates how the cost of the above order might be detailed if the costs were departmentalized. Overhead rates vary in the three factory departments.

	Foundry	Machine Shop	Assembly	Total
Direct labor	$1,000	$200	$1,300	$2,500
Direct material	200	...	400	600
Departmental overhead	1,250	350	1,020	2,620
Material overhead	6	...	16	22
Special tools	...	250	125	375
Factory cost				6,117
Administrative expense				612
Sales expense				1,835
Total cost				$8,564

In addition to the departmental rates, note that overhead to cover material storage and handling is separately identified. The costs of special tooling (to be absorbed in this one order) could have been added in the previous example.

Ordinarily, *cost accounting* in the going concern ends with the factory cost (or manufacturing cost). But knowledge of total cost is often essential, for example—to determine the cost of a cost-plus contract, or to estimate the profitableness of individual products. We have not described how the forementioned overhead rates are established. Let us consider the general aspects of this problem. The techniques in detail are an accounting specialty.

Excluding strategic and administrative objectives, the purpose of establishing departmental overhead rates is to make the individual work orders absorb their fair shares of total overhead costs. The ideal result is the condition in which the overhead charged to all the individual orders during a year will equal the total overhead cost during that period. This perfect balance is never accomplished. The accounting adjustments required and the administrative controls are beyond the scope of this book. In principle, however, the steps in the process of distribution in a manufacturing enterprise are:

1. Distribute a fair share of all anticipated overhead costs among all departments. The total for each department is its overhead budget for the accounting period.
2. Redistribute to all manufacturing departments or work centers all overhead of the nonmanufacturing departments in the factory division.

3. Establish an overhead rate for work done in each of the producing departments in accordance with the department budgets and the anticipated volume of work.
4. Charge overhead to individual work orders in accordance with the established rate.

The process is similar for organizations concerned with construction, transportation, and other types of industry. The first three steps are periodic, monthly to yearly. The last step applies when work is done or estimated.

Overhead Budgets

A preliminary study of organization and facilities is needed to determine a suitable basis for distributing overhead costs among divisions and departments or work centers. This is a matter of experienced judgment. It may seem most appropriate to distribute building costs (rent, depreciation, and maintenance) on the basis of area occupied. Heat and light may be treated similarly. Horsepower of equipment may be the best indicator for sharing of power cost. The number of personnel, labor hours, salaries and wages paid, direct labor only, or direct material handled may be appropriate. Of course, overhead costs confined to the organization unit belong to that group —the foreman's salary and depreciation on the department's equipment, for example. There are times when the budgeting or apportionment of overhead is somewhat arbitrary or unusual. For example, during World War II, one large concern with several plants apportioned administrative and sales expense among the plants according to the outstanding orders assigned to each. In that case, government accountants objected to the charge and negotiated a considerable reduction in a contract settlement.

The purpose for reapportioning all the factory overhead costs to the producing departments or work centers is to provide a means for charging all the overhead to work turned out. It is production that must pay for all the costs. This applies to any primary service rendered to outside consumers—power, water, transportation, and the like.

Budgets may be revised frequently (e.g., monthly) to conform with actual expenditures and changes in forecasts. When costs are greater or credits (charges to work done) are less than anticipated, overhead is said to be underabsorbed. And the opposite (overabsorption) can be true. These differences between the budget and the actual are matters for accounting adjustments, with which the person engaged in economy study is rarely concerned. The estimator must be guided by forecasts.

Departmental Rates

Decision as to the distribution of overhead to cost of work done can be a controversial issue even among expert accountants, whether or not the charges are made on a departmental or company-wide basis. What seems to be the fair share? It depends on conditions. The decision can be arbitrary (as in budgeting) or a matter of expediency. Ordinarily, overhead is apportioned according to direct labor hours, direct labor cost, direct material cost, prime cost, direct material quantity, machine-hours, or a combination of these. Various departments in the same organization can be handled differently. In a shop with some very costly and some inexpensive machines, it would be hardly appropriate to charge overhead based on labor for all the work turned out; a suitable rate per hour should be charged for work on each machine. Perhaps the most common basis is direct labor cost because this cost is always recorded, and it may also be assumed that higher-priced labor should bear more of the overhead share. Direct material is not often used except as a basis for a separate charge (as in the previous example), but it could be used when its cost or quantity is a good measure of the work done. Accountants should be consulted about the pros and cons of these bases when the indications are not clear.

An overhead rate is customarily established for application to work done. This rate is derived from the overhead budget and the anticipated amount of work that will be accomplished. For a department using direct labor cost as the base, the budget may be $100,000 and the anticipated labor $60,000. Then the rate is:

$$\text{Overhead rate} = 100{,}000/60{,}000 = 1.67 = 167\%$$

which means that each dollar expended for labor on a job should be accompanied by $1.67 for overhead.

To review the principles that have been described, assume that a factory of modest size (the one represented in the example on page 75 is in a suburb where lunch facilities are not available. The company must operate its own cafteria at a loss estimated at $8,400 per year. This cost is to be charged to the three producing departments, to be charged in turn to the work which they turn out. It seems most reasonable to make the apportionment on the basis of number of employees as follows:

	Foundry	Machine Shop	Assembly	Total
Number of employees.......	35	60	45	140
Percentage of total.........	25%	42.86%	32.14%	...
Apportionment............	$2,100	$3,600	$2,700	$8,400

Now assume that the overhead budget for the year, including the above item and a good many other charges, totals up as follows:

	Foundry	Machine Shop	Assembly	Total
Overhead budget..........	$131,200	$437,500	$157,500	$726,200
Anticipated direct labor.....	$105,000	$250,000	$180,000	$535,000
Departmental rate.........	125%	175%	87.5%	(149%)

The last percentage listed is the single factory rate that would be obtained if the overhead were not departmentalized; it is not the average of the three departmental rates. The department rates are not based on the total $726,200, but on the budgets of the individual departments. For example, for the foundry:

$$\text{Overhead rate} = 131,200/105,000 = 1.25 = 125\%$$

Overhead rates vary greatly in practice. Rates based on labor cost may range from 50% to 500%, depending largely on the extent of mechanization. Where automation is extensive, the rate would hardly be based on labor but on machine time. High overhead does not necessarily indicate high product cost. It is the total per unit of output that is significant.

Administrative expense if related to factory cost is usually low, perhaps 5% to 15%. It could be much higher for a concern that requires a relatively large amount of engineering and development work that is classed with administrative cost. Sales expense may be high related to factory cost, depending on the character of product and method of selling. Some products cost more to sell direct to consumers than the cost accumulated in those products as they go into stock. Low sales expense incurred by the producer does not necessarily permit low price to the consumer. Distribution may involve costs (and profits) to a chain of agencies to reach the consumer.

PERIODIC COSTS AND UNIT COSTS

In the appraisal of an enterprise as a whole, the departmental costs and the cost details of projects, products, and orders are not always significant. Most important are the periodic sums of the basic classes of cost, usually the monthly or annual totals. Direct labor and direct material may be identified in the financial summary (profit and loss statement). Factory cost (or manufacturing cost) is often designated *cost of goods sold*. Administrative and sales expenses may be combined in one total.

The overhead rates that have been described are applied to work orders in the accounting process. Individual work orders may cover separate projects, customers' orders or contracts, or production lots of various products. Departmental rates are most significant in the fair cost appraisal of such orders and for estimating new work or new projects. Therefore, they are important in economy studies.

When an economy study is concerned with a product that is produced in lots or batches, the *unit cost* is always important. Of course, it is significantly related to the price at which the product can be sold. Unit factory cost plus administrative overhead indicates to the sales organization the cost and profit margin available for their operations.

Unit cost is simply a periodic total or order cost divided by the units of output involved. The same overhead rates apply to the units of output as to the quantity represented by the period or order. The choice of unit may not be obvious. It should be the unit by which the product is distributed or sold. This applies also to service operations. Examples of appropriate units are: tons of refined ore, 1,000 cubic feet of gas, ton-miles of freight, room-days for a hotel, kilowatt-hours for power, square feet of storage space, car-miles for highway travel, cwt. (100 lb. units) for certain refined metals.

PROBLEMS

6.1.   Following is a list of typical operating costs that could apply to a manufacturing establishment.

Telephone bills
Electric power bills
President's salary
Advertising
Material going into product
Salaries in accounting office
Loss in food service
Real estate taxes
Chemicals for electroplating
Salesmen's commissions

Supplies issued to producing departments
Depreciation on production equipment
Depreciation on general equipment (elevators, etc.)
Clerical salaries in production office
Wages to operators of production machines
Depreciation and maintenance on building

a) Classify these costs as *direct labor, direct material,* or *overhead.*
b) Subclassify the overhead items indicating those that could be charged exclusively to *factory, administration,* or *sales,* and those that would require apportionment.
c) Identify the overhead items that could be charged directly or apportioned to the factory, and suggest an appropriate basis for their distribution to producing departments.

6.2.   Assume that the following overhead expenses in a manufacturing division are to be apportioned to several producing departments. State an appropriate basis for the apportionment of each item, assuming that supporting data are available.

Compressed air
Factory office salaries
Electric power
General heating
Sanitary supplies
Office supplies
General maintenance of machinery
Building depreciation and maintenance
Trucking service (predominantly raw material)

Depreciation on office equipment and furnishings
General janitor service
Maintenance of interdepartmental conveyor system
Operating cost of interdepartmental telephone service
Medical supplies for first-aid stations
Shipping costs from factory to warehouse (finished products)

6.3.   The following overhead budgets have been assigned to four producing departments. Also indicated are the anticipated amounts of direct labor hours, average wage rates, and direct material consumed in each department.

Dept.	Overhead	Direct Labor Hours	Average Wage per Hour	Direct Material
A	$15,000	4,250	$2.50	$10,000
B	16,000	2,550	3.00	1,500
C	9,000	3,400	2.25	2,500
D	12,000	5,100	2.00	3,000
Totals	$52,000	15,300		$17,000

a) Compute by four methods the overhead rates that could apply to work done, without departmentation (a single factory rate).
b) Compute departmental rates by each of the four methods.

6.4.   Referring to the situation described in Problem 6.3, assume that an order has been completed with the following returns:

Dept.	Hours	Wages	Material
A	55	$130	$350
B	60	188	125
C	42	96	3
D	5	10	75

a) Compute the total *factory* cost based on one set of departmental rates determined in Problem 6.3. Also use a similar single factory rate and compare results. Which is the more reasonable?

b) Under what conditions would the results of departmental rates and a single factory rate be identical (by any of the four methods) in computing an order cost?

c) If you were to attempt a precise cost estimate for an entirely new product handled in the four departments, which of the demonstrated methods would you employ? Why? (Assume that overhead rates would not be seriously affected by the new product.)

6.5. As a sequel to Problem 6.4, it is desired to estimate the total cost of the order to check against the selling price. The normal administrative expense rate is 10% based on factory cost, and sales expense is 25% on the same basis. Using the departmental rates of the previous problem, determine the total cost. Enumerate conditions that would cause you, as a manager, to question the significance of the computed cost.

6.6. A large company employing 16,000 workers is considering the use of a comprehensive aptitude test for new employees to fit them into the proper jobs. It is estimated that these tests will reduce labor turnover 5%. The turnover ratio at the present is 30%, which means that 4,800 replacements are being hired annually. The cost of hiring and training each new employee is $55. The proposed new plan will cost $10,500 annually to administer plus $5.00 in wages for each new employee who takes the test. Determine:

a) The annual cost of replacements under the present system.

b) The annual cost of replacements under the new system.

c) The economic justification for *adopting* or *not adopting* the new system, including intangible considerations. (PE Pa. revised)

6.7. For the past 10 years a certain small city has spent an average of $2,500 per year to maintain a certain section of pavement on one of its main streets. A politician, campaigning for election, claimed that the city could have had a new pavement for less than was paid for repairs on the old one. A conservative estimate indicated that the new paving could have been installed 10 years ago for a total cost of $19,000, which could have been financed by the sale of $19,000 worth of 10-year 4% non-callable bonds. The annual cost of maintenance of the new paving would have been $300.

a) Was the politician's claim a correct statement?

b) Justify your answer by annual cost figures to the city for the new paving venture. (PE Pa.)

6.8. A centrifugal pump is to operate against a head of 135 ft. and is to discharge 250 gallons of water per minute. The pump has an efficiency of 65%. Calculate:

a) The water horsepower.

b) The brake horsepower required to operate the pump.

c) Assume that 180,000 gallons per day is the average output. The electric motor which drives the pump has an efficiency of 85%. The cost of electricity is 1.8¢ per K.W.H. What is the cost of operation for a 30-day month? (PE Pa.)

6.9.   A certain electric motor-driven water-pumping plant has a capacity of 2,500 gallons per minute operating against a 132-ft. head. At full load the plant operates at 75% over-all efficiency, i.e., from electric input to water delivered to the pond. At half load it operates at 45% efficiency. The plant operates at full load 4,000 hours per year, and at half load 3,760 hours per year. The costs associated with the plant operation are as follows:

> First cost installed........................$5,500
> Annual fixed charges......................15%
> Average cost for electricity...............1.4¢/K.W.H.
> Weight of water...........................8.34 lbs./gal.

From the above data determine:

a) The total annual cost of operating the plant.

b) The average cost per 1,000 gallons pumped. (PE Pa.)

6.10.   With reference to the pumping plant of Problem 6.9, now assume that the half-load operation for 3,760 hours is to be paid for by a customer. The charge is to be based on an appropriate share of the annual cost of operations. For this customer, what is the annual cost and the cost per 1,000 gallons?

6.11.   A certain company is a manufacturer of novelties of miscellaneous types. All production is on a job-lot basis. There are three producing departments, designated A, B, and C.

The company's cost system is essentially as follows: All *factory overhead* costs are allocated directly to the producing departments. Any reasonable basis is used for these allocations, depending on the character of the individual cost item. The anticipated totals for each of these departments constitute their overhead budgets for the fiscal period. These budgets are the bases for overhead rates that are applied to individual products and orders. The rates are expressed as a percentage of direct labor cost. When it is necessary to estimate total cost of individual products or orders, an administrative rate (percentage) is applied to the factory cost. The sales expense percentagewise is applied to *production* cost (factory cost plus administrative expense). The knowledge of production cost gives the sales organization a cost basis for promoting and pricing the product.

The cost estimates for the fiscal period are as follows:

Anticipated direct labor:
Department A..$ 700,000
Department B.. 1,600,000
Department C.. 800,000
Anticipated direct material:
Department A.. 550,000
Department B.. 300,000
Department C.. 50,000
Factory overhead items:
Charged directly to individual departments:
Department A.. 250,000
Department B.. 350,000
Department C.. 150,000
Indirect labor and salaries................................ 1,250,000
Buildings depreciation and maintenance.................... 750,000
Heat and light... 250,000
Electric power... 400,000
Depreciation on general equipment........................ 1,300,000
Indirect materials....................................... 100,000
Miscellaneous items...................................... 200,000
Administrative expense................................... 1,000,000
Sales expense.. 2,500,000
Total operating cost.....................................$12,500,000

The following information is available for possible use in distribution of overhead:

	Dept. A	Dept. B	Dept. C
Floor area. sq. ft.	40,000	50,000	10,000
Rated horsepower	900	1,250	100
Direct labor hours	450,000	700,000	350,000
All employees	250	380	195

a) Determine the overhead rates for administration, sales, and individual producing departments; also a single factory rate.

b) Determine the *total* cost for a special order on which the returns were as follows:

	Dept. A	Dept. B	Dept. C
Direct material	$1,500	$ 200	$600
Direct labor	2,500	1,800	500

Compute the costs using departmental factory rates, also the single factory rate, and compare results. Under what conditions would the two results be the same? What conditions as to sales or operations regarding this order would modify management's opinion regarding the computed cost.

6.12. Select some substantial manufacturing industry with which you are familiar. You are to make an economy study of an entirely new product that is proposed for adoption. The existing buildings, organization, and general equipment will be used without change. The project will require production equipment and activities in the factory and sales organization that will have effect on overhead charges.

Assume that the capital requirements have been determined. Your immediate problem is to estimate the annual operating cost. Make a comprehensive list of the costs that will have to be considered. Items that are similar (e.g., costs of individual production operations) may be grouped under single titles. The details listed, however, must be appropriately grouped according to operating division and class of cost.

CHAPTER 7

Income, Profit, and Yield

INCOME

THE term *income* has various refinements of meaning in accounting practice and tax regulations. The Supreme Court has accepted the following definition: "Income may be defined as the gain derived from capital, from labor, or from both combined, provided it be understood to include profit gained through a sale or conversion of capital assets." There is a gross income (gross profit) which is prior to deductions for administrative and sales expense, a taxable or net income after deduction of operating costs and interest before income tax, and a final net income after taxes (net profit). To clarify our discussion we shall adopt a definition that conforms more nearly to the layman's concept. *Income,* as used here, is the receipts from operations, excluding certain financing transactions such as borrowing or payments received on the principal of a loan, and accounting adjustments such as capital gain (unless the latter is an objective of the enterprise).

In economy studies, we are principally interested in the receipts from the sale of products or services. Government enterprises may have similar interests—toll charges, rentals, and sales of power, water, transportation, and fertilizer, for example. Income, then, depends on two primary factors: selling price per unit of product or service, and quantity sold. We shall assume that the buyer's obligations to the seller are met in accordance with the selling price (the net amount).

Selling Prices

Prices were mentioned in connection with expenditures for capital goods and operating materials. Those prices affect investment and operating cost. Equally or more important are the selling prices that control income—the prices charged for the products or services provided by the enterprise. The establishment of selling prices is a critical management problem. And the estimation of selling prices is essential in the economy study of a proposed new project that involves sales.

To illustrate the critical nature of pricing, consider an actual situation of the late 1930's. A new product was developed to outperform all similar offerings by several competitors. The product was priced the same as the competing devices (which were about equal to each other). Very soon after introduction of the new product, however, the competitors reduced their prices; and quality advantage in the new product was not sufficient to offset the ensuing price disadvantage. Unfortunately, the cost of the new product was too high to permit its price reduction, and it was withdrawn from the market in five years. Almost all new enterprises incur similar risk as to price potentials.

In profit-making enterprises, it must not be presumed that price is customarily based on cost. In the routine pricing of items in a line of products, a fixed mark up (a percentage perhaps) may be added to cost. Some contracting is done on a cost-plus basis—cost plus a percentage of cost, or cost plus a fixed dollar allowance. But in the usual strategy of pricing, cost simply indicates the level below which profit cannot be realized. Even as a guide to pricing, cost estimates are unreliable because unit cost varies with output or rate of operations.

Price is influenced by trade strategy, competition, economics of supply and demand, government controls at times, and miscellaneous economic or social factors that may affect a particular situation. The effects of prices in a major industrial group or in the nation at large are major problems in the science of economics. Price potentials in a particular enterprise are a subject for market research. Pricing is a major aspect of the game of trade—anticipating the competitors' as well as customers' reactions. The theory of games is an advanced mathematical approach to this problem. And, of course, many price agreements are arrived at by bargaining, the result being between the minimum that the seller will accept and the maximum that the buyer will pay. There is obvious difference between pricing for maximum immediate gain and pricing for long-term advantage.

Price and Quantity

Everyone knows that unit prices for large lots are lower than those for the purchase of a few. There may be trade strategy in such quotations, but there is usually cost justification in the price-volume relationship. In the large lots, the cost of order preparation, tool setups, and other fixed expenses are spread over a greater number of units. Also, there may be packaging economy as in grocery products. Cost is a prime factor in these price variations, and competitors are similarly influenced.

The preceding remarks applied to price variation according to quantity in unit of sale. There is another relationship between the price at which a product is sold and the quantity that can be disposed of to the market in a substantial period of time—the economic effect of supply and demand. The law of supply and demand is most conspicuous in industries as a whole, and in trusts, cartels, or monopolies. Increase in demand or shortage of supply results in higher price, and the reverse is true for reduction of demand or oversupply. The same principle applies to individual enterprises. The practical price range is then more limited because of competition with other producers. Of course, all supply and demand relationships are affected by other outlets for the customer's dollar or by alternative types of goods and services (e.g. steel versus aluminum and trucking versus rail freight).

Figure 7–1 represents a supply and demand situation for a hypothetical enterprise. The graph (assumed a straight line) shows that only about 200,000 units could be sold at a price of $12 each and that the potential is 1,000,000 units for $7 each. This is a forecast by a market research organization. It is assumed that competition would prevent appreciable sales at a price higher than $12 and that the market would be saturated at above 1,000,000 units. For most products, keen competition would necessitate a much narrower price range, and the graph would be much more horizontal.

It must be recognized that quantitative conclusions, as shown by the figure, are highly speculative. One of the most important risks is the uncertain reaction of competitors to a price decision. Price cutting may induce similar action by competitors (as in a local gasoline price "war") with the result that no greater share in a limited market may be realized. Price cutting by the several competitors in an industry may broaden the entire market, however, with advantage (in quantity sold) to all. But as to competition, the differences

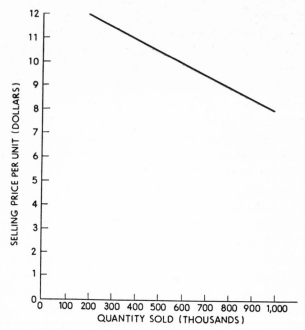

FIG. 7–1.   Selling price of a product versus quantity that can be sold.

in detail characteristics of competing products or services (as in automobiles of a certain price class) may make possible a considerable range in price due to individual consumer preferences. All this is the major aspect of the game of trade. The application of the *theory of games* to such problems was previously mentioned; and a real-life example was cited, in which competitors' reactions were incorrectly judged.

From the seller's viewpoint, the optimum price is not the one that yields the greatest sales in physical volume of product or service, or in total dollars. The optimum price is the one that realizes the maximum profit. Both income and operating cost vary with volume of output and sales, with results that will be discussed in later chapters. For the present, *it will be assumed that a suitable fixed price is arrived at and that all the units produced will be sold at that price.* Applying this price and physical volume to a fiscal period establishes the income for that period.

PROFIT AND YIELD

Profit or return in the financial sense is the difference between income and cost. There are, of course, intangible types of profit (or loss) in all undertakings—intangible benefits or disadvantages. But apart from intangibles, the amount of profit in dollars is not by itself a measure of the success of an enterprise. Profit should be compared with investment, and often with total cost or sales dollars. A one thousand dollar annual profit on a million dollar investment or three million in sales is an accomplishment that is poor indeed compared with the same profit on a ten thousand dollar investment or thirty thousand dollars in sales. The profit ratio of greatest significance in most economy studies is the comparison with investment, a ratio known as *yield*. As a decimal, yield = profit/investment. Yield is based on annual profit, unless otherwise specified, and it is usually expressed as a percentage.

Profit (or return) and yield often require a modifying adjective or phrase to define them explicitly. Profit to whom? And is it the profit after all obligations are met, or is it figured at some intermediate stage in the accounting? There can be profit, investment, and yield that apply to an individual owner or financial contributor, to the enterprise as a whole, or to an individual product, order, project, division, and the like. Stages in the profit picture come about on account of a succession of demands in addition to operating cost. In the following examples, equivalent terms often used in accounting will be indicated in parentheses. *Net profit* (net profit or net income, after income taxes) is the final result to the organization or individual—the ultimate criterion for decision when compared with investment. There is a profit before income tax (net income)—before federal, state, or local tax, the bases for which may not be the same. There may be deductions for profit-sharing bonuses to employees and interest on debt, which define stages of profit. We shall avoid the term *gross profit,* often used to indicate profit over manufacturing or factory cost. We shall use the term *economic return* to indicate the profit based on operating cost before deductions for interest, income taxes, and profit-sharing bonuses. *Economic yield* will be based on total investment, including that of owners and long-term lenders.

Economic Return and Yield

It is often useful to consider the potential profit or gain from a project or enterprise without regard to financial structure and ownership. The project or enterprise is looked upon as an entity by itself. Its obligations to financial contributors, the government, and other sharers in profit may be exceedingly varied. We prefer the term *eco-*

nomic return for the profit considered in that sense. Similarly, the term *economic yield* neglects financial structure.

and $\begin{cases} \text{ECONOMIC RETURN} = \text{INCOME} - \text{OPERATING COST} \\ \\ \text{ECONOMIC YIELD} = \text{ECONOMIC RETURN/INVESTMENT} \end{cases}$

Only in a simple proprietorship free from long-term debt and in a society without income tax do economic return and yield indicate the reward to the owner. In economy studies, however, economic return is significant because its calculation is a step in the determination of *net* profit and yield, or because financial structure and claims against profit are not yet known. Financial structure and participation in profit by financial contributors will be discussed at length in Chapter 16. The common deductions from economic return will be considered presently.

Operating Cost and Economic Return

The purpose of many economy studies is to predict the effect of a proposal on operating cost. The enterprise involved may or may not be a profit-making one. If income is not involved, cost may be the sole monetary criterion for decision. In the profit-making enterprise, cost is a profit criterion. And if income is fixed, saving in operating cost means equal increase in economic return; or the reverse is true for operating cost increases. It must be understood, however, that the *net* profit or loss resulting from change in cost is seriously affected by the *variable* deductions from economic return, such as income taxes and profit-sharing bonuses. For example, the seemingly extravagant outlays for bonuses and entertainment by some firms during World War II were largely offset by an income tax of 70% to 80% that would have been due on the equivalent profit. To properly appraise an increment in cost and economic return, adjustments must be made to reflect the *increment* in deductions from profit. The tax penalty in this case must be computed at the rate applicable to the profit *increment*, not the average rate charged against the firm's total taxable profit. This distinction will be apparent in the subsequent discussion of income taxes.

Deductions from Economic Return

In private industry, economic return is always shared by the government (in the United States) and by participating owners. It may be shared by outside financial contributors (lenders of money) and by employees in profit-sharing plans.

Interest on debt is treated here as an obligation against economic return, although it is an amount due whether profit is realized or not. From the viewpoint of the owners, interest is a cost of operations.

Profit-sharing bonus plans are exceedingly varied. They may be related to economic return after interest or to profit after taxes. Or the bonus may be figured from profit after allowances for minimum returns to owners. It has been legally established (*United States* v. *Lincoln Electric Co.*) that the bonus based on profit is a proper deduction from the taxable profit. In theory, then, such bonuses are wage and salary costs. It is more practical to exclude them from operating cost, as we employ the term, because the amount may not be known until all other profit deductions are known. The bonus computation is complex if it is based on profit *after* income taxes and minimum returns to stockholders.

Miscellaneous taxes, other than profit taxes, are treated here as elements in operating cost. Sales and "use" taxes on purchased material and equipment are included in their costs. Taxes on property (real estate and other assets), various fees, licenses, and the like are items of overhead. Excise taxes, as on gasoline, are included in their prices. The employer's share in Social Security is among the "fringe benefits" that accompany the costs of wages and salaries (direct labor and overhead).

By far the most important cut out of profit in private enterprise is the income tax based on profit—in recent years between 25% and 55%. Obviously, then, the tax situation is a critical factor in management decisions based on cost, income, or profit.

Income Taxes

The federal income tax was authorized by constitutional amendment in 1913. Income taxes are now imposed by more than half the states and by some communities. The federal tax and the others, in general, as applied to a profit-making enterprise are based on profit. There are exceptions. In at least one state (Indiana in 1957), the tax is based on gross income—a relatively small percentage that is due whether profit is realized or not.

The profit base for taxation (taxable "income") has always provided for deduction of certain business expenses in addition to operating cost (as previously defined). In federal regulations, interest on debt and taxes paid to state and local governments has always been deductable. The treatment of profit-sharing bonuses has been mentioned. At the time this was written, the federal tax on incorporated business was at a fixed rate (30% on operating profit in 1960) plus an additional percentage (22% in 1960) on the increment of profit above a certain amount ($25,000 in 1960). Capital gain may be taxed at a different rate (25% in 1960). State and local taxes vary greatly. Some are based on profit before income tax (New York, 1957). Others employ the federal tax base (Pennsylvania, 1960). In at least one state, the taxable profit excludes the federal tax (Alabama, 1957). In one community known to the author, there is a tax on wages and salaries earned within the community plus another tax against residents based on occupation.

Tax regulations concerning the tax bases, allowable deductions, and methods of computation are complex and subject to changes at the will of legislative bodies. Published tax rates can be misleading without detailed information. No economy study can be complete and precise without tax information that is current as to time and place. For this reason, the reader is cautioned against acceptance of the rates and computing methods illustrated in this book and the practice problems.

Computing Corporation Income Taxes

Following is a demonstration of income tax computing methods for corporations, using general formulas and illustrative numeric values. Only state and federal taxes will be considered. Varied types of profit-sharing plans are neglected. The derivation of the formulas and effects on yields are given in Appendix E.

Notation and Assumed Numerical Values

P' = profit before income taxes ($100,000)
P_s = base for state tax
P_f = base for federal tax = $P' - T_s$
C = amount of P_f excluded from surtax ($25,000)
r_1 = normal rate for federal tax (30%)
r_2 = surtax rate for federal tax (22%)
r_3 = rate for state tax (6%)
T_s = state tax
T_f = federal tax
P = net profit after taxes = $P' - T_s - T_f$
r = over-all tax rate = $(T_s + T_f)/P'$

When there is no state income tax (on profit):

$$P_f = P'$$

When $P_f \leq C$,

$$T_f = r_1 P_f$$

When $Pf > C$,

$$T_f = (r_1 + r_2)P_f - r_2 C$$

e.g.,

$$T_f = (.30 + .22)(100{,}000) - .22(25{,}000) = \$46{,}500$$

and

$$r = 46{,}500/100{,}000 = .465 = 46.5\%$$

When the state tax is based on profit before income taxes:

$$P_s = P', \; P_f = P' - T_s, \text{ and } T_s = r_3 P'$$

When $P_f \leq C$,

$$T_f = (r_1 - r_1 r_3)P'$$

When $P_f > C$,

$$T_f = (r_1 + r_2)(1 - r_3)P' - r_2 C$$

e.g.,

$$T_s = (.06)(100{,}000) = \$6{,}000$$
$$T_f = (.52)(100{,}000)(.94) - .22(25{,}000) = \$43{,}380$$
$$r = 49{,}380/100{,}000 = 49.4\%$$

When the state tax is derived from the federal base:

$$P_s = P_f = P' - T_s \text{ and } T_s = r_3 P'/(1 + r_3)$$

When $P_f \leq C$,

$$T_f = r_1 P'/(1 + r_3)$$

When $P_f > C$,

$$T_f = P'(r_1 + r_2)/(1 + r_3) - r_2 C$$

e.g.,

$$T_s = (.06)(100{,}000)/1.06 = \$5{,}660$$
$$T_f = (100{,}000)(.52)/1.06 - .22(25{,}000) = \$43{,}557$$
$$r = 49{,}217/100{,}000 = 49.2\%$$

When the state tax is computed after deduction of federal tax:

$$P_s = P' - T_f \text{ and } T_s = r_3(P' - T_f)$$

When $P_f \leq C$,

$$T_s = P'r_3(1 - r_1)/(1 - r_1r_3)$$
$$T_f = P'r_1(1 - r_3)/(1 - r_1r_3)$$

When $P_f > C$,

$$T_s = \frac{r_3(1 - r_1 - r_2)P' + r_2r_3C}{1 - r_1r_3 - r_2r_3}$$

$$T_f = \frac{(r_1+r_2 - r_1r_3 - r_2r_3)P' - r_2C}{1 - r_1r_3 - r_2r_3}$$

e.g.,

$$T_s = \frac{(.06)(.48)(100,000) + (.22)(.06)(25,000)}{1 - .018 - .0132} = \$3,313$$

$$T_f = \frac{(.52 - .018 - .0132)(100,000) - 5,500}{1 - .018 - .0132} = \$44,777$$

$$r = 48,090/100,000 = 48.1\%$$

It is interesting to note that the amount of the state tax does not as seriously increase the *total* tax because the federal tax base is reduced by the amount of the state tax. On account of the complexity of the last set of tax formulas, the State of Alabama (1957) permitted the tax payer to *estimate* the federal tax in order to compute the state tax, making a correction for the estimate in the following year's return. A similar procedure could be used for profit-sharing plans based on deduction of profit taxes and minimum returns to stockholders.

For economy studies concerned with projects within a going enterprise, the criteria for decision are *increments* of investment, operating cost, income, and profit. In such studies, the *increment* in profit taxes is significant. If the firm already operates in the surtax level of profit, any increase in taxable profit would be subjected to the higher federal tax rate ($r_1 + r_2$ in the formulas) neglecting the term containing C (i.e., $C = 0$). To demonstrate the result, consider the foregoing example with the state tax derived from the federal tax base.

$$T_s = .06(100,000)/1.06 = \$\ 5,660, \text{ as before}$$
$$T_f = 100,000(.52)/1.06 = \underline{\ 49,057}$$
$$\text{Total income tax} = \$54,717$$
$$r = 54,717/100,000 = 54.7\%$$

This effective tax rate is 5.5% more than the rate previously computed, a rate that depended on the total profit situation of the enterprise. The 54.7% assumes that the firm's taxable profit would be in the surtax bracket without inclusion of the project being studied; and the same rate would then apply to any increment of profit or change in cost. When there is no state tax in this situation, the rate applicable to increment profit is $r_1 + r_2$ (52% in 1960).

The federal tax on *capital gain* was 25% in 1960. Long-term capital gain has not been treated as ordinary profit. During a year, the capital losses may be deducted from the capital gains to determine the net subject to tax. Net capital loss, however, could not be deducted from operating profit to reduce the taxable profit. In studies that involve disposal of long-term assets (such as equipment or buildings), the anticipated tax on capital gain should be deducted from the salvage value realized. It would be improper to consider such a tax as an annual cost because it is a one-time penalty for the project in question.

Profit taxes have been discussed in considerable detail because of their obvious importance in deriving the net costs and profits that are criteria for decision. The reader is reminded that tax rates change frequently and that tax regulations are complex. The person engaged in economy studies must keep up to date on the current situation.

PROFIT AND LOSS SUMMARIES

The accountant's periodic report that summarizes income, cost, and profit (or loss) is known as the *profit and loss statement*. This statement combined with the balance sheet indicates the financial condition of the enterprise. The forms of profit and loss statements and the detail in which they are presented vary considerably in practice—depending on character of enterprise, persons to whom reports are directed, and management policies. All of these statements arrive at *net profit* as the final result. Total receipts or revenue (income) and operating cost are shown. Manufacturing (factory) cost or "cost of goods sold" and administrative and sales expenses may be listed separately. Then there are deductions for interest on debt, profit-sharing bonuses, other special deductions, and income taxes. In some statements, the total of *all* taxes may be listed. We shall employ here a simple form of profit and loss summary that can apply to an enterprise as a whole, to one of its divisions, or to an individual project, product, service, or order. It is to be understood that the time period is annual, unless otherwise specified or implied (as for a single order).

To illustrate the type of summary suitable for our purpose, let us assume an enterprise that realizes the $100,000 taxable profit used in the previous income tax demonstration. The firm's net worth is $600,000 and an additional $200,000 has been borrowed at 4½%. The income, cost, and profit summary is shown in Table 7–1. The

TABLE 7–1

INCOME, COST, AND PROFIT SUMMARY FOR A
HYPOTHETICAL ENTERPRISE

Net worth..	$ 600,000
Long-term debt......................................	200,000
Total investment[1].................................	$ 800,000
Units of output.....................................	700,000
Unit selling price..................................	($2.20)
Income (from sales).................................	$1,540,000
Operating cost......................................	1,421,000
Unit operating cost.................................	($2.03)
Economic return.....................................	119,000
Economic yield[2]...................................	(14.88%)
Interest on debt[3].................................	9,000
Profit before bonuses and income taxes..............	$ 110,000
Profit-sharing bonuses[4]...........................	10,000
Profit before income taxes.........................	$ 100,000
Income taxes[5].....................................	49,380
Net profit..	$ 50,620
Net yield[6]..	(8.44%)

[1] Investment of owners and financial interests.
[2] Based on total investment, $800,000.
[3] 4½% on $200,000.
[4] Profit-sharing plan calls for 10% on profit before income taxes.
[5] State tax at 6% on federal tax base. Federal tax at 30% on taxable profit plus 22% surtax on profit increment over $25,000. See example on page 94.
[6] Net yield is net profit/net worth.

appended notes show the bases for calculations. Items such as operating cost could be broken down, if desired (e.g., into direct labor, direct material, depreciation, and other overhead).

In the example, note that economic yield is based on net worth plus long-term debt, and net yield is based on net worth. These bases are most appropriate for the usual engineering economy study. Businessmen may be interested in yield on *total assets,* which include values that are offset by current liabilities, because short-term creditors may make substantial contributions to the capital employed. The owners of a business are certainly most interested in net yield on their investment (net worth). In case of doubt, the basis for a stated yield should always be specified.

The importance of yield as a measure of operational success has been mentioned. It is particularly significant in a summary of the type just described, and it may serve as a means for comparing competing proposals. The appropriateness of a yield will be discussed in the next chapter.

PROBLEMS

7.1. Refer to Problems 6.3, 6.4, and 6.5. Assume that the company received $3,400 for the order mentioned. Determine the apparent profit or loss from that order.

7.2. Refer to Problem 6.11. Assume that the special order mentioned was sold for $22,000. Compute the apparent profit or loss by the two methods of charging overhead in the factory. If this order was an average in results for the year, and if the total of annual costs were as anticipated, what would be the annual total of sales (income)? Assume departmental factory rates in this case.

7.3. A certain product is selling for $8.20. The production cost plus sales expense is $7.38.
a) What per cent of the selling price represents profit?
b) What per cent of reduction in cost will increase the margin of profit 60%. (PE Pa.)

7.4. A part has a finished value of $4.80. Of this amount, 40% is material, 30% labor, 20% overhead, and 10% profit. If material goes up 25%, labor pay rate goes up 20%, labor production rate goes down 15%, and overhead is the same, what is the new value (selling price) to clear 10% profit? (PE Pa.)

7.5. A general contractor is required to install and operate a temporary wellpoint system during a 6-month phase of construction of a riverside powerhouse. The necessary equipment will cost $800 a month to rent. A pump operator will have to be in attendance continuously, and must be paid an hourly wage of $3.00 for each 8-hour weekday shift, $4.50 for each 8-hour Saturday shift, and $6.00 for each Sunday and legal holiday shift. (Assume 26 full weeks with two legal holidays that occur on days other than Saturday and Sunday.) Payroll taxes and insurance are 13% of wages. Fuel is estimated at $20 per day. Overhead and maintenance charges are 15% of wages, fuel, and rental charges.

Payment for successful completion of the wellpointing operation will be one lump sum at the end of the 6-month period. If financing costs the contractor 6% per annum (average debt, 2 months operating cost), and he desires profit and allowance for contingency amounting to 10% of his costs, what would be his lump-sum bid for the wellpointing operation? (PE N.Y.)

7.6.   A small industrial building is constructed for $65,000 on a lot that cost $5,000. The depreciation life is 30 years. Annual maintenance is estimated at $950, property taxes and insurance at 2.5% of first cost. The building has been leased at $10,860 per year. The income taxes are at the rates of 6% to the state based on profit before tax, and 30% federal after deduction of state tax.

a) What is the over-all rate of income tax (state plus federal)?

b) What is the percentage of net profit based on income?

c) What is the net yield on investment? Consider investment at the beginning and at the end of the 15th year.

7.7.   The following data were secured in making efficiency tests on certain electric and gas water heaters.

```
Amount of water heated.................1,340 gals.
Temperature rise in water...............  100° F
Electricity consumed....................  401 K.W.H.
Gas consumed............................  121 lbs.
1 K.W.H. = 3,412 B.T.U., 1 lb. gas = 21,600 B.T.U.
```

a) What is the over-all efficiency of each heater?

b) If fuel costs are to be equal and electricity sells for 1.5¢ per K.W.H., what will the gas have to sell for? (PE Ohio)

c) If fuel costs are equal, what are the major economic and intangible factors that would influence decision?

7.8.   You are employed as a consultant to a group of merchants who plan to develop and operate a parking lot. They would like to operate so as to recover cost of operation and, in addition, to recover initial cost at the rate of $1.50 per square foot per year. Conditions:

```
Size of lot 28,200 sq. ft., all space to be used.
220 sq. ft. per stall if attendant parking is used.
282 sq. ft. per stall if self-parking is used.
```

Annual costs:

```
Taxes....................................5¢ per sq. ft.
Clerical help............................$2,400
Parking attendants.......................3 at $3,000
Utilities, insurance, maintenance..........$8.00 per stall
```

Assume 300 working days per year and an average of 50% capacity used during the 12-hour working day.

a) Under the conditions given above, and using parking attendants, compute:

(1) Total annual cost.

(2) Cost per stall per year.

(3) Minimum hourly charge per stall.

b) Under the conditions given above, but using self-parking, compute:

(1) Total annual cost.

(2) Cost per stall per year.

(3) Minimum hourly charge per stall.

c) If the merchants will be satisfied with a profit of 25¢ per square foot per year, other conditions remaining the same, what is the hourly charge per stall? (PE Pa.)

7.9. The net worth (owner's equity) of an enterprise is $1,650,000. Profit for the year, before deductions for interest, bonuses, and income tax, is $350,000. Interest on long-term debt is $25,000. A profit-sharing plan calls for bonuses to employees, figured after payment of interest, in the amount of 15%. The federal income tax rate is 30% plus a surtax of 22% on the increment of profit above $25,000. There is also a state profit tax of 5%. Compute the *net profit, net yield* on owners' investment, and the *over-all tax rate* (state plus federal) for each of the following conditions:

a) State tax applying to profit before considering federal tax.

b) State tax applying to same base as federal tax.

c) State tax computed after deduction of federal tax.

The company is considering an annual expenditure of $1,200 for prizes to worthy students in a local college. Under the state tax conditions described in (a) above, what is the actual net cost of the proposed donation?

7.10. In the enterprise described in Problem 7.9, a proposed process improvement indicates a saving of $40,000 per year in operating cost. The investment required is $180,000. Capacity of plant and income from sales are not affected. None of the funds required will be borrowed. Depreciation in this case is computed straight-line to 10% salvage value for an expected life of 10 years, and the amount has been considered in estimating the above annual savings. The state income tax previously mentioned is computed on the same base as the federal income tax.

Determine the net results of the proposal as requested below. Computation should be confined to this project only, without determining the profit details for the enterprise as a whole.

a) What is the net annual return from the project?

b) What is the net yield on the proposed investment based on its average book value during expected life?

7.11. A small textile manufacturer has been averaging $20,000 annual profit, before income tax. Net worth is $185,000. The federal income tax rate is 30%, plus 22% surtax on the profit increment above $25,000. There is no state income tax.

The firm is now considering a new product. The required investment is $160,000 (equipment and working capital). The estimated annual factory cost, including depreciation, is $140,000; and sales expense is $35,000. Administrative expense is not increased. Predicted income from sales is 188,000.

a) What is the yield on proposed investment before income tax?

b) What is the *net return* and the *net yield* on the venture?

c) Does the proposal seem favorable to you based on the present record of earnings?

CHAPTER **8**

Yield and Return Requirements

THE economic appraisal of any enterprise or individual project involves both investment and operating advantage (cost saving or profit). The importance of yield, relating profit or saving to investment, has been emphasized. Having determined the return and yield, however, does not answer the natural query: "Is the result satisfactory?" Consider an example. Suppose that an investor is considering the purchase of a conservative bond that yields 4%, compared with a speculative industrial stock that is estimated to yield the same percentage. Certainly the yield estimates do not indicate that the alternatives are equally good. A layman would recognize that the stock should promise greater yield to compensate for the risk.

The same question may arise in other types of projects, in which advantage (or disadvantage) can be measured in money, even in "nonprofit" enterprises. A proposed government project may promise savings to the public (in taxation or cost of service) in the amount of $1,000,000 annually, but it requires a capital expenditure of $50,000,000. The equivalent yield is only 2%. But, what if the investment were $20,000,000 and the yield 5%? It is apparent that a measuring device is required to judge the adequacy of monetary advantage or yield.

REQUIRED YIELD AND REQUIRED RETURN

As a basing point for appraisal of yield, a *minimum* may be established for each venture, a hurdle that must be cleared if that venture is to merit consideration. This requisite yield is variously titled: *interest* (rate), *expected yield, charge for the use of capital* (rate), and *required yield.* Among engineering economists and analysts of business, the terms may vary somewhat in significance. Interest on borrowed capital may be involved in any project. But, in general, *interest* does not necessarily imply borrowing; it refers to return from investment. The author prefers the term *required yield* to indicate the minimum rate of return necessary to justify a particular investment. The reader should recognize the alternative expressions, although their interpretations may be somewhat obscure on occasion. *Interest* is most commonly used in the literature.

A corollary of required yield (a decimal or percentage) is *required return* (dollars). Required return is the amount of return or profit necessary to justify an investment. It is the product of that investment and required yield.

Types of Required Yield and Return

The concept of required yield or return can be applied to various stages in the profit picture and to portions of the total capital. The modifying adjectives or phrases previously mentioned in connection with yield and return or profit (page 89) are similarly appropriate when we refer to the minimum requirement. From the viewpoint of an investor (an owner or lender of capital), it is his *net* yield that is of interest. From the viewpoint of an engineer investigating an equipment or process problem in a plant, the criterion for decision may be savings in factory cost compared with the capital expenditure. It is obvious, then, that the terms *required yield* and *required return* will need explicit definition unless the context implies the answer to the questions: "What investment?" "What gain (or loss)?" "Yield to whom?"

In Chapter 16, we shall consider the yields and returns to the various participants in ownership and financing. Neglecting these financial interests, there are three types of required yield or return that are most useful in economy studies. Saving in factory cost may be gaged by a required return or charge for the use of capital *before administrative and sales expenses and deductions from profit*. Required *economic* yield or return applies after the inclusion of administrative and sales expenses (overhead). Required *net* yield and return apply to the final result to the investor, assumed to be the firm or institution, unless otherwise specified.

Required Yield before Income Taxes

Required yield *before* income taxes should be much higher than the *net* requirement because of the currently high level of taxation.

When the tax rate is 50%, the required yield *before taxes* is double the net after taxes. If there are no other deductions from profit, such as interest on debt or profit-sharing bonuses, the percentage before taxes is the same as *required economic yield*. If such a standard is adopted for various types of project studies in an enterprise, it is unnecessary to detail the income tax costs or benefits.

Let us consider the effects of income taxes based on the computing methods and illustrative data demonstrated previously (pages 92 to 94). Notation and illustrative values in addition to those of page 92 are as follows: (For derivation of formulas, see Appendix E.)

I = investment ($800,000)
i = required *net* yield (8%)
i' = required yield *before taxes* (to be determined)

When there is no state income tax:

$$\text{If } P_f \leq C, \quad i' = i/(1 - r_1)$$

$$\text{If } P_f > C, \quad i' = (i - r_2C/I)/(1 - r_1 - r_2)$$

For example,

$$i' = (.08 - 5{,}500/800{,}000)/(1 - .30 - .22) = .152 = 15.2\%$$

When a state tax is based on profit before income taxes:

$$\text{If } P_f \leq C, \quad i' = i/(1 - r_1 - r_3 + r_1r_3)$$

$$\text{If } P_f > C, \quad i' = (i - r_2C/I)/(1 - r_1 - r_2 - r_3 + r_1r_3 + r_2r_3)$$

For example,

$$i' = (.08 - 5{,}500/800{,}000)/(1 - .30 - .22 - .06 + .018 + .0132)$$
$$i' = .162 = 16.2\%$$

When a state tax is derived from federal tax base:

$$\text{If } P_f \leq C, \quad i' = \frac{i}{1 - r_1 - r_3/(1 + r_3) + r_1r_3/(1 + r_3)}$$

$$\text{If } P_f > C, \quad i' = \frac{i - r_2C/I}{(1 - r_1 - r_2)[1 - r_3/(1 + r_3)]}$$

For example,

$$i' = \frac{.08 - 5{,}500/800{,}000}{(1 - .30 - .22)(1 - .06/1.06)} = .161 = 16.1\%$$

When a state tax is based on prior deduction of the federal tax:

$$\text{If } P_f \leq C, \quad i' = i(1 - r_1r_3)/(1 - r_1 - r_3 + r_1r_3)$$

$$\text{If } P_f > C, \quad i' = \frac{(1 - r_1 r_3 - r_2 r_3)i - r_2(1 - r_3)C/I}{1 - r_1 - r_2 - r_3 + r_1 r_3 + r_2 r_3}$$

For example,

$$i' = \frac{(1 - .018 - .0132)(.08) - (.22)(1 - .06)(25{,}000/800{,}000)}{1 - .30 - .22 - .06 + .018 + .0132}$$
$$i' = .157 = 15.7\%$$

The above formulas apply to an enterprise as a whole. A project within a going enterprise involves an *increase* or *decrease* in the total income tax. The effect of increment tax rate on return and yield was discussed in Chapter 7. The same considerations apply to required yield. When an economy study is concerned with a project that involves possible gain or loss within the federal surtax bracket, the above formulas (for $P_f > C$) are applicable if the C factor is omitted (i.e., $C/I = 0$). Assume, for example, that the previous illustration relates to a company that already pays federal tax on more than \$25,000 profit. Then:

$$i' = (1 - .018 - .0132)(.08)/(1 - .30 - .22 - .06 + .018 + .0132) =$$
$$17.2\%$$

From the examples, it may be observed that the basis for the state tax and its percentage does not as seriously affect the required yield as might be expected. The total difference between net required yield and that before income taxes, however, is important.

Required Yield before Interest and Other Deductions

In many large corporations, projects must be appraised, if not finally decided upon, by local executives who may not be fully informed about the various deductions from economic return that determine net profit. A gross required yield may be the appropriate criterion for decision. To arrive at such a gross requirement, when borrowed capital, profit sharing, and other demands are to be met, involves more than a simple formula. One way to accomplish this is to work the problem backwards from a known required net yield or return.

The following example illustrates a method, which must be adjusted for individual conditions. Let us assume conditions of the previous example at the increment tax level. It is assumed further that capital is borrowed in addition to the amount (I) supplied from the company's resources. The company's fiscal policy is to borrow 25% of its total requirements, and the average interest rate is 5%. There is also a profit-sharing plan that calls for distribution of 20% of the *net* profit to employees. The conditions of our immediate problem are:

Total capital required for a project $= I'$
Owners' share of total investment $= I = .75I'$
Borrowed portion of total investment $= .25I'$
Required net yield on owners' investment $= i$ (to be specified)
Required economic yield on total investment $= i'$ (to be determined)
Federal income tax rate $= 52\%$
State income tax rate $= 6\%$ after deduction of federal tax
Profit-sharing bonus $= 20\%$ of required net return (iI)

The principal unknown at this point is the income tax amount, which should be expressed in terms of total investment (I'). The over-all or effective tax rate (r), applied to profit before tax, may be derived from the tax formulas (page 92 and Appendix E) and also from a computed value of i'.

over all tax Rate
or
$$r = 1 - i/i'$$
Effective tax Rate

in which the ratio i/i' is, in this case, dependent only on the tax rates since i' is a multiple of i. Based on the previous example:

$$r = 1 - .08/.172 = .535 = 53.5\%$$

This rate, however, applies to profit before tax, which is unknown. The relationship with the net profit (iI) would be:

$$r' = r/(1 - r) = .535/.465 = 1.15$$

We now have the details necessary to compute the gross (economic) return:

Required net return $=$	$.75iI'$
Income taxes $= 1.15iI =$	$.8625iI'$
Profit-sharing bonus $= .20iI =$	$.15iI'$
Interest on debt $= (.05)(.25I') =$	$.0125I'$
Required economic return $=$	$.0125I' + 1.7625iI'$
Required economic yield $(i'') =$	$.0125 + 1.7625i$

In the previous example, $i = .08$; so that, in the present case, i'', applicable to the total investment, is:

$$i'' = .0125 + (1.7625)(.08) = .154 = 15.4\%$$

Required yields such as i'' are often expressed as a required payoff period. If depreciation on the proposed investment enters into the

computation of gross profit or savings and other appropriate overhead is included, then:

$$\text{Payoff period} = 1/i'' = 1/.154 = 6.5 \text{ years}$$

Very often the savings or profit mentioned neglects depreciation;
and an average depreciation must be considered in the specification
of a payoff period. Let us assume that this average depreciation is
10% of the first cost. The effect is to add .10 to the value of i''.

$$\text{Payoff period} = 1/(i'' + .10) = 1/.254 = 3.94 \text{ or } 4 \text{ years}$$

Specification of Required Yield

The adoption of a required net yield, a standard that should differ
with various classes of projects, is a decision involving tangible and
intangible considerations. Factors that may be pertinent include:

The current interest rate on borrowed money.
Yields experienced from similar investments.
Yields anticipated from alternative uses for capital.
Yield experienced by the enterprise in its over-all operations.
Yield demanded by present or potential financial contributors to the
    enterprise.
Risk—as to forecasts of cost, income, and life of project.

If the project involves borrowed funds, the required *economic*
yield should exceed the interest rate by a substantial amount. Otherwise why borrow? Yield experienced from similar projects is good
for comparison, but trends must be recognized. An appraisal of a
new project must look to the future. And any business project,
including those of nonprofit institutions, must compete with other
demands for capital. What yields can be expected from those competing prospects?

The experience of a firm in its over-all operations is another gage
for comparison. Managers are usually reluctant to consider a proposal that does not promise at least as well as its usual experience.
Individual projects within an enterprise, however, can be expected
to deviate from the average. Perhaps a long-term project such as a
power plant should not be expected to earn as great a yield as the
many shorter-lived ventures (new product models, new processes,
and the like).

Risk is the principal factor that dictates greater or lesser yield
requirements for different kinds of ventures. Greater profit potential
should be demanded of a successful oil well than from the manufac-

ture of petroleum products. Perhaps only one well comes in for eight or ten exploratory drillings. On the other hand, there is much less risk in a general-purpose building or machine tool, and almost no risk in a federal bond. Referring to a previous example, an industrial stock should certainly deserve higher required yield than the government bond, although unusual market conditions may alter that picture. The evaluation of risk and other intangibles is discussed at greater length in Chapter 17.

Some idea of appropriate yield requirements may be gained from the yield experience of industrial groups during a successful business year. In Table 8–1, the yields for several typical industries were

TABLE 8–1

YIELDS REALIZED BY U.S. INDUSTRIAL CORPORATIONS, 1956 TO 1957

(Dollars in millions)

Industrial Groups	Total Assets	Shareholder's Equity (Net Worth)	Net Profit	Yield on Net Worth
Extractive industry	$ 10,409	$ 7,373	$ 812	11.01%
Construction	8,642	3,634	509	14.00
All manufacturing	203,801	133,487	13,313	9.97
Food products	13,398	8,685	769	8.85
Textile mills	8,198	5,844	362	6.19
Apparel	3,066	1,715	154	8.98
Paper products	8,641	6,070	675	11.12
Chemicals	19,015	12,690	1,566	12.34
Petroleum and coal products	33,583	24,494	1,293	5.28
Primary metals	21,267	13,663	1,450	10.61
Fabricated metal products	8,792	5,894	646	10.95
Machinery, except electric	17,949	11,553	1,371	11.88
Electric machinery and equipment	10,230	5,801	635	10.95
Motor vehicles	14,567	9,620	1,254	13.04
Public utilities	106,174	55,172	3,148	5.71
All trade	64,574	36,085	3,385	9.38

SOURCE: *Statistics of Income . . . 1956–1957, Corporation Income Tax Returns,* U.S. Treasury Department, Internal Revenue Service, Publication No. 16 (3–59).

derived from corporation income tax statistics for fiscal years ending between July 1, 1956 and June 30, 1957. The net yields are based on net worths (shareholders' equities). Note the considerable difference between the various industrial groups.

It is apparent that the specification of a required net yield is a management decision based on conditions and operating policy. Standards may be established for various types of projects within an enterprise. These standards can be designed for any desired level of profit computation—the *net*, profit before income taxes and other deductions, gain at the level of total operating cost or economic return, or at the level of factory cost. Of course, the basic criterion is the required net yield.

APPLICATIONS FOR REQUIRED YIELD AND REQUIRED RETURN

There are three general ways in which required yield or required return can serve useful purposes in economy studies.

1. Required yield or return can be used as a standard to judge whether or not the anticipated yield or return from a venture is satisfactory.
2. In problems where cost is the immediate criterion for decision, required return can be treated as if it were an element of cost to be added to the other costs. In this sense required return is a *charge for the use of capital.* It is return that the investor is deprived of (hence, a cost) because the capital is not used for some other comparable investment; and it is, therefore, a necessary factor in determining possible cost advantage from a project.
3. As a corollary to the above concept, required yield can be used as the interest rate in time value computations. It is the rate of return that should be expected from investments that could be substituted for the anticipated future costs.

Anticipated Yield versus Required Yield

The significance of *required* yield as a standard for appraisal of *anticipated* yield is usually quite obvious. Consider the profit and loss statement on page 96. In that example, the net yield was 8.44%. If the investors in that business believed that a yield of 6% was necessary to attract capital, the result would be considered satisfactory. But if the enterprise were a hazardous one, the 8.44% would be much less than a reasonable yield requirement. If the figures were the estimate for a proposed enterprise, the proposal would then be rejected.

In the yield calculations mentioned previously, it has been assumed that the investment, cost, and profit figures were fixed amounts. The effects of variable cost and income will be covered in Chapter 9 and several others. At this point, it is important to consider time changes in the value of investment, because investment is the basis for computing required return or anticipated yield. In the evaluation of a business, it might be assumed that the over-all investment would remain fairly constant, or that increase in net worth would be accompanied by a proportionate increase in profit. In the appraisal of an individual project, however, it may be necessary to recognize that fixed assets representing the investment will decline in value (e.g., by depreciation), which changes the basis for yield and required return year after year. In the economy study that estimates results beyond the immediate future, time changes must be taken into account. The technique of doing this will be discussed presently.

Charge for Use of Capital

The concept of required return as a cost, a charge for the use of capital, was previously mentioned. The combined costs may be termed *cost plus required return,* using an appropriate adjective before *cost* to indicate the inclusiveness of that cost and that required return. The three most common types of cost to be treated in this manner, in this book, are *factory* cost, total *operating* cost, and *total* cost including income taxes, all of which are to be supplemented by the required returns appropriate at those levels of computation. Of course, the defining adjectives need not be used if the meaning is evident from the character of the study.

The combinations of cost and required return are most useful for comparing alternative proposals from the cost viewpoint. It may be difficult to apportion income and profit to a particular project within an enterprise, or there may be no income and profit involvement. The charge for the use of capital provides a means for realistic comparison of the project that effects large savings in operating cost with large investment against the alternative showing less annual savings but lower investment. The addition of required return may alter the cost comparison conspicuously, as will be demonstrated in subsequent examples.

The effect of time changes (in investment) on yield and required return have been mentioned. When capital has been recovered by depreciation, depletion allowances, or amortization, it is improper to use first cost as the basis for computing required yield. Theoretically, a reappraisal of the worth of the investment should apply for each year of the study. The length of the study period is obviously pertinent. That is, for how long a period does the economic estimate apply. The project may have a definite limited life, or it may extend indefinitely into the future. Or the investor may be unwilling to base decision on a long-term prospect. If immediate results are the criterion, adjustments for future time changes may not be important. But when the value of the investment declines substantially during the study period, the changes must be recognized in the required return. Two methods for doing this will be described in this chapter. A special procedure (MAPI method) will be discussed in Chapter 15.

Exact Method

The "exact" method treats capital recovery and required return on a present worth basis, time valued for the requisite study period. Actually the method is no more exact than are the contributing factors in the computation, but time value is recognized. The present worth of the investment (assumed to be its cost at the beginning of the study period) is equivalent to the combined present worths of periodic depreciation, periodic required return, and salvage value at the end of the study period.

Notation:

$$I = \text{initial investment,}$$
$$D = \text{periodic depreciation}$$
$$R = \text{periodic required return}$$

Then:

$$I = (D + R) \left[\frac{(1 + i)^n - 1}{i(1 + i)^n} \right] + \frac{S}{(1 + i)^n}$$

and

$$(D + R) = I \left[\frac{i(1 + i)^n}{(1 + i)^n - 1} \right] - S \left[\frac{i}{(1 + i)^n - 1} \right]$$

The formula for $(D + R)$ usually appears in other forms. In the numerator in the bracket following S, add and subtract the factor $i(1 + i)^n$. Then:

$$(D + R) = I \left[\frac{i(1 + i)^n}{(1 + i)^n - 1} \right] - S \left[\frac{i(1 + i)^n}{(1 + i)^n - 1} \right] + S \left[\frac{i(1 + i)^n - i}{(1 + i)^n - 1} \right]$$

and

$$(D + R) = (I - S) \left[\frac{i(1 + i)^n}{(1 + i)^n - 1} \right] + iS$$

If, instead of the above, the factor i were added and subtracted from the numerator in the bracket following I, the result would be:

$$(D + R) = I \left[\frac{i(1 + i)^n - i}{(1 + i)^n - 1} \right] + I \left[\frac{i}{(1 + i)^n - 1} \right] - S \left[\frac{i}{(1 + i)^n - 1} \right]$$

and

$$(D + R) = (I - S) \left[\frac{i}{(1 + i)^n - 1} \right] + iI$$

The last formula shows that $(D + R)$ is equivalent to sinking fund depreciation plus required return based on first cost (I). However, it can be proved that the combined amount $(D + R)$ would be the same if the time value were computed for any method of depreciation—assuming that the same study period, salvage value, and interest rate were used.

To justify the general application of this theory, let us assume any sequence of periodic depreciations $(D_1$—D_m—$D_n)$, and the corresponding book values $(B_1$—B_m—$B_n)$ after deducting depreciation. B_n is the same as salvage value (S). B_o is the initial value (I). Now consider the relationship between these book values and the present worths of the subsequent depreciations, returns on investment, and residual values. For convenience, we shall start with *any* period designated $m-1$.

$$B_{m-1} = D_m + B_m = D_m/(1 + i) + i(D_m + B_m)/(1 + i) + B_m/(1 + i)$$

Simplifying the terms of the right half of this equality demonstrates its validity. This is equivalent to stating that the book value of a property at the beginning of any time period is equal to the sum of the present worths of the depreciation, return on investment, and residual value for the *following* period.

Now consider a valuation sequence that starts with the beginning of the last period, which means that n may be substituted for m in the previous formula, and S may be substituted for B_m.

$$B_{n-1} = D_n/(1 + i) + i(D + S)/(1 + i) + S/(1 + i)$$

In this case, known values $(D_n, S,$ and $i)$ determine the book value B_{n-1}. Then, if we evaluate B_{n-2}, the foregoing known factors can be substituted for B_{n-1} in the present worth determination. This process can be repeated until we arrive at the initial book value $(B_o = I)$. Therefore, the initial value (I) is the present worth of all succeeding values of depreciation, periodic returns on investment (based on book values at the beginning of each period), and residual value at the end of the study period.

To show that the above principle is general in application, let us try it on two extreme cases: (1) All depreciation takes place in the first period, when the property is written off to its terminal salvage value; and (2) depreciation is deferred until the nth period.

Case 1:

$$B_1 = B_2 = B_3 \cdots = S, \text{ and } D_2 = D_3 = D_4 \cdots = D_n = 0$$

The present worths of the depreciation, periodic interest on investment, and final salvage value sum up as follows:

$$I = D_1 + S = D_1/(1 + i) + iD_1/(1 + i)$$

$$+ iS \left[\frac{(1 + i)^n - 1}{i(1 + i)^n} \right] + S/(1 + i)^n$$

The equality can be verified by simplifying the equation.

Case 2:

$$B_1 = B_2 = B_3 \cdots B_{n-1} = I, \text{ and } D_1 = D_2 = D_3 \cdots = D_{n-1} = 0$$

The present worths sum up as follows:

$$I = D_n + S = D_n/(1 + i)^n + i(D_n + S) \left[\frac{(1 + i)^n - 1}{i(1 + i)^n} \right] + S/(1 + i)^n$$

As in the previous example, simplifying the equation verifies the equality.

In the general theory developed above, it is apparent that depreciation need not be a uniform periodic amount. On the other hand, only a *uniform periodic* (annual) *equivalent* is usable in the practical formula for $(D + R)$ given at the outset. In the usual economy study, it is the annual "average" for D and R in which we are interested, similar to the time average of other cost and income items within the study period. Therefore, we can rightly substitute straight-line depreciation when declining balance or sum of digits are actually used, because the straight-line amount is the annual average of the other depreciations. Then the annual equivalent for R is:

$$R = (D + R) - D$$

in which $(D + R)$ is computed by the formula and D is the straight-line depreciation.

As to the length of the study period (n) employed in these computations and in the average-interest method, to be described presently, some analysts recommend a time equal to the customary depreciation life. The common objection to this practice is that managers and investors would not consider so long a period for justifying an investment on the basis of its returns. It is therefore reasonable to adopt a shorter study period, provided that the salvage value used fairly represents the anticipated value of the property at the end of that period. This salvage value (S) could be the book value computed from the desired method of depreciation.

Exact Method with Continuous Depreciation

It may be useful to consider *continuous* depreciation and compounding in the foregoing concept. (See page 14.) Continuous depreciation may be more realistic than the annual increments, capital turnover may be rapid, or the desired interest rate may not be available in the tables. The adjusted formula becomes:

$$(D + R) = i(I - S) \left[\frac{e^{in}}{e^{in} - 1}\right] + iS = (I - S) \left[\frac{i}{e^{in} - 1}\right] + iI$$

In this formula, D, R, and i are annual quantities. The sum $(D + R)$ derived in this way is somewhat lower and less conservative than results from the conventional formula because the average investment is less; but the difference is not great. Consider the following comparison based on four situations (A, B, C, and D).

	A	B	C	D
Initial investment (I)...................	1,000	1,000	1,000	1,000
Study period (n), years.................	5	10	5	10
Salvage value (S)......................	500	0	500	0
Interest rate (i), per year...............	20%	20%	10%	10%
$D + R$ (annual depreciation)............	267.2	238.5	181.9	162.8
$D + R$ (continuous depreciation)........	257.2	231.2	177.2	159.2

Average-Interest Method

The "average-interest" method of computing required return has long been recommended by some authorities and is often specified in state license examinations. As the name implies, the interest or required return is based upon the average worth of the investment during the life of the project or during the specified study period. The commonly recognized formula (recommended by Eugene L. Grant) assumes straight-line depreciation in annual increments as in conventional accounting. Using the previous notation: *Conventional*

$$\text{Average required return} = R = i(I - S)\frac{(n + 1)}{2n} + iS$$

It should be observed that the average investment (book value), being based on discrete annual depreciations, accounts for the factor $(n + 1)/n$. Actually, a capitalized physical asset could incur continuous, not intermittent, depreciation. In fact, depreciation is a monthly charge in some organizations. In accordance with this concept, the author recommends a simplified formula:

$$\text{Average required return} = R = i(I + S)/2$$

The simplified average interest formula gives a value of R somewhat less than obtained by the more complex formula—most conspicuous for low values of n. In neither case have we accounted for the time value of money provided for by the exact method. The difference in result is most evident for larger values of n and i.

As in the exact method, the principal objection to average interest arises from the usual assumption that the study period is the life of the asset that would be used in computing depreciation. If, for example, the required return on a well-built structure were based on a life (n) of 50 years and no salvage value, the required return would be half the amount based on first cost. No investor would be willing to appraise such a project on the basis of a valuation of 25 years hence. To meet this objection, a shorter study period should be adopted, accompanied by short-term depreciation and salvage value. The study period in this case is not the expected life of the asset; it is the period of time within which the investment must be justified by adequate return.

Required Return Based on First Cost

Required return based on first cost combined with the most appropriate method of depreciation is the simplest way of providing for capital recovery and charge for the use of capital. Of course, this does not recognize either the time change in the worth of the investment or the time value of money. The amount of depreciation plus required return, the penalty against the project, is greater than that of the forementioned methods, unless sinking fund depreciation is employed.

A cost summary that includes required return based on first cost ($R = iI$) indicates immediate results. Business managers are often influenced by immediate potential, discounting the future. The continued success of most enterprises, however, depends on decisions that speculate on future results. Basing required return on first cost may unduly penalize worthwhile proposals that are reasonably assured of substantial life. Uncertainties of the future could be taken care of by raising the required yield (rate of return) and computing the return requirement for a reasonable study period.

Payoff Period

When changes in process or facilities are proposed, a common method of appraisal is to compute the number of years required for the investment to pay for itself by advantages realized. This involves the increments of (changes in) investment and operating cost. In other words, an increased investment of $10,000 with an operating cost advantage of $4,000 per year would pay off in 2½ years. In a sense, this amounts to a yield of 40%. As a gage for appraisal, it is customary to specify the *minimum* number of years in which a class of projects is required to pay off in order to merit consideration. This minimum payoff period is equivalent to a *required* yield.

The payoff period method does not recognize time effects on worth of investment or money value. Its significance also depends on methods of computing increment investment and increment operating cost. Depreciation and overhead items may or may not be included. Perhaps income and profit are involved. When cost details are equally complete, this method is equivalent to evaluation with required return based on first cost as previously described. The method is discussed further and illustrated in Chapter 15 on analysis of replacement.

Comparison of Methods

To demonstrate methods of computation and to compare results, let us assume the following situation. Two competing proposals, processing methods (A and B), are being compared. Proposal A requires much less investment but is higher in operating cost. The specified required yield is 15% (economic yield, before income taxes and other deductions from profit). The study period is 5 years. The estimated salvage value for 5 years is based on the estimated life and straight-line depreciation. (Of course, the 5-year salvage value could be estimated independently of the customary long-term depreciation figure.) Essential preliminary data may then be summed up as follows:

	A	B
First cost	$30,000	$100,000
Depreciation life	12 yrs.	18 yrs.
Salvage value	$3,000	$10,000
Depreciation per year	$2,250	$5,000
Study period	5 yrs.	5 yrs.
Salvage value in 5 years	$18,750	$75,000
Required economic yield	15%	15%
Operating cost less depreciation	$18,000	$5,500

Operating cost plus required return, and an advantage in favor of one proposal or the other, will now be computed by three methods.

	A	B
Exact Method:		
Depreciation plus required return..................	$ 6,169	$18,708
Operating cost less depreciation...................	18,000	5,500
Operating cost plus required return..............	$24,169	$24,208
Advantage.......................................	39	
Average-Interest Method:		
Depreciation.....................................	2,250	5,000
Other operating cost.............................	18,000	5,500
Required return..................................	3,656	13,125
Operating cost plus required return..............	$23,906	$23,625
Advantage.......................................		281
Return Based on First Cost:		
Depreciation.....................................	2,250	5,000
Other operating cost.............................	18,000	5,500
Required return..................................	4,500	15,000
Operating cost plus required return..............	$24,750	$25,500
Advantage.......................................	750	

In the exact and average-interest methods, the 5-year study period is used. Depreciation is straight line. If the amounts of required return by the exact method were to be identified separately, the straight-line depreciations should be deducted from the combined values computed above. The average-interest computation is by the simplified formula which assumes continuous straight-line depreciation.

The situation just illustrated is a borderline case. Two methods of computation favor proposal A; the other favors B. But the differences are not as conspicuous as would be the case if the study were extended to the full depreciation lives, 12 years and 18 years respectively. In that event, the exact and average-interest methods would show very considerable advantage in favor of proposal B.

In general, the three methods of applying required return compare as follows. The exact method is certainly the most reasonable for long-term projects because it provides for time value of money. The average-interest method is a fair approximation for moderately long-term appraisals, and it is more easily understood by many managers. Required return based on first cost is the simplest and most easily understood concept. It appeals to many managers because it indicates immediate results and is the most conservative (it imposes the greatest penalty on investment). The last-named method, however, charges unreasonably for investment, when time changes should be considered in making a decision. Time may bring about cost changes in addition to interest on investment, which is another problem in economy study. This is recognized in the MAPI method of replacement analysis discussed in Chapter 15.

PROBLEMS

8.1. A power plant is to be erected to serve a factory. The annual requirement for electricity is estimated at 800,000 K.W.H. The first cost of the plant is $60,000, depreciation life 20 years to zero salvage value, annual operation and maintenance $7,500, insurance and taxes $1,500. What are the total annual cost and the cost per K.W.H.? Include the charge for use of capital at 12%, exact method.

8.2. A refinery can provide for water storage with a steel tank on a steel tower adjacent to the plant, or a concrete standpipe on a hill some distance away. The elevated tank is estimated to cost $82,000, while the standpipe installation and extra length of service line is estimated to cost $60,000. The standpipe installation will require an additional $6,000 for pumps and controls; and operating and maintenance cost for this setup is estimated at $150 per year. The maintenance cost of the elevated tank is estimated to be $150 per year. The estimated service life of both installations is 30 years with no salvage value. Required yield is 10% based on first cost, to be included as a charge for use of capital.

Assuming declining balance depreciation at the maximum rate allowed for income tax purposes, what is the average annual cost of each proposal for the first 5 years of operation? (PE N.Y. revised)

8.3. A new apartment building was erected at a first cost of $550,000. This cost included a lot purchased at $40,000. Depreciation on the building (less the lot) is straight line based on 30-year life to zero salvage value. Insurance and tax on real estate is $2\frac{1}{2}\%$ of first cost. Maintenance and other operating expenses are estimated at $20,000 per year. There are 50 apartments of approximately equal value. The financial backers require a yield of 15% (before income tax) to justify this investment.

Determine the minimum average monthly rental per apartment necessary to meet required return. Compute by each of the following methods:

a) First cost basis.
b) Average interest for a 10-year study period, based on continuous depreciation.
c) Exact method based on a 10-year study period, with salvage value estimated from straight-line depreciation. What is the annual required return on this basis?

8.4. A lot was bought 5 years ago for $1,200. Taxes were paid at the beginning of each year of ownership as follows: $20, $20, $25, $25, and $20. Now, after 5 years, the lot is to be sold.

a) What price should be asked to realize a yield on investment (before income taxes) of 24%?

b) What is the yield if the lot is sold for $1,800? (PE Pa. revised)

8.5.   Two methods, A and B, are proposed for a certain operation in a plant. Method A requires considerably less investment but is much higher in labor cost. The economic comparison is to be based on a 5-year study period. Required economic yield is 24% of average investment during the study period, based on continuous straight-line depreciation. The essential data are estimated as follows:

	Method A	Method B
First cost	$15,000	$50,000
Salvage value at end of study period	5,000	30,000
Annual costs		
Labor	15,000	6,000
Electric power	200	300
Floor space	1,200	600
Maintenance	500	1,200
Property taxes and insurance	400	1,300

Other expenses are equal for the two methods, and income from operations is not affected by the choice. Straight-line depreciation is used. Compute the annual totals that indicate the preference from the viewpoint of economy.

8.6.   An automatic machine is being considered for a manufacturing process. Although considerable savings in operation are anticipated, the exact amount is unknown. The equipment will cost $60,000 installed. Depreciation by the straight-line method, used for tax accounting, will assume a 10-year life to a salvage (resale) value equal to 15% of first cost. Removal cost would be $500. The required economic yield on this class of investment is 20%.

a) Determine the annual operating savings, before deducting depreciation, that would be just sufficient to justify the investment. Compute by the following methods:

(1) First cost basis.

(2) Conventional average interest, annual depreciation.

(3) Average interest based on continuous depreciation.

(4) Exact method assuming straight-line depreciation.

b) Now assume that the 20% applies only to return based on first cost. What interest rate would produce the same result if the exact method were used?

8.7.   A corporation is considering location for a new plant. There are now three proposals in different states. The tax situation is being studied. In location A, the state income tax is at 6% based on profit before computing the federal tax. In location B, the rate is 5½% applied to the federal tax base. In location C, a state tax of 7% is based on profit after deduction of the federal tax. The firm already operates well into the surtax bracket, so that the effective federal tax on additional profit would be at 52%. Local taxes are about the same in the three locations.

a) What is the over-all tax rate on profit (federal and state) in the three states?

b) If the required net yield on investment is 10%, what is the required yield that would apply before income taxes?

8.8.   The purchase of a piece of suburban farm land is being considered for future development. It is proposed to wait 10 years before offering lots for sale, at which time it is estimated that the lots should be sold for at least $140,000. Real estate tax is now $120, payable at the beginning of each year, and the rate is not expected to change until the property is developed for sale. The presale development in 10 years is expected to cost $45,000. There will be no income on the land in the meantime.

If the real estate operator requires a yield of 15% (before profit tax) on his investment in the land, what is the maximum price that should be paid for it?

8.9.   A certain mining property has a first cost of $2,500,000. The ore body is estimated at 3 million tons. At a feasible rate of extraction, the mine is expected to last at least 10 years, after which salvage value would be negligible. The mining equipment costs $75,000 new, and the average straight-line depreciation rate is 7%. The cost of ore extraction is estimated to average $3.75 per ton (excluding depreciation and depletion). The required yield on investment prior to income tax is 25% based on the conventional average-interest method.

At what value per ton for extracted ore can the mine operator expect to recover the investment and required return? Assume continuous operation at the forementioned rate of extraction.

8.10.   The management of a corporation requires justification for any major capital expenditure on the basis of a *payoff period*—years or months required for profit or savings to equal investment. The controller is expected to establish payoff requirements for various classes of projects based on probable life and risk. The general considerations are as follows: The firm has been realizing profit well above $25,000 per year, so that the federal tax on increment profit or savings is at 52%. There is a state income tax of 6% applicable before federal tax computation. A profit-sharing plan requires a bonus payment amounting to 12% of profit before income taxes and after interest payments. Of the capital, 20% used by the firm is borrowed at an average interest rate of 5%. Straight-line depreciation is used in cost accounting. For manufacturing operations, the *payoff* period relates to total investment (including the borrowed portion) and the saving in *factory* cost without capital recovery.

A certain class of factory equipment is now being considered. The useful life is assumed to be 10 years, depreciated to zero salvage value. The required net yield on the firm's investment (which excludes the borrowed money) is 12%. The simplified average-interest method is used for required return. Interest on debt for individual properties is similarly estimated. The class of equipment under consideration is not expected to affect sales expense, administrative expense, or income. The *payoff period* specification is determined as follows:

a) What is the amount (percentage of first cost) that should be added to required economic return to determine the required savings in factory cost (which are assumed to be estimated without depreciation allowance)?

b) What is the required yield on the firm's investment (80% of the total) at the following stages of profit computation:

   (1) Before federal income tax?

   (2) Before state income tax?

   (3) Before profit-sharing bonus?

   (4) Before interest on debt (basis for economic required return)?

c) Compute the required payoff period in years. (Hint—a total investment of $1,000 could be used as a basis for the computation.)

Can you suggest a practical reason why such a payoff period should be specified as a guide for subordinate executives and staffs? What objections would you offer to such a specification?

CHAPTER 9

Cost, Income, and Profit versus Rate of Operations

OST, income, and profit are obviously affected by the rate of operations or utilization of facilities. In the economic appraisal of any proposed project, it can rarely be assumed that demand is fixed in amount, and that the costs, income, and profit are consequently fixed. The rate of operations is the most common and most important independent variable in project economy. Its consideration may be most significant in the appraisal of a complete enterprise; but it can be equally important in the study of an isolated project within the enterprise.

FIXED AND VARIABLE COSTS

Costs may be affected by a number of variables that are evident to the estimator. The terms *fixed cost* and *variable cost* usually refer to variability with relation to the rate of operations, and the costs are periodic totals (e.g., annual or monthly) rather than amounts per unit of output. It is in this sense that the terms are employed in this chapter. *Fixed costs* are those that do not change with the rate of operations. *Variable costs* are the costs that are affected by the rate of operations. The rate of operations may be measured in various units: operating level in per cent of capacity, output in physical units, duration of operations in time (e.g., days or hours), or sales volume in dollars. In many problems, there is a fixed relationship between the different measures for rate of operations; convenience and significance are the criteria for usage.

Fixed Costs

Some fixed costs are easy to identify—for example, depreciation or amortization based on time, taxes and insurance on fixed assets, interest on long-term debt, sinking fund deposits, rent, fixed charges for public utilities, and like obligations.

Other fixed costs may be more difficult to estimate because they are the minimums of costs that normally vary—for example, minimum salaries of key personnel, minimum maintenance, minimum heat and light, minimum security (e.g., watchmen), minimum office work and supplies. It may be necessary to decide whether the fixed concept should apply to long-term shutdown, or to temporary inactivity which would not seriously reduce the core organization and its sustaining activities.

One method of estimating total fixed cost is to derive it from the downward trend of total cost. The total costs for a reasonably expected range of operating rates may be known. The cost curve can then be extrapolated to zero output, which indicates the level of fixed cost. This derivation will become apparent from the patterns of variable cost to be described presently.

Among the fixed obligations are interest on debt and required return on investment, which are not operating costs as defined in this book. These two obligations, however, deserve consideration along with the fixed operating costs.

Interest on debt, which may be considered a cut out of economic return, may be partly fixed and partly variable. The fixed portion would apply to long-term debt. Short-term borrowing may be related to the rate of operations, increasing with business volume. In computing taxable profit and net profit, interest on debt is treated as a cost.

Required return as a charge for the use of capital may be treated as a cost, as described in the previous chapter. This charge may be partly fixed and partly variable. The portion that applies to working capital may vary because working capital may vary with rate of operations. This variability can be very important in some economy studies—those that involve inventory, for example. To simplify the problems presented with this book, *required return is to be considered a fixed charge*, unless working capital variation is clearly indicated.

Variable Costs

All direct labor and direct material are variable costs, with rare exceptions. Many items of overhead are also variable—supplies, heat, light, power, indirect labor, sales activities, shipping, travel, depreciation based on output, depletion, and the like. Some of these items may have fixed (minimum) levels, which are therefore fixed costs.

Added to the variable operating costs are other variable obligations or charges. Interest on short-term borrowing and required return on variable working capital were previously mentioned. Then there are deductions from profit such as profit-sharing bonuses and income taxes, which are variable. At this point, let us consider the characteristics of variable *operating* cost.

Figures 9–1 to 9–4 are graphs representing four patterns of operating cost versus rates of operations. The upper halves of these figures show the unit costs, to be discussed later. The lower portions show the costs for the fiscal period (assumed to be a year, unless otherwise specified). In these graphs, the characteristics of variable costs in the aggregate are shown for typical situations.

Figure 9–1 represents a simple straight-line condition in which the variable cost increases in direct proportion to rate of operations. Although this situation is rare if applied to an enterprise as a whole, it may be a fair approximation for a reasonably expected range of operating rates. The labor and material rates per unit of output may be fixed; and the hiring or release of indirect labor and office people may be in small increments. Variable budgets are often prescribed on a straight-line basis. In our practice problems, *straight-line cost variation is to be assumed,* unless conditions are introduced that dictate other treatment.

In Figure 9–2, the cost rises in steps that could result from increase in personnel as required by increasing work loads. A pattern as conspicuous as this would characterize a small enterprise.

In Figure 9–3, the slope of the variable cost line changes at one or more operating levels because of definite change in some element of cost. Overtime wages could increase the slope. A change in process justified by increased production, or advantage of quantity purchases, could reduce the cost trend.

Figure 9–4 is a typical cost-efficiency curve. It could represent a power plant, for example. At low outputs, the efficiency is low and the cost curve is steep. At the minimum slope, the efficiency is maximum. This could be the operation at rated capacity, perhaps. Then, overload operation may reduce the operating efficiency (indicated by the steeper trend).

In the figures described above, the graphs represent aggregates of

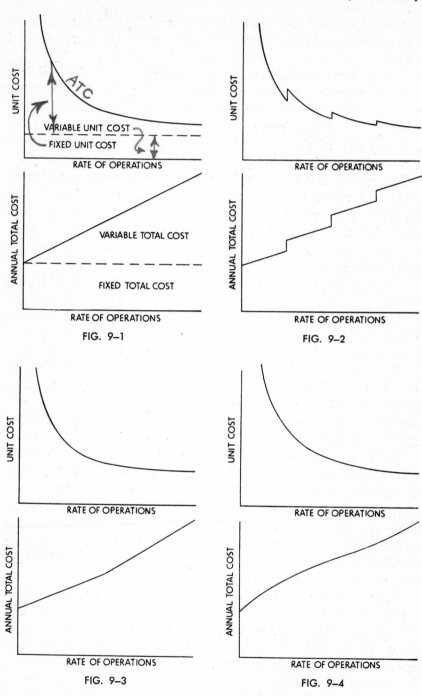

FIG. 9–1

FIG. 9–2

FIG. 9–3

FIG. 9–4

Typical patterns of operating cost versus rate of operations.

fixed and variable cost. It may be useful for analysis or reporting to indicate various items or classes of fixed and variable cost. Items such as wages, salaries, materials, or power may be outstanding enough to warrant conspicuous identification in a graphic report. For estimating the totals at various rates of operations, consideration of all variable costs in detail is necessary. But detail costs need not be computed separately for each rate of operations if straight-line variability can be assumed.

Total Operating Cost

After all operating costs have been classified as fixed or variable, the total operating cost is, obviously, the sum of the two groups of cost. The total is variable, as indicated in Figures 9–1 to 9–4. Now let us assume that *total* costs have been estimated for several operating rates within a likely range of probability, but that the amount of *fixed* cost has not been determined exactly. This range could be from 50 to 100 per cent of capacity, for example. The fixed cost can then be estimated by extrapolating the total cost curve to the point of zero output, as was previously suggested. Although fixed cost determined in this manner may not be the exact amount that would be incurred under shutdown conditions, the estimate is useful for break-even point computation, as will be explained later.

Unit Operating Costs

Unit operating cost was discussed in Chapter 6. The unit represented by the cost should be the same as employed in measuring the rate of operations, preferably the unit in which the product or service is sold. If the project or enterprise involves a miscellany of products or services, unit operating cost may be expressed as cost per sales dollar.

Variability in unit cost does not parallel the variability in components of total cost. The portion of unit cost that corresponds with fixed periodic cost varies from ∞ at zero output to a minimum at maximum output. In other words, that portion of unit cost is inversely proportional to the units produced. Fixed overhead is distributed over as many units as are indicated by the rate of operations.

A portion of the unit cost can be fixed, corresponding with straight-line variation in the periodic variable cost. For example, if direct labor and direct material costs vary in direct proportion to output, the corresponding unit cost elements would be fixed.

Unit operating costs are indicated in the upper portions of Figures 9-1 to 9-4. The portion of unit cost below the broken-line graph in Figure 9-1 corresponds with the variable portion of total (periodic) cost, both graphs being drawn to the same horizontal scale. Note that unit cost can increase under some conditions with increase in rate of operations. Ordinarily, increased output means reduction of unit cost until operating efficiency is seriously impaired by overloading the establishment.

VARIABLE INCOME AND PROFIT

The variability of cost is an essential consideration in the economy study of any project subject to variable rate of operations. Operating cost plus required return may be the criterion for decision. When such a study involves income, however, it is obviously necessary to consider the variability of that income and the resulting profit or loss.

Variable Income

Income is a function of rate of operations in almost all operating enterprises, public or private. In most industry or trade, the portion of income that is fixed with relation to operating rate is usually minor—rentals, patent royalties, income from securities, interest on loans, and the like. In these enterprises, the major income is from sale of products or services. In the following discussion, we shall neglect the possible fixed items of income. It will also be assumed that the quantity produced is equal to the quantity sold, which is certainly the reasonable long-term prospect in any commercial enterprise.

If selling prices are fixed (or assumed to be stable), income from sales is in direct proportion to quantity sold. For a single product, income equals selling price times the quantity sold. In general, income equals some appropriate coefficient times the rate of operations. This simple *straight-line pattern of income is assumed in all our practice problems unless other conditions are specified.* Two exceptions to this assumption, described below, will be discussed further in Chapters 12 and 14.

Prices often vary with the size of orders. There are also price discounts for prompt payment. For the long-term study, it is reasonable to average such variable units of income. In some cases, however, the disposal of large increments of output may require special pricing. Sales to large mail-order establishments and the "dumping" of excess inventory are examples of this practice. The slope of the income line must change with these price changes.

Another exception to the straight-line pattern of income is the possible adjustment of prices to make possible a desired volume of sales and output, recognizing the price-demand relationship shown in Figure 7–1 (page 88). Under these conditions, the income-output graph would be curved downward as unit price decreases. Then, the optimum unit price is the one that produces the maximum total profit, which may correspond with a rate of operations that is less than maximum capacity.

Variable Profit

Economic return and the subsequent deductions that arrive at net profit were described in Chapter 7. The same treatment of cost and profit data applies at all rates of operations. It will be apparent that profit does not vary in proportion to income or operating cost patterns. An example will be demonstrated later. At this point, let us consider the factors in profit determination. We shall refer, however, to Figure 9–6, which is a graph representing the forementioned example.

Economic return is realized when income exceeds operating cost. The point where they are equal will be designated *economic break-even point*. By some authors, this point has been termed "no gain–no loss break-even point." The latter designation is true from the owners' viewpoint only if there is no interest on debt or other fixed obligations in addition to operating cost.

Interest on debt, and certain other fixed obligations, can be due whether or not economic return is realized. These obligations may be treated as *fixed* costs. In a cost graph such as Figure 9–6, these costs could be represented by a line above and parallel to the graph of total operating cost. In a profit and loss summary, they should be immediately deducted from economic return (or added to economic loss).

Profit-sharing bonuses to employees depend on the amount of profit; but the formulas or payment policies vary greatly. From the owners' viewpoint, these bonuses are *costs* to be added to operating

cost plus interest, but only at operating rates at which profit is sufficient. Computation is simple if the profit share is a specified percentage of profit before income tax deduction. It would be a complex
determination if the bonus were based on *net* profit or on the residue
after a minimum return to owners.

Income taxes are variable costs that usually commence when
economic return exceeds interest on debt. The tax rate now (1961)
changes when the base for federal tax on corporations reaches the
surtax level. Rate changes are frequent in taxation on personal income. These rate changes will affect the slopes of the total cost and
profit graphs.

Required Return

Required return is a fixed amount except as it may be affected by
variable working capital. In any economy study that involves variable rate of operations, the concept of required return is important.
In the profit-making enterprise, it represents the level of accomplishment necessary to justify the investment. When net profit
breaks even at required return, the project may be considered a
success. (See Figure 9–6.) This is termed the "make-out" point by
some authorities.

Required return may also be regarded as a charge for the use of
capital, as described in the previous chapter. This concept is particularly significant in studies that do not lead to profit determination.
In this case, the graph should be represented by a line above the
total cost line. The upper line is total operating cost plus required
return, a graph that is most important for comparing competing
proposals at various rates of operations or output.

In many economy studies, required return can be assumed to be
fixed, because variation in working capital is negligible—in equipment problems, for example. And this simplifying assumption applies to most of the practice problems of this book. Under these
conditions, required return is equivalent to a *fixed* cost (a fixed
obligation that must be met). If indicated separately in a graph, it
would be shown by a line above and *parallel* to the total cost.

For graphic analysis, the *economic* required return is most convenient, particularly when operating cost can be represented by a
straight line as in Figure 9–6. Operating cost plus required return
may then be drawn parallel to the line representing operating cost
and spaced above it at a distance equal to required economic return.
As described in Chapter 8, the required economic return includes

allowances for income taxes and other deductions from profit at that level of accomplishment. The required economic yield, used for determining the return, is computed from the required net yield as described in the previous chapter and Appendix E.

It should be understood that this simple treatment of required return for determining the break-even or "make-out" point, as will be described presently, is appropriate for that purpose only. Actually, *economic* required return at various rates of operations varies with demands on profit, such as income taxes and bonuses. Hence, a graph that truly represents operating cost plus required return would be parallel with and above the graph that represents the sum of all costs, as shown by the broken line in Figures 9–6 and 16–1, which also intersects the income line at the forementioned break-even point. It is this graph (the broken line) that indicates amount of profit greater than or less than required return at various rates of operations.

BREAK-EVEN POINTS

The condition of breaking even at required return (the "make-out" point) has been discussed. There are other break-even points relating to an enterprise as a whole or to individual projects that are useful in economy studies and that can be analyzed graphically or by computation. In the study of an incorporated enterprise, there can be a succession of break-even points that indicate the rates of operations at which various demands on economic return are met—for example, breaking even at:

Operating cost (economic break-even point)
Interest on debt
Preferred stock dividend requirement
Common stockholders' required return

The last named of these break-even points is equivalent to that at economic required return (which includes all the demands on economic return). The shares of return to financial contributors and owners will be discussed further in Chapter 16.

Calculation of Break-Even Points

For nonlinear types of variable cost and income patterns, the graphic solution of break-even points may be the most convenient. When the cost and income patterns are linear (a satisfactory assumption in many studies), an algebraic solution is simple and most accurate. Consider the general straight-line situation depicted in Figure 9–5. For the break-even point determinations, the following notation will be used:

> x = rate of operations in terms of units of output (or other more suitable units of measurement, such as per cent of capacity or of dollars of sales)
>
> y = dollars of cost, income, or return (annual or monthly)
>
> a = unit variable cost, in units used for x
>
> R = required return
>
> b_1 = fixed operating cost
>
> b_2 = fixed operating cost plus required return = $b_1 + R$
>
> p = income per unit of operations, in units used for x.

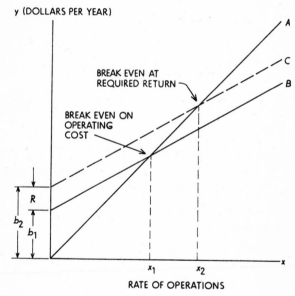

FIG. 9–5. Graphic guide for break-even point computation. A = income, B = operating cost, C = operating cost plus required return.

In the figure, line A represents income, line B is operating cost, and line C indicates operating cost plus required return. The break-even points are:

> x_1 = rate of operations at operating cost equals income
>
> x_2 = rate of operations at operating cost + required return equals income

The determination of x_1 and x_2 is based on the well-known straight-line formula:

$$y = ax + b$$

in which x is the independent variable. Then:

the income line is $y = px$
operating cost is $y = ax + b_1$
operating cost + required return is $y = ax + b_2$

The value of x that satisfies the first two equations is x_1. In this case:

$$x_1 = b_1/(p - a)$$

Similarly, x_2 is derived from the first and third equations:

$$x_2 = b_2/(p - a)$$

A common mistake in the above calculations is failure to employ the same units of measurement for x, a, and p. When a single product is dealt with, it is most convenient to use the unit by which the product is sold (e.g., yards, pounds, tons) so that p is then the selling price. The answers, x_1 and x_2, can then be converted into any units desired, such as per cent of capacity or dollars of sales. If a miscellany of products is involved, the formulas can be in terms of sales-dollars, so that the income line (A) is mathematically at 45° with respect to the x and y axes $(y = x)$.

Other Break-Even Point Applications

The break-even point concept need not be confined to analyses of profit versus rate of operations. The concept is significant in comparisons of competing proposals that are affected by rate of operations. For example, at what degree of utilization will two alternative machines be equal in operating cost plus required return (no choice); or beyond what rate of operations will it pay to invest in the higher-priced but more efficient equipment? The forementioned algebraic method will be appropriate for such problems if the formulas for operating cost plus required return versus rate of operations are linear. This concept of breaking even will be illustrated in several succeeding chapters.

VARIABLE COST, INCOME, AND PROFIT SUMMARIES

In most studies that involve compilations of data, an effective tabulation of data and results is important for the checking and analysis of figures, and for presentation of findings to those who read and act upon reports. Graphic summaries are useful aids to reporting. ("A picture is worth a thousand words.") And graphic methods may be the best for solution of some problems. These principles apply to economy studies of the type considered in this chapter.

Methods of Tabulating and Charting Results

In general, the devices used and the form of tabulations for summarizing data and results depend on the character of the problem and the policies or needs of those who use the information. An effective method of tabulating and charting an economy study will be demonstrated in a summary of the following hypothetical case, which illustrates variable cost, income, and profit. In the tabulation, Table 9–1, pertinent data are summarized. (More detail could be listed if desired.) Figures are rounded to simplify the illustration.

TABLE 9–1

INCOME, COST, AND PROFIT VERSUS RATE OF OPERATIONS

	20%	40%	60%	80%	100%
Capacity..............					
Output, 100-lb. units....	125,000	250,000	375,000	500,000	625,000
Sales.................$	500,000	$ 1,000,000	$1,500,000	$2,000,000	$2,500,000
Fixed operating costs:					
Depreciation.........$	80,000				
Other fixed expense...	420,000				
Total fixed costs......$	500,000	$ 500,000	$ 500,000	$ 500,000	$ 500,000
Variable operating costs:					
Direct labor.........	120,000	240,000	360,000	480,000	600,000
Direct material.......	20,000	40,000	60,000	80,000	100,000
Variable overhead....	180,000	360,000	540,000	720,000	900,000
Total variable........$	320,000	$ 640,000	$ 960,000	$1,280,000	$1,600,000
Total operating cost....$	820,000	$ 1,140,000	$1,460,000	$1,780,000	$2,100,000
Operating cost/cwt......	($6.56)	($4.56)	($3.89)	($3.56)	($3.36)
Income...............	500,000	1,000,000	1,500,000	2,000,000	2,500,000
Operating cost........	820,000	1,140,000	1,460,000	1,780,000	2,100,000
Economic return.......$	−320,000	$ − 140,000	$ 40,000	$ 220,000	$ 400,000
Interest on debt........	16,000	16,000	16,000	16,000	16,000
Profit before bonus and tax...........$	−336,000	$ − 156,000	$ 24,000	$ 204,000	$ 384,000
Profit sharing.........	...	...	2,400	20,400	38,400
Profit before income tax................$	−336,000	$ − 156,000	$ 21,600	$ 183,600	$ 345,600
Income tax............	...	...	6,480	89,972	174,212
Net profit............$	−336,000	$ − 156,000	$ 15,120	$ 93,628	$ 171,388
Net yield.............	(−33.6%)	(−15.6%)	(1.51%)	(9.36%)	(17.14%)

Break-Even Points at:	Capacity	Cwt. Output	Sales
Operating cost.......55.6%		347,222	$1,388,888
Interest on debt......57.3		358,333	1,433,332
Required return......76.5		478,080	1,912,320

The chart, Figure 9–6, is derived from the tabulated data and shows certain break-even points, which are also determined by algebraic computations.

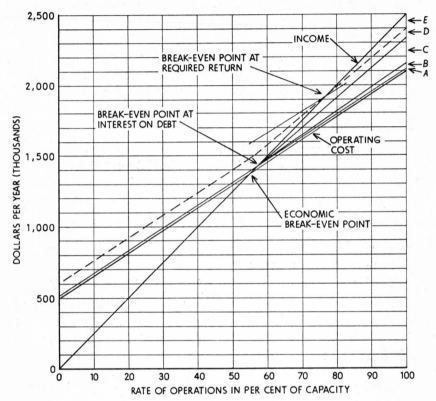

FIG. 9–6. Graphic analysis of a commercial enterprise. A = interest on debt, B = profit-sharing bonuses, C = income tax, D = net required return, E = profit in excess of required return.

The following preliminary information applies to the hypothetical enterprise:

Net worth (owners' equity)........ $1,000,000
Long-term debt at 4% interest...... 400,000
Total investment................$1,400,000
Profit-sharing bonuses based on 10% of profit *before* bonus and income tax.
Income tax (federal only) at 30% on taxable profit plus surtax of 22% on increment of profit above $25,000.
Required net yield on net worth, 8%.
The product (a chemical) is sold at $4.00 per cwt. (100 lb. units).

The income, cost, and profit summary, tabulated in Table 9–1, is based on three simplifying assumptions: (1) stable investment, (2) uniform fixed selling price for product, and (3) linear cost patterns. Break-even point computations are demonstrated below.

Break-Even Points

The preceding problem is now used to illustrate break-even point computation. The calculations are in terms of 100-lb. units of output. Results are then converted to volume of sales (dollars) and per cent of capacity.

At operating cost:

$$\text{Income} = y = 4.00x$$
$$\text{Operating cost} = y = (1{,}600{,}000/625{,}000)x + 500{,}000$$

Then,

$$1.44x = 500{,}000$$
$$\text{Break-even point} = x = 347{,}222 \text{ cwt.} = \$1{,}388{,}888 = 55.6\%$$

At payment of interest on debt:

$$1.44x = 500{,}000 + 16{,}000$$
$$\text{Break-even point} = x = 358{,}333 \text{ cwt.} = \$1{,}433{,}332 = 57.3\%$$

At required return: It is first necessary to determine the required economic return. This is derived from the net requirement (at 8%) and the various required deductions from profit. (See interest and tax formulas on page 103.)

$$\text{Required yield before tax} = \frac{[.08 - (.22)(25{,}000)/1{,}000{,}000]}{(1 - .30 - .22)} = .1552$$

$$\text{Required yield before bonus} = .1552/(1 - .10) = .17244$$

$$\text{Required return before bonus} = (.17244)(1{,}000{,}000) = \$172{,}440$$

Required payment of interest at 4%............$ 16,000
Required economic return.....................$188,440
Fixed operating cost.......................... 500,000
Fixed operating cost + required return..........$688,440

To determine the break-even point using the previous coefficient for x:

$$1.44x = 688{,}440$$
$$\text{Break-even point} = x = 478{,}080 \text{ cwt.} = \$1{,}912{,}320 = 76.5\%$$

Appraisal of Results

The chart, Figure 9–6, demonstrates the critical effects of income and cost factors on the break-even points. Due to the acute angle of incidence between the income and operating cost lines, slight differences in selling prices or costs will make conspicuous changes in the rates of operations required to break even. This condition typifies many businesses that operate on a small margin of profit. The income in most enterprises is more than the net worth, perhaps several times that amount. In such cases, the percentage of profit per dollar of income can be considerably less than the yield on investment, resulting in the critical condition that has been described. In 1954, for example, the profit on sales for all manufacturing corporations was only 3.3%; but yield on net worth was 7.4%.

The values of the break-even points are particularly significant. The operating rate necessary to keep the enterprise out of the red is 57.3% of capacity. At 76.5% the enterprise may be considered successful, having accomplished required return on net worth. At 100% of capacity, however, the yield is more than double the net requirement. These figures indicate the conspicuous difference in results between a good year and a poor one in typical enterprises such as the case demonstrated.

Analyses of profit versus rates of operations are particularly useful for comparing alternatives. Obviously, a comparison of profits or yields at a fixed rate of operations does not tell a conclusive story —the comparison may be very different at some other reasonable operating rates. Two competing proposals may be said to break even (no choice) at the rate of operations where the net yields are equal, if the same required yield is specified for both.

PROBLEMS

9.1. Refer to Problems 6.1 and 6.2. Make a list of the costs enumerated and identify them as to probable variability—v = variable, f = fixed, fv = partly fixed and partly variable.

9.2. Two pumps, A and B, are being considered for basement drainage. The pumps are equal in output but differ in price and efficiency. Electricity costs 2¢ per K.W.H. Expected yield on investment, based on first cost, is 15%. The following data have been obtained:

	Pump A	*Pump B*
Cost installed	$350	$450
Expected life to zero salvage value	10 years	15 years
Maintenance cost per 1,000 hours of operation	$25	$20
Current consumption at full load	6.0 kw.	5.8 kw.

The pump will operate intermittently but at full load. At how many hours per year of operation will the choice be equal? If the demand is greater than this, which pump is the better?

9.3. Two machines of different types and capacities are available for a production job to which they would be assigned exclusively. The choice will depend on a forecast of the annual demand for product. The maximum demand is assumed to be the capacity of the more rapid machine; but more than one of the slower machines can be used, if necessary, to accommodate demand up to the stated maximum. The following estimates were obtained for each of the two machines. Required yield is 20% by the exact method.

	Machine A	Machine B
First cost........................	$3,000	$40,000
Expected life to zero salvage value..	10 years	10 years
Fixed operating cost except depreciation.................	$1,400 per year	$4,800 per year
Variable cost per piece produced...	60¢	35¢
Capacity, pieces per year.........	15,000	40,000

Fixed operating costs that are the same for both methods have not been included in the comparison. Note that the data on Machine A are for one machine only.

    a) Determine the annual operating cost plus required return for each method for a production of 15,000 pieces, 30,000 pieces, and 40,000 pieces per year.

    b) From the computed data, plot graphs, operating cost plus required return versus output, on the same set of coordinates so as to reveal the break-even point.

    c) Confirm the graphic determination of the break-even point by algebraic computation.

    d) Confirm the above conclusion by computing the annual operating cost plus required return at that output for both methods.

9.4. The complete cost of constructing a new all-season hotel is $980,000. The cost of the land is $300,000 and is considered not to depreciate in value. Fixtures will cost $150,000, and a working capital of 30 days' gross income at 100% capacity will be required. The investment in fixtures should be recovered in 7 years, and the investment in the structure should be recovered in 25 years.

When the hotel is operating at 100% capacity, the gross income will be $1,200 per day. Operating expenses, exclusive of capital recovery and interest, will amount to a fixed cost of $115,000 per year and a variable cost, varying in proportion to the level of operation, of $78,000 per year at 100% capacity.

If interest is taken at 12% compounded annually, at what per cent of capacity must the hotel operate to break even? (Hint—the exact method for required return is equivalent to sinking fund depreciation and interest on first cost. Assume property is depreciated to zero salvage value.) (PE N.Y. revised)

9.5.   The Sweep Company manufactures vacuum cleaners. The labor cost is $15 per unit, and materials cost $10. The fixed costs are $8,000 per month. The capital investment is $300,000, and the fair rate of return is 8% net per year. The plant has a normal capacity of 500 units per month. The unit selling price is $55. The estimated income tax rate is 30% on taxable profit.

a) Draw the monthly total operating cost chart with the x axis showing capacity and the y axis showing cost. Include income and profit tax so as to reveal break-even points.

b) Calculate the outputs to break even on cost and to make out (break even at required return) on a monthly basis. (PE Pa. revised)

9.6.   A manufacturer produces a product at a direct labor cost of $2.75 per unit and with material cost of $3.50 per unit. The fixed charges of the business are $75,000 per month. The business has fixed assets of $150,000 and working capital of $35,000. Maximum production is 6,000 units per week.

a) Draw the operating cost pattern for the project with the x axis showing per cent capacity and the y axis showing cost.

b) Assuming a return rate of 10%, what selling prices do we need for an economic break-even point of 50% and for a make-out point of 60% (breaking even at required return)?

Make all calculations on a 52-week-per-year basis. (PE Pa.)

9.7.   A local shop which specializes in the production of plastic bags operates 8 hours per day, 300 days per year. The shop, now operating at 75% of its theoretical capacity, is producing at the rate of 100,000 bags per day. Under these operating conditions, the estimated yearly costs are:

	Fixed	Variable (In Proportion to Output)
Labor	$ 6,750	$28,250
Material		45,600
Tools and dies		5,200
Power and light	700	4,900
Heat	450	
Water	70	
Taxes	1,530	
Supplies	200	700
Equipment and tool maintenance		3,270
Building maintenance	960	
Insurance	2,200	
Depreciation	23,200	
Administration	15,000	
Selling	10,000	

The owners of the shop consider a return of $12,000 on their investment necessary to justify their business. Sales quotations have been based on a selling price of $6.00 per 1,000 bags.

a) Draw a break-even chart based on the above data.

b) Compute the break-even points for no profit–no loss and for required return.

c) What is the required selling price to earn the required return when the shop is operating at 40% capacity?

d) If market conditions are such that bags can be sold for only $4.00 per 1,000, would you recommend that the plant shut down rather than accept orders at this price? Conditions are assumed to be temporary. Explain your answer. (PE Pa.)

9.8. A manufacturer has been having his gear cutting done by an outside machine shop and now is considering the purchase of his own equipment. In the opinion of management, the machine would have to demonstrate an annual cost advantage of at least 20% of investment, by the exact method based on a five-year study period. Ordinary depreciation would be computed by the straight-line method, and book values or intermediate salvage values would be so estimated. Other essential facts have been collected as follows:

Purchase price (f.o.b. plant).........................	$45,000
Preparation for service (installation, etc.)...............	$1,500
Estimated service life..............................	15 years
Estimated trade-in value in 15 years...................	$4,500
Hours per year:	
Maximum normal daytime operation.................	2,000 hours
Maximum practical overtime.......................	1,000 hours
Wage rates for machine operator:	
During normal day...............................	$2.50 per hour
During overtime.................................	$3.50 per hour
Fringe benefits.......................................	10% of labor cost
Other overhead except depreciation:	
Fixed..	$1,800
Variable.......................................	75¢ per hour

a) Make an economy study leading to annual totals and unit costs plus required return. Tabulate results for 500, 1,000, 1,500, 2,000, and 2,500 hours of operation per year. Assume that there will be no overtime unless the annual total is expected to exceed 2,000 hours.

b) If the outside shop has been charging $10.50 per hour for the gear work, what annual demand would have to be exceeded to make the machine purchase a profitable venture?

c) If the forecasted demand for the coming year is 1,750 hours, what would the outsider have to bid (charge per hour) to encourage the manufacturer to defer the purchase of equipment?

9.9.   Two manufacturing methods have been proposed for a new production requirement. One method involves *two* general-purpose machine tools that cost $15,000 each, installed. The other method would employ *one* special-purpose machine that would cost $45,000. In both cases, the production rate would be 20 pieces per hour (during operation) with a potential of 2,000 hours per year. The first method requires two men (one for each machine) at $3.00 per hour. The special machine requires one man at $3.50 per hour. The depreciation rate for each type of equipment is 6% per year, straight line. Required yield on investment is 24% at the level of factory cost, based on average investment for a study period of 5 years. Other essential data follows:

	General-Purpose Machine (Each)	Special Machine
Power cost per hour	20¢	30¢
Fixed maintenance	$300	$500
Variable maintenance per hour	10¢	18¢
Miscellaneous fixed charges per year	$1,600	$2,100

The miscellaneous fixed charges include insurance, taxes, and floor space. They exclude depreciation and required return.

a) At what output will the two methods break even on operating cost?

b) At what output will the two methods break even on operating cost plus required return?

c) At the latter break even point, what is the operating cost plus required return per piece? (Neglect direct material and other charges, not listed above, that are assumed to be the same for both proposals.)

9.10.   A firm is considering the purchase of a truck for delivery and pick-up service, a service that has been previously furnished by a local trucking company. The trucker was paid $6,800 last year for an estimated 21,000 miles of travel. The firm's management believes that private trucking can be justified only if the savings per year exceed 22% of the average investment based on straight-line depreciation. Data on the proposed trucking operation follow:

Purchase price for truck	$4,800
Preparation for service (name, etc.)	$150
Estimated service life	5 years
Estimated trade-in value in 5 years	$1,400
Estimated average miles per hour	25
Estimated total mileage required	50 to 150 per day
Working days per year	255
Truck driver's wages	$2.75 per hour
Fringe benefits	12% of wages
Gasoline, oil, and maintenance	10¢ per mile
Licenses, insurance, garage space	$425 per year

The trucking operation is to be charged with driver's wages only when the truck is in service. The driver is used for other work when not driving.

a) Make an economy study leading to trucking costs per mile plus required return for annual mileages from minimum to maximum of estimated demand?

b) Compute the mileage at which purchased and private trucking would break even.

c) If management decides to speculate on an annual requirement of 25,000 miles of trucking, what would the trucking concern have to charge (in average per mile) to obtain consideration?

9.11.   The capital required to operate a plant making milk-bottle caps has been estimated as follows:

Cost of land... $ 9,000
Planning and construction of building.................... 23,000
Equipment.. 45,000
Working capital:
    Fixed... 15,000
    Variable, in proportion to output (at 80% capacity)...... 18,000

The normal rate of plant operation is expected to be at 80% of capacity, and the following estimates are on that basis.

Output (at 80% capacity)........................1,200,000 caps per day
Working days per year...........................   250
Fixed cost, except depreciation.................. $67,000 per year
Variable cost at 80% capacity.................... $340,000 per year

Straight-line depreciation is based on a 3% rate for the building and 10% for the equipment. The owners have established a required net yield on investment of 10% as the basis for planning (using the average-interest method and a 5-year forecast). The federal income tax rate is 30% on taxable profit plus 22% on the profit increment above $25,000. The state income tax is at 5% computed before federal tax.

a) Tabulate the results of an economy study for operation at 40%, 60%, 80%, and 100% of capacity, and leading to annual and unit figures for operating cost. The unit of sale is 1,000 caps.

b) What selling price would have to be obtained to break even on required return at 65% of capacity?

c) Using the above selling price, compute economic return, income taxes, net profit, and net yield on 5-year average investment for operation at 80% capacity.

9.12.   A company specializing in small portable radios has a net worth of $1,500,000. The normal capacity of the plant is 160,000 sets per year, an amount that can be increased to 240,000 by operating a night shift. Only one model is being offered, at a wholesale price of $20 per unit, and this price is fixed because of highly competitive market conditions.

The sales cost is estimated to rise in greater than straight-line proportion to sales because of the greater sales effort required (e.g., advertising and promotion). Required net yield on net worth is considered to be 10%. The only deduction from economic return is the federal profit tax at 30% plus 22% surtax on the profit increment above $25,000. Annual costs at various rates of operations have been estimated as follows:

		Variable Sales Expense
Fixed overhead................................	$ 750,000	
Variable factory cost:		
For 80,000 units.............................	840,000	$200,000
For 120,000 units............................	1,260,000	320,000
For 160,000 units............................	1,680,000	460,000
For 200,000 units............................	2,300,000	625,000
For 240,000 units............................	2,900,000	830,000

a) Construct a break-even chart based on the above estimates. Assume that the curves representing costs and income taxes are continuous through the outputs specified in the estimates.

b) From the break-even chart, what is the output or outputs at which the net profit would equal the required return?

c) From the chart, estimate the quantity produced and sold that would yield the maximum return, assuming that the relation between sales and selling cost proves to be valid.

d) Compute the net profit and net yield on net worth at the output derived in (c).

9.13. The economy of a proposed power plant for an industrial establishment is being studied. The proposal competes with service offered by a public utility. The public utility would charge a fixed amount (demand charge) of $1,500 per month plus 1.1¢ per K.W.H. for electricity consumed. The proposed power plant would have a rated output (100% capacity) of 3,500 kw., but overloading up to 20% would be considered feasible. For this type of investment, the required yield (before income tax) is to be 16% by the exact method and based on a 10-year study period.

The engineers consulted for the design and construction of the plant (coal-fired boiler, turbogenerator, and accessories) have quoted $700,000 for the project. The value of the land on which the plant would be erected is $5,000. The estimated thermal efficiencies of the over-all plant at various rates of operation are as follows:

Capacity	Efficiency	Capacity	Efficiency
30%...............	19.8%	80%...............	23.9%
40	21.2	90	24.0
50	22.4	100	23.9
60	23.2	110	23.7
70	23.7	120	23.1

Coal rated at 13,000 B.T.U.'s per pound can be obtained for $5.00 per ton.

Operating costs, other than fuel, have been estimated on an annual basis as follows:

Depreciation on plant (except land)............straight-line at 3%
Fixed maintenance.......................... $14,000
Variable maintenance (at 100% capacity)....... 10,500
Other operating cost, fixed................... 41,000

For computing required return, the plant's 10-year salvage value is to be estimated from the straight-line depreciation rate. The plant is to operate 24 hours a day, 365 days a year.

The results of the economy study are to be reported so as to show:

a) Annual operating costs plus required return for operating rates from 30% to 120% of rated capacity.

b) Costs plus required return per K.W.H. at above operating rates.

c) A break-even chart indicating the operating rate at which privately produced and purchased power are equal in economy.

d) If demand for the coming year were estimated to range from 70% to 90% of power-plant capacity, what would be the gain or loss in dollars per year and yield for each of these conditions? Yield is to be based on average investment.

CHAPTER 10

Estimating

ECONOMY study is a process of estimating and analysis. Conventional accounting is based primarily on historical records (what has happened). Economy studies aim to *predict* results. Such studies usually involve *estimates* of life of the project, cost, required return, income, and profit or equivalent cost advantage. In prediction, there is the uncertainty inherent in forecasting. The accumulation of pertinent data may require most of the time and effort in the economy study. The extent of the preliminary fact finding and estimating depends on the character of the project, the objectives of study, and the detail and precision required for meeting the objectives.

It is obviously impractical to attempt in any one volume a discussion of estimating techniques for all types of projects. Each class of industry has individual problems and practices. Principles to be discussed in this chapter are general in application. We shall be concerned mostly with data and estimates that are the bases for project analysis. Subsequent treatment of these data are the topics of other chapters.

PRELIMINARY CONSIDERATIONS

Objectives

A well-defined objective is a prerequisite of any effective, organized activity. Unrestricted search for facts and subsequent analysis is extravagant and often ineffective. When several persons are involved, common understanding as to objective is essential for coordination. The basic objective of economy study is cost or profit prediction; but subordinate objectives are also important. Is the purpose of study a rough preliminary estimate that may or may not encourage further investigation? Is the estimate to be a basis for a firm bid or commitment? Is it to be the basis for a costly long-term program? Naturally, the objective controls the extent and character of investigation.

Economy of Investigation

The character of the project and objective of study impose limits on the time and cost of investigation. A study to guide decision on a $1,000 tool would not warrant the weeks of time and elaborate report that might be appropriate for a million-dollar venture. A problem for manager and analyst is to balance the cost of a proposed study against the cost of possible error in decision that could be avoided by the study. The law of diminishing returns applies. Excessive detail and effort at precision can negate the gains that might be realized. These considerations will be illustrated in the following situations.

An architect is called upon by a prospective client for a preliminary estimate on an interesting home design. Knowing that the plans are tentative, the architect can not afford to spend time on an item-by-item estimate. He would probably present an over-all figure based on a cost per square foot of floor area that seems appropriate for the desired grade of construction. A much more careful estimate would be expected of a contractor bidding on the job. Even then, the average home does not call for detailed item-by-item computation. A large building project, however, does justify detailed estimates on all items, major and minor.

Now consider a new product that is being developed for manufacture. Several stages of economy study may be called for. Among the initial steps are the establishment of goals as to product cost and quality and an appraisal of development cost. Development may appear so uncertain as to cost and outcome that a succession of appropriations should be made. Each succeeding appropriation would then depend on the progress and prospects revealed during the course of development. When certain of the product specifications become definite, economy studies may be made to determine whether the cost prospect is reasonably satisfactory. When specifications are tentatively final, an accurate, detailed economy study is necessary. The project may then be approved for production, require revision, or it may be abandoned. After the new product has been manufactured and sold for a reasonable period, the cost, income, and profit situation may be reappraised. At this stage, the analyst has the benefit of accounting records; but the future still requires prediction.

Engineers and management experts are often employed to assist financing agencies in the appraisals of status and prospects of enterprises that may be aided or purchased. These situations are problems in evaluation and forecasting which may involve detailed study much beyond the inspection of accounting records.

From the examples cited, it is apparent that the character of the project and the objective of the study control the allowable time, extent, precision, and cost of estimating.

BUSINESS FORECASTS

Operating costs and income change with the business conditions affecting the industry. An economy study may be confined to conditions that are immediate and local. Long-term projects depend on future economic and market conditions, appraisals of which are specialties of the economist and market researcher. The costs of capital, purchased products, labor, and taxes, and the prospects of market and income are affected by conditions that must be professionally forecasted or guessed at. Uncertainty increases with remoteness of events. Investors, owners of business, and top managers, however, must make decisions that speculate on the future, with or without the aid of professional economists or market experts.

A comprehensive discussion of economic and market forecasting is not to be attempted here. But, to aid the reader in appreciation of the problem and its relation to economy study, some general observations may be of interest.

General Business Conditions

Everyone knows that business in general fluctuates irregularly in short-term and long-term cycles. Although interesting formulas have been proposed to predict the depth and timing of these cycles, no such formulas have proved to be reliable. World-wide economic conditions and international relations have been unpredictable factors in our economy. And respected economists differ in their forecasts. It is known only that periods of boom, inflation, depression, and deflation are to be expected. It is also expected that federal agencies, with the support of a more knowledgeable public, will be able to reduce the severity of these cycles.

Several metropolitan dailies (e.g., the New York *Times*) and financial journals publish statistics which are watched closely by businessmen. For example:

Business loans   Electric power output
Money supply   Steel production
Money in circulation   Steel operating rate
Business failures   Oil production
Commodity index   Motor vehicle production
Consumer's price index   Construction contracts
Number employed   Freight car loadings
Number unemployed   Inventories
Personal income   Exports
Industrial production index   Imports

In addition to these are the market statistics on basic commodities
and securities and interest rates. The significance of these figures
is in the changes and rates of change revealed by successions of such
reports. The *trends* are important.

Seasonal Variations

In economy studies relating to activities that are seasonal in character (clothing, toys, canning operations, and the like), one must
recognize the extent and timing of demand and material supply. An
ideal objective is the plan for products, facilities, and schedules that
effects the optimum balance in investment, rate of operations, operating costs, inventories, and sales or services. The problems of minimum cost and maximum profit will be discussed in Chapter 14. The
businessman naturally considers diversification to offset fluctuating
seasonal demand.

To the analyst, statistical past experience is the best guide for predicting seasonal variation. In the toy business, for example, the percentage of annual sales devoted to Christmas trade can be anticipated quite accurately. In the canning enterprise, the dates of crop
maturity can usually be predicted within a few days.

Another kind of seasonal variation affects buying and material
cost. It may be good policy to buy and accept delivery of fuel in the
early summer because decline in demand may depress prices. But,
the uncertainty of price fluctuation and the costs of storage and
capital may discourage stockpiling.

Secular Trend

Secular trend characterizes the history of many products and industries that are not of basic type. The trend is graphically represented by an inclined "f" curve (business volume versus time).
Most new developments have a slow beginning. Then, the product

becomes known, costs and prices decline, the market broadens, and the industry may expand at a rapid pace. Finally, competition and saturation of the market slow down expansion. Business is then sustained by population growth and needs for replacements, or changes in conditions may cause actual decline. This is the history of moving pictures, radio, TV, electric refrigeration, air conditioning, and similar industries. The secular cycle is short for novelties or products with transient appeal (e.g., the games Mah Jong and Canasta).

Quantitative *prediction* of secular trend is highly speculative, of course. If the economy study deals with a product or service that has made a beginning, the progress curve can be plotted up to date. It is necessary to extrapolate that curve into the future as a basis for estimating. The forecast of secular trend must be combined with a forecast of general business conditions. Consider the problem of the radio manufacturer in 1929. Radio business was then expanding rapidly. But 1929 was also the eve of the Great Depression.

The manager concerned with secular trend naturally tries to maintain favorable progress against the slowing-down tendency. This necessitates introduction of improvements in product, cost reductions, price reductions, and increased sales effort. New types of products may then be introduced to take up the slack. The radio business has been sustained by automobile radios, portable sets, and high fidelity. Radio manufacturers expanded into TV and all sorts of electronic equipment, with the obvious advantage of diversification.

Sales Forecasting

As a subject of study, engineering economy may seem mostly concerned with analysis and prediction of cost. But the economic objective of a business project is profit; and profit is as dependent on income as on cost. Income is often the most speculative factor in project economy. In construction, extractive industries, manufacture, public utilities, and trade, income is from sales.

The prediction of business conditions, seasonal variations, and secular trend is part of the sales forecasting problem. Outguessing competitors (the game of trade) is another aspect of the problem. Then there is the relationship between price and quantity that can be sold, and a similar relationship between sales volume and sales effort. The offerings of competitors and alternative outlets for the consumer's dollar are obviously critical factors. All these subjects are specialties of economics and market research.

The person engaged in economy study may not have professional competence in forecasting sales. If not, he must be assisted by specialists or by the sales and business executives who must assume that responsibility. Certain aspects of sales prediction can be subjected to mathematical analysis—procedures for determining optimum conditions as to risk, selling prices, rate of operations, product mixes, capacity of facilities, and investment, all of which involve income. These matters will be discussed further in Chapter 14.

In the study of public projects or nonprofit enterprises, the predicted utilization of facilities is comparable with the sales forecast. What will be the demand for output from a public power project? What will be the traffic density on a superhighway in five years? Trends in population, industrial growth, and popular demand are critical factors in the economy of such projects.

ESTIMATING COST DETAILS

The treatment of major classes of cost has been previously described. Depreciation, income taxes, and required return (as a charge for the use of capital) have been discussed in considerable detail. At this point, we shall consider the techniques of estimating some of the important cost factors.

Prices of Purchased Items

For purchased products in immediate demand, the firm quotations of suppliers are an obvious source of price information. For materials currently being purchased, accounting records supply the needed data. Also, there are the usual catalogs and price lists that may apply to the estimate. For many economy studies, however, the prices that will be incurred are not known so definitely; they must be estimated. This is true of all projects that involve purchases beyond the time limit of available quotations, including all long-range forecasts. Prices also vary with conditions that may not be certain until action is decided upon.

Prices usually vary with quality, quantity, delivery requirements, accessory services, and terms of settlement. This means that the estimator must recognize these critical factors. It may be appropriate to compare alternative conditions. The lot-size problem is a topic of Chapter 14. It must also be recognized that, in business or industrial operations, there is considerable range for price negotiation. Buying is a professional specialty beyond the scope of discussion here. Of immediate interest is the effect of these variables on the precision of estimates. The actual prices can deviate considerably from the estimates used in the economy study.

Geographical location may be a conspicuous factor in prices. Prices are often quoted f.o.b. shipping point (or basing point, such as port of entry). Nearness to sources of supply is a factor in plant location. And local price situations vary—most conspicuously for bulky materials, fuels, and purchased power. Local price situations may not be revealed in the trade publications. Local chambers of commerce and the departments of commerce of the various states may be called upon for information. On-the-spot investigation may be necessary. Transportation facilities at the plant site or construction works can be important factors.

It may be necessary to estimate prices from past experience and trends. Price trends may be evident in the purchasing records of the enterprise. Or it may be necessary to study the recent historical statistics of the industry at large. In this manner, for example, an estimator who knows about the cost of certain construction materials in 1950 can now estimate a similar project on the basis of published price indexes for that class of goods. Price indexes are published in trade and financial periodicals. Longer-range historical data are available in the statistical publications of the U.S. Department of Commerce. These are distributed by the U.S. Government Printing Office, Washington 25, D.C., and lists of appropriate publications can be obtained from them.

The forecasting of future prices is a speculation related to fluctuating supply and demand and business conditions. Trends of the past may be used as a guide; but extrapolation of such trends into the future is guesswork at best. In 1960, it was expected that steel prices would rise because of increase in labor rates; but no economist could make a certain prediction. Some prices have actually decreased because of improved technology. Prices in general may be expected to increase gradually because of long-term inflationary trend. Witness the decline in the purchasing power of the dollar during the past half century. The same trend, however, applies to other costs and to income as well.

Construction Costs

The construction project is particularized here because it is usually a major investment that may involve many cost details. In this class of estimating may be included buildings, various other structures, roads, equipment erected at its site, and properties that involve masonry, steelwork, carpentry, excavation, and the like. Detail estimating for such a project involves purchased items, labor, and overhead discussed elsewhere.

The cost of purchased construction is known when a fixed-price contract is agreed upon. But it may be necessary to evaluate the bids, or preliminary estimates may be required for planning. A program for construction may extend considerably into the future. In many such estimates, the classes of work are aggregated into groups, or the entire job may be considered as a whole; extreme detailing of costs is not justified.

The techniques for estimating price apply, in general, to estimating classes of construction cost. Gross estimates may be based on area, volume, tonnage, and the like. Current costs and indexes are listed in trade and technical journals. The publications of the F. W. Dodge Corporation and *Engineering News Record* are prominent in the construction industry. Indexes on construction cost and construction activity are also available in the publications distributed by the U.S. Government Printing Office, previously mentioned.

As in the case of prices, construction costs vary considerably with location. Local chambers of commerce are possible sources of information. Allowances must be made for conditions at the exact site.

Construction estimates should be generously "padded" for contingencies. Unfortunately, most large construction projects, public works particularly, cost more than originally estimated.

Labor Cost

When wage rates are known, the estimate of labor cost is essentially that of time or man-hours. In the going enterprise, the rates and time standards for operations like those being studied are the obvious sources of estimating data. Complications arise when: (1) operations are different from those previously experienced, (2) work is to take place in a new location, and (3) the estimate is a forecast of *future* costs.

For rough estimates, labor cost may be based on the size of the project. A class of construction may be estimated in cents per square foot, excavation in cents per cubic yard, sand castings in cents per pound, and so on. The manufacturer that has produced many job lots of metal products will have records from which can be averaged labor cost per pound for machine-shop work. These estimates require experience in the particular industry. They do not recognize detail differences in the individual projects.

To estimate new manufacturing operations in detail, the synthetic methods of time study can often be applied. Procedures such as Methods-Time-Measurement, for example, can develop reliable time standards for most human manipulations. Conventional machine operations can be estimated from published recommendations as to speeds and feeds (surface speed of cutting tool and advance per cut). Engineering handbooks and suppliers of tools and materials provide such data. To illustrate this, assume that a cylindrical part 12 inches long and 2 inches in diameter requires a lathe operation. The recommended speed is 250 feet per minute and the feed 1/32 inch. Then for each piece:

$$\text{Revolutions required} = 12/.03125 = 384$$
$$\text{Circumference} = 2\pi/12 = .523 \text{ feet}$$
$$\text{R.p.m.} = 250/.523 = 478$$
$$\text{Time} = 384/478 = .804 \text{ minutes}$$

To this must be added time for loading, starting, stopping, unloading etc. Such detail is justified when quantity production is anticipated. In some cases, the performance of machines and other processing equipment is guaranteed by the supplier. Very unusual new work may require experimental trials. And the most important may justify the cost of a pilot production line or plant.

Labor rates that are not known to the estimator, as for a new class of work, require a job evaluation of some sort. If the concern already uses a job evaluation system, the labor rate can be predicted on that basis (with the aid of the personnel staff). Regional rates for similar labor may be investigated. Estimating rates for an entirely new location is a problem similar to that of material costs. Labor rates vary greatly with location. Table 10–1 illustrates the variation in rates in the textile and needle trades during the years 1952 to 1957. The data are extracted from bulletins of the Federal Bureau of Labor Statistics. Trade publications publish similar data. *Factory Management and Maintenance,* for example, publishes every few months the regional rates for indirect labor. State departments of labor and industry and local chambers of commerce are appropriate sources of wage data.

Projections into the future involve the risks inherent in forecasting. Past trends can be used as a guide. It is noteworthy that since

TABLE 10-1

REGIONAL WAGE RATES—EXAMPLES FROM THE TEXTILE AND GARMENT
INDUSTRIES

Industry, Date, Region	Occupational Wages, Dollar per Hour			

Synthetic Textiles, 1954	Loom Fixers	Truckers	Weavers, Women	Stenographers
U.S.A. average	$1.74	$1.07	$1.49	$1.34
Mid-Atlantic	1.92	1.14	1.55	1.34
Allentown	1.92	1.07	1.56	..
Scranton	1.82	1.02	1.39	..
Southeast	1.69	1.04	1.44	1.32
Charlotte	1.65	1.02	1.36	..
Greenville	1.73	1.05	1.49	..

Full-Fashioned Hosiery, 1952	Adjusters	Boarders	Knitters	Stenographers
U.S.A. average	$2.18	$1.41	$2.09	$1.20
Mid-Atlantic	2.24	1.60	2.07	1.27
Philadelphia	2.28	1.58	2.00	..
Reading	2.19	1.77	2.19	1.31
Southeast	2.16	1.31	2.11	1.19
Charlotte	2.35	1.45	2.16	1.28
Hickory, N.C.	2.11	1.35	2.17	1.18
Tennessee	1.66	1.01	2.24	1.16

Men's and Boys' Dress Shirts, 1954	Cutters	Hand Pressers	Sewers	Clerks, Women
Alabama	$1.42	$0.84	$0.91	$0.94
Georgia	1.36	1.12	1.00	1.05
New York	2.08	1.50	1.28	1.12
Pennsylvania (1954)	1.74	1.29	1.16	1.12
Allentown (1956)	1.89	1.57	1.44	..
Pottsville (1956)	1.89	1.31	1.31	..

Women's and Misses Coats and Suits, 1957	Cutters	Hand Pressers	Hand Sewers	Sewing Machinists Section Method
Baltimore	$2.31	$2.62	$1.67	$1.54
New York City	3.35	3.46	2.42	2.45
Paterson, N.J.	3.25	1.91	1.80	2.03
Philadelphia	2.94	3.09	1.63	2.34

SOURCE: "The Textile Industry in Pennsylvania," *Engineering Research Bulletin* B-74, College of Engineering and Architecture, The Pennsylvania State University, May, 1958.

the beginning of this century wage rates (and salaries) have steadily risen except during the depression period of the 1930's. The same general rate of increase, however, has not applied equally to all regions. The percentage increases in some of the southern states have been double those of the industrial North so that wages are now equal in some occupations. In a region that is developing industrially, a similar trend is to be expected.

Wage rates are not the sole criterion of comparative labor cost. Skill, productivity, and stability are cost factors. If these conditions are not measurable in dollars, they must be given weight as intangibles. *Fringe benefits must always be added to labor cost.* Fringe benefits include the employer's contribution to social security, unemployment insurance, hospitalization and life insurance, retirement funds, and employee services. These costs now exceed 20% of the regular pay in many concerns. Although some of these expenses may be included in overhead in accounting practice, it is most reasonable to treat the over-all fringe benefits as a percentage of wages and salaries in an economy study.

Miscellaneous Costs

Classification of costs into fixed and variable components is important in most economy studies. The principle was discussed in Chapter 9. Some types of cost are mixed—e.g., fixed maintenance and variable maintenance, fixed heat and light and the variable increment, and so on. This distinction is particularly important when the rate of operations is variable.

Much of the overhead may be fixed. When one is dealing with individual projects in the going enterprise, fixed overhead can often be neglected since it is unaffected by the project. Overhead and other costs that are the same for alternatives can usually be neglected in comparing those alternatives. Exceptions are the problems in which *total* cost is a decision factor.

Among the interesting problems in economy study is the cost of sales effort. A new product (or service) may be introduced with a burst of advertising and promotion which may level off as the product takes hold. Developments, such as secular trend or competition, may then stimulate additional sales effort. Selling expense is an exceedingly important factor in most commercial projects; in some enterprises it may exceed the manufacturing cost. The economy of sales effort is discussed in Chapter 14.

A precaution is necessary in the application of overhead rates that may be already established in the going concern. Often, certain elements of overhead must be analyzed separately—depreciation, tool-setup costs, storage, maintenance, power, floor space, for example. *When this is done, these particularized costs must be deducted from the more general type of overhead to avoid duplications.*

The long-range prediction of overhead is a problem similar to that of the forementioned price and labor situations. After an enterprise has become established, overhead does tend to increase at a rate greater than that of prices and labor. It is an unfortunate tendency in bureaucratic institutions, often in government enterprises. A more legitimate reason is increase in automation and in the complexity of processes and facilities. Increase in overhead may be accompanied by decrease in total cost per unit of output. Long-range predictions of this kind can hardly be detailed.

Precision of Estimates

Estimates may be imprecise because of time and cost limits imposed on estimating, errors by the estimator, and lack of exact knowledge about the costs. Uncertainties in predicting the future have been mentioned previously. The precision of estimates is certainly an important factor in economy study and decision making. Let us consider some practical aspects of this problem.

One principle of engineering computations is that the precision of a result can be no greater than the precision of a *multiplying* factor. For this reason, it is absurd to use compound interest factors (as given in most interest tables) that show more than three or four significant digits, when the other multiplying factors are considerably less accurate. For the same reason, slide rule computation is adequate for most estimating.

When several factors are to be multiplied (or divided) in an estimate, the probable error of the product is not the product or sum of the probable errors of the factors. The formula for the probable error (E) is:

$$E = \sqrt{e_1^2 + e_2^2 + e_3^2 \cdots + e_n^2}$$

This situation would apply to the estimating of annual fuel cost for a power plant operation, for example.

For time value estimates, the effect of uncertainty in the estimates of interest rates (i) and time (n) is often more serious than in simple multiplications because the compound interest factors are geometric in character. Time, however, is not critical for the long-term present worth of a series which approaches capitalized cost (infinite time).

Individual cost items that are to be added should be as precise as practical to estimate them, even though the error in a minor component that is roughly estimated may not have a serious effect percentagewise on the total. In many economy studies, some of the costs may be known exactly; others may have to be approximated.

The novice in a field of estimating should be encouraged to be as accurate as facilities for computation and data permit. It is unwise to round out the results of computations until the end, because the results of such rounding can not always be anticipated. The *final* figures, however, may be appropriately rounded to indicate that no greater accuracy is expected or required. Some cost estimates, submitted for bidding purposes, are stated in dollars or cents far beyond the precision possible in the estimating. A possible justification for this is that such figures may indicate to the reader that the estimate has been developed with precise details.

Uncertainties in estimates may be accounted for by several techniques:

1. If the probability of occurrence for an uncertain event can be numerically estimated (failure of an electronic device, for example), the probable cost can be included in the estimate.
2. Any item of cost can be "padded" to guard against unexpected increases. The total cost may be similarly adjusted.
3. A separate item for contingencies (the unexpected) may be included in the estimate.
4. Risk and uncertainty can be reflected in the specified yield requirement.
5. The degree of risk or uncertainty can be expressed *qualitatively*, along with other intangible considerations, as a guide for decision.

The probability technique is the most accurate of the methods mentioned, but its accuracy is limited to the reliability of the estimated probability. The probability of an occurrence may be mere judgment on the part of one or more persons, or it may have reliable statistical foundation. Then, too, it must be recognized that deviations from the most probable result are to be expected. Quantitative determination of probabilities (as in statistical mathematics and theory of games) is too extensive a subject for discussion here. A few problems that make use of statistics will be demonstrated presently. At this point, let us consider simple probabilities.

Assume that the history of a certain type of equipment indicates the probability of 30 stoppages during a year, causing an average delay of one hour. Assume further that the time value of this facility is $75 per hour, labor that would be idled is worth $30 per hour, and the average cost of corrective maintenance is $10 for each stoppage. Then:

Probable cost of stoppages = $(30)(75 + 30 + 10)$ = $3,450 per year

Cost estimates of this type are dominant factors in the economy of preventive maintenance (a regular schedule for replacement of light bulbs and electronic tubes, for example).

Allowances for contingencies are common in practical estimating. They may be combined in the individual or total costs, or they may be itemized separately. Such allowances are usually figured as a percentage of the cost. The percentage depends on the estimator's experience and judgment and the seeming degree of uncertainty in the particular project.

The reflection of risk or uncertainty in required yield and time value computations is a somewhat controversial issue. In the author's opinion, this is a reasonable device for recognition of risk and the hazards inherent in forecasting. All professional investors do this in appraising the worth of investment. The nonprofessional demands more when he recognizes risk. Probably it is most appropriate to include in the required yield allowances for risk or uncertainty that can not be readily accounted for in details of the estimate.

The forementioned allowances have the effect of adding to cost or subtracting from profit. One should not lose sight of the fact that costs may be *less* than estimated, or the enterprise may prosper much more than conservatively predicted. That is the incentive for risk taking. All intangibles affect decisions. Analysis of intangibles is the topic of Chapter 17.

Statistical Analysis in Estimating

The role of statistics in economy estimates is important. Those unfamiliar with the subject will find it necessary to pursue the study or to use the assistance of mathematicians. For the benefit of readers with some knowledge of statistical mathematics, the following examples will suggest the possibilities.

Problem 1: In an automatic packaging process, the net weight of the contents is to be not less than 16 ounces. Some variation in the weight is to be expected. The standard deviation is found to be .50 ounce. The problem is to estimate the quantity of material (package contents) that will satisfy the *minimum* requirement, based on the assumption that not more than 1% of the packages will be underweight. Reference to a table of normal frequency distribution indicates that 1% will exceed 2.326 standard deviations from the average weight. Hence, the average weight to meet the forementioned requirements should be:

$$(.50)(2.326) + 16.00 = 17.16 \text{ ounces}$$

Problem 2: To obtain interchangeability of parts in a precise assembled product, it is necessary to maintain a tolerance of $\pm$ .0005 inch. Experience with the grinding equipment indicates a standard deviation of .0002 inch in practical operation. The economy study requires an estimate of the probable percentage of rejects in the grinding process. According to tolerance specifications, parts should be rejected when larger or smaller than 2.5 standard deviations from the required mean. The table of normal frequency distribution shows a probability of $\pm$.0062 for rejection size. Thus, the expected quantity of rejects will be:

$$(2)(.0062) = .0124 = 1.24\%$$

Of course, this percentage will increase with wear in the grinding equipment. This involves another economy problem—the balancing of cost of machine adjustments and replacements against the cost of rejected work. If, for example, the tool wear amounted to .0002 per 100 pieces, an amount equal to one standard deviation, the undersize production would be negligible, but rejections for oversize would increase to 6.7%.

Problem 3: Two makes of cutting tools are being compared as to tool life. Samples of each make were tested and were found to average 23.5 hours and 19.4 hours respectively. Is it reasonable to assume that the 23.5-hour tool is significantly better than the other? Variability in performance is the critical factor. The pertinent statistical data are as follows:

	n	$\bar{X}$	s^2	ns^2
Sample 1	10	23.5	5.1	51.0
Sample 2	12	19.4	4.5	54.0

In this case, it is assumed that distribution is normal, that population variances are about equal, and that the 5% significance level (.975 confidence interval) is appropriate. Then:

$$\text{Degrees of freedom} = n_1 + n_2 - 2 = 10 + 12 - 2 = 20$$

And, according to the Fisher tables, if there is no significant difference in the two makes, $|t| \leq 2.09$. The above data give the following results:

$$\text{Pooled variance} = s^2 = (n_1 s_1^2 + n_2 s_2^2)/20 = \frac{51 + 54}{20} = 5.25$$

$$\text{Pooled standard deviation} = s = \sqrt{5.25} = 2.29$$

$$t = \frac{\bar{X}_1 - \bar{X}_2}{s\sqrt{1/n_1 + 1/n_2}} = \frac{23.5 - 19.4}{2.29\sqrt{.1833}} = 4.18$$

Since 4.18 is much greater than the critical value 2.09, there is a significant difference in the two makes; the 23.5-hour tool is better.

Problem 4: Forecasting is required for any important project that extends into the future. It may be necessary to base such a forecast on the extrapolation of a trend revealed by recent history. Assume that a power company is planning for an expansion that aims to accommodate demand for the next 20 years. The company has statistics showing the energy consumed year by year for the past 20 years. After neglecting the war years, these data are carefully plotted for study of the trend, and a formula is to be developed to show demand for energy versus years. Details of computation are too extensive for demonstration here; but the procedure, in general, is as follows.

A line that corresponds with the data according to theory of "least squares" is the best estimate of the trend. If the trend appears to be linear, the records of annual demand would be squared in deriving the formula. The linear function would be written in the form:

$$y \text{ (K.W.H.)} = ax \text{ (years)} + b$$

If the trend appears to be exponential, as would be revealed by plotting the data on logarithmic paper, it would be necessary to square the logarithms of kilowatt hours. Then the least-squares line (linear on logarithmic paper) would take the form:

$$\log y = \log a + n(\log x)$$

More complex trend approximations are also possible. The trend line is to be extended (extrapolated) into the future. The demand for any year, according to this trend, can be determined by substituting the year for x in the formula.

The significance of the trend line may be judged by computing the coefficient of correlation, which measures the conformity of statistical data to the line. It may also be desirable to derive curves above and below the least-squares line to represent upper and lower limits to the projection. For the most part, the forecast depends on the assumption that the trend will continue as in the past. It may be modified by knowledge of anticipated changes in conditions, as in the secular trend previously described.

FORMS FOR ESTIMATING

Almost any type of investigation can be aided by the systematic listing or tabulation of data. The practice helps the estimator and makes it easier for the report reader to check and interpret results. It is a practice that must be developed promptly by the beginner in the subject of economy analysis.

When certain types of economy study are to be repeated often (e.g., machine replacement problems and job estimates), special printed forms may be justified. A well-designed form will contain a list (a "check list") of all the items that should be considered, and it will provide a convenient means for tabulating initial data and computed results. The needs of different industries and types of projects are obviously specialized and varied. Whether estimates are to be approximate and inclusive, or detailed and precise, is also pertinent. A few examples will illustrate the possibilities.

Most industrial projects require material listings. Figure 10–1 is

SHOP MATERIAL LIST

MACH. #116 Hypoid Generator ASB. IN ______ BENCH ______ ASB. NO. G16SC—23HB

LOT NO. ASB. NAME ______ 3 SHEET NO. 2

PART NO.	NAME	QUAN. THIS ASB.	QUAN. ISSD.	REMARKS	NO. PCS. S OR P	NO. PCS. L	NO. PCS. +	COST PER PIECE TIME HRS.	COST PER PIECE TIME MIN.	COST PER PIECE MATL.	COST PER PIECE PROD. LABOR	COST PER PIECE BURDEN	COST PER PIECE TOTAL EACH	TOTAL COST
G16SC-1037A	Work Spindle Front Brg. Cap	1												
G16SC-1064	Work Spindle Brg. Spacer	1												
G16SC-1567	Bearing Roller Spacer	2												
G16SC-1732	Wk. Spindle Oil Seal (Front)	1												
G16SC-2922	Inspection Hole Cover	1												
G16S--1454	Oil Line Restrictor	2												
136-C8	Pull Dowel in G16SC-1037A	1												
136-C10	" " G16SC-107B	2												
136-D12	" " G16SC-73B	2												
TOTAL														

LAST LOT 3 SHEET NO. 2 ASB. NO. 23HB

Courtesy: A prominent manufacturer of precision machine tools

FIG. 10–1. A typical form for bill of material.

a typical bill-of-material form, used by a prominent machine tool manufacturer. This particular form applies to regular production lots, but it can be used equally well for new projects or special job estimates. This manufacturer also provides a separate form for listing the sequence of operations and tools required for each part. For operations that are repeated often, there is a standard procedure

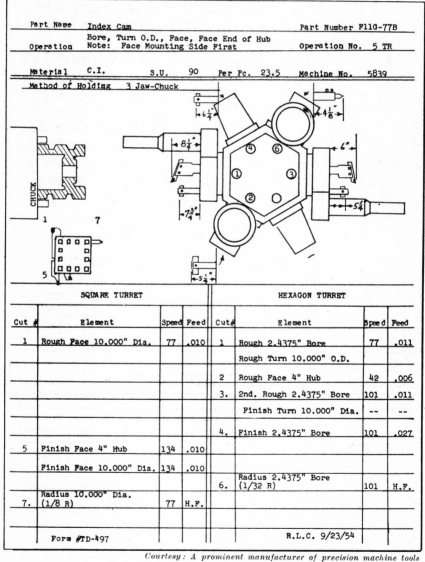

Courtesy: A prominent manufacturer of precision machine tools

FIG. 10–2. A standard procedure form for machining operations.

form that details the tool setup and work elements in the operation. (See Figure 10–2.) In estimating work, the latter would be justified only for quantity production.

The forms that are appropriate for different classes of construction work differ considerably. Requirements for estimating excavation are very different from those applying to electrical contracting. Figure 10–3 shows a portion of a form distributed by the National Automatic Sprinkler Association. This form goes into unusual detail for a construction estimate; but such detail is advisable here because the specifications are worked out along with the cost estimate.

A complex, costly project, such as a large building, a public works, or a manufacturing establishment, would require several types of estimating forms to cover subcontracted work, purchased units, raw materials, labor, and the like. The essential features of the forms are provisions for detailing and consolidating the cost items, for listing the sequence of events or operations in the program, and for classifying and totaling the costs. Spaces for "remarks" are desirable for cross references, suggested alternatives, mention of intangibles, and similar notes.

Several of the trade and technical associations distribute forms for estimating or economy study. Figure 10–3 is an example. The Machinery and Allied Products Institute provides forms for replacement analysis. Table 15–1 (Chapter 15) is an adaptation of the MAPI form. Other forms must be "tailor made" to fit the individual type of project. When an estimator is responsible for an important and unusual type of economy study, it is worthwhile for him to prepare a preliminary check list of all pertinent considerations and to design an effective form of presentation for data and computations.

PROBLEMS

10.1. A factory building was constructed in 1950—120,000 square feet at a cost that averaged $2.50 per square foot. It is now proposed to add a wing of 40,000 square feet to the original structure. The same type and grade of construction is intended. A rough estimate of cost is desired for preliminary consideration.

Obtain from a suitable reference (e.g., *Engineering News-Record*) indexes of construction cost from 1950 to the latest available reference date, in your area if possible. Then extrapolate the trend to the current date. Using this estimated index, estimate the cost of the proposed structure.

FIRE PROTECTION ESTIMATE
EIGHTH EDITION

DATE   ESTIMATOR   AGENT   DEPARTMENT

ESTIMATE FOR (GIVE FIRM NAME AND STATE WHETHER OWNER, TENANT, ARCH'T. CONTRACTOR, BROKER, ETC.)   INDIVIDUAL NEGOTIATING AND TITLE

STREET AND NUMBER   CITY   STATE

NAME OF OWNER OR PROPERTY TO BE EQUIPPED   LOCATION OF PROPERTY   STREET AND NUMBER   CITY AND STATE

OCCUPIED BY OWNER OR TENANT   KIND OF BUSINESS   NAME OF ARCH'T. OR ENG'R. IF NOT SHOWN ABOVE

DOES ESTIMATE COVER { NEW EQUIPMENT / EXTENSION TO PRESENT SYSTEM   WATER SUPPLIES—SINGLE-CITY-TANK-PUMP   CITY PRESSURE

OCCUPANCY OF BUILDING TO BE EQUIPPED   UNDER CONSTRUCTION   OCCUPIED—RUNNING

PLANS AND EQUIPMENT TO BE APPROVED BY

READY FOR ENGINEER—APPROX. DATE

NAME OF R. R. LOCATED ON OR NEAREST DELIVERY

DETAIL OF ITEM 100

LOCATION OF SPRINKLERS   MATERIAL   LABOR

A	B	C	1	2	3	4	5	6	7	8					
NAME OR NUMBER OF BUILDING	FLOOR OR SECTION	TYPE OF HAZARD	TYPE OF LAYOUT	NO. OF SPKRS. ON LINE	NO. OF LINES ON MAIN	DIST. BET. SPKRS. ON LINE	DIST. BET. LINES ON MAIN	TOTAL NO. OF SPKRS.	LIST PRICE PER SPKR.	TOTAL LIST PRICE	LABOR CLASS	WET OR DRY	LIST PRICE PER SPKR.	TOTAL LIST PRICE

EXTRAS DESCRIBE FULLY   FOR HANGERS OTHER THAN U HOOKS, EXTRA FLOOR HEIGHTS, EXTRA HEAVY OR GALV. PIPE OR FITTINGS, SPECIAL COATED SPRINKLERS, MAKING ON FITTINGS IN FIELD, CONCEALED WORK, CORK CEILING, CEILING PLATES IN OFFICES, STAGING, ETC.

TOTALS   XXXX   TOTALS

THESE TOTALS ARE TO BE ENTERED UNDER ITEM 100 ON OTHER SIDE

MEMO. OF ITEMS FIGURED IN DETAIL

ITEM NO.	NUMBER, SIZE AND DESCRIPTION	PRICE		ITEM NO.	NUMBER, SIZE AND DESCRIPTION	PRICE	
		MATERIAL	LABOR			MATERIAL	LABOR

TOTALS   TOTALS

TOTALS ARE TO BE ENTERED UNDER THEIR RESPECTIVE ITEMS ON OTHER SIDE

SPECIAL INSTRUCTIONS AND OTHER INFORMATION HELPFUL TO ENGINEERING AND CONSTRUCTION DEPARTMENTS

COPYRIGHT 1953   F 17148   PRINTED IN U. S. A.

Courtesy: National Automatic Sprinkler and Fire Control Association

FIG. 10–3. A form for estimating sprinkler installations.

BUYER WILL FURNISH	SELLER WILL FURNISH	ITEM	SPECIFICATIONS NOTE:—WHENEVER WORD "DETAIL" OCCURS, ITEMS SHOULD BE FIGURED ON REVERSE SIDE OF THIS SHEET AND TOTALS TRANSFERRED TO THIS SIDE.	COLUMN NO. 1 MATERIAL LIST PRICES	COLUMN NO. 2 LABOR LIST PRICES HOURS	COLUMN NO. 2 LIST PRICES	COLUMN NO. 3 SUB-CONTRACTS AND EXPENSE ITEMS
		100	SPRINKLERS—NUMBER : TOTAL—SECTION A				
		200	ALARM VALVES 3' 4' 5' 6' 8'				
			CUTTING INTO OLD RISER NO. EXCESS PRESS. PUMP				
			D. P. VALVES 2' 3' 4' 6'				
		202	CUTTING INTO OLD RISER NO. DUMMIES NO. SIZE				
			ACCELERATOR—EXHAUSTER NO.				
			CUTTING INTO OLD SYSTEM				
		204	VALVE HOUSES NO. TYPE HEATER—LIGHT				
		210	AIR COMP. CAPACITY AC-DC- VOLTS PHASE				
			WIRING CONN. FOUNDATIONS				
		211	AIR PIPING NO. CONN. FT. ¾' PIPE FT 1' PIPE				
			NO. CONN. FT. ¾' PIPE FT. 1' PIPE				
			ELEC. ALARMS NO. TYPE GONGS NO. HOODS NO.				
		220	TOTAL FT. SINGLE WIRE TOTAL FT. CONDUIT				
			ANNUNCIATOR NO. NO. POINTS				
		221					
			EXPANSION CASES (INSERTS ...) DRILLING				
		302	OTHER HANGERS (DETAIL)				
		303	SPRINKLER CABINET NO. NO. OF SPRINKLERS				
		310	SMALL HOSE CONNECTIONS SIZE FT. OF PIPE NO. OF OUTLETS				
			HOSE EQUIPMENT INSIDE EQUIP. NO. SIZE				
		311	FT. HOSE KIND				
			STEEL HOSE CABINETS NO.				
			HYDRANT HOUSE EQUIP. NO. KIND FT. HOSE				
		312	HYDRANT HOUSES NO.				
			FOUNDATIONS—KIND				
		313	FIRE DEPT. CONNS. NO. SIZE FT. OF PIPE				
			TYPE				
		612	PAINTING (DETAIL)				
		615	SPECIAL				
			TOTAL—SECTION B		XX	XXXX XX	XXXX XX
			SOCKET PIPE 4' 6' 8'				
		500	CLASS OR KIND 10' 12' 14'				
			WINTER WORK NO OF JOINTS				
		501	SOCKET FITTING JOINTS (DETAIL)				
			WINTER WORK NO. OF JOINTS				
		502	SOCKET CLAMPS 4' 6' 8' 10' 12' 14'				
		504	IND. POST AND VALVES 4' 6' 8' 10' 12' 14'				
		505	HYDRANTS TWO WAY THREE WAY				
			MAKE WITH OR WITHOUT IND. GATES				
		508	FLANGED FITTINGS 6' 8' 10' 12'				
		510	UND. GATE VALVES HUB END ONLY				
		511	UND. CHECK VALVES HUB END ONLY				
		513	VALVE PITS NO. TYPE				
		514	CITY WATER CONN. NO. SIZE				
			TOTAL—SECTION C		XX	XXXX XX	XXXX XX
		600	RECEIVING, SHIPPING, DISTRIBUTING NO. SPKS. LIST PRICE PER SPK.				
			UNDERGROUND				
			FREIGHT SPRINKLER MATERIAL RATE PER SPRINKLER				
		601	UNDERGROUND MATERIAL				
		614	ENGINEERING				
			TRAVEL TIME & EXPENSES				
			TOTAL—SECTION D				XXXX XX
			TOTAL COLUMN 2 & COLUMN 3				

ITEMS	LIST TOTALS	OFF DISCT.	NET $	NOTE:
COL. 1—SEC. A				
" " B				
" " C				
" " D				
COL. 2				
	NET TOTALS	% ADDED		
COL. 3				
BONDS				
TAXES CLASS A				
SPECIAL:				
TOTAL				
ADD SALES OR USE TAX CLASS B				
TOTAL PRICE				

10.2.   A 2-wire feeder circuit runs from the meter to the point of use. The voltage at the meter is 120. The monthly bill at 2¢ per K.W.H. was $6.00. There was a 15% voltage drop in the original wiring. The voltage drop was reduced to 2% by rewiring.

   a) For a water-heater load only, 4,000 watts at 120 volts, what will be the monthly bill after rewiring? The same amount of water is heated as before.
   b) If the load is entirely lighting, 4,000 watts at 120 volts, what will be the monthly bill after rewiring? The lamps are used the same number of hours as before. (PE Pa.)

10.3.   Estimate the monthly (30 days) power bill for pumping 3 million gallons of water per 24-hour day from a reservoir into a distribution system where the velocity is 4 feet per second and the gage pressure is 150 pounds per square inch. The water level in the reservoir and the distribution system are both 10 feet lower than the pump, and friction losses may be neglected. The over-all efficiency of the pump and motor is 70%. Electricity costs .975¢ per kilowatt hour. Pumping is continuous and at a uniform rate during the month. (PE Pa.)

10.4.   An architect is to provide field inspection for a modern office building during its construction. The inspection will cover a 6-day workweek consisting of 9-hour days Monday through Friday, and a 6-hour Saturday. The fee for the inspection is to be based on the following schedule:

   For weekdays (Monday through Friday), the charge is to be cost plus 80% for overhead plus out-of-pocket expenses which shall not exceed $5.00 for any one day.
   For Saturday work, cost plus 100% for overhead.
   For overtime (exceeding 8 hours in the week day), cost plus 90% overhead.

   The engineer who is to be sent to the field for the inspection is to be paid an hourly wage of $3.50. He is to be paid time and a half for weekday overtime, and double time for Saturdays. His actual out-of-pocket expenses average $7.00 per day, for which he must be paid by the architect.

   What is the total cost to the architect for 4 weeks of this inspection service? What is the amount of his bill to the client according to the above agreement? (PE N.J. revised)

10.5.   A telephone company purchases its power on the schedule quoted below. Its maximum demand is 50 kw., and it uses 12,000 K.W.H. during the month. The power factor of the load at the time of maximum demand is 70.7%. Compute the amount of the power bill. The rate schedule is as follows:

Energy charge:

First 150 K.W.H. @ 3.3¢ per K.W.H.
Next 350 K.W.H. @ 2.2¢ per K.W.H.
Next 1,000 K.W.H. @ 1.1¢ per K.W.H.
Excess @ .88¢ per K.W.H.

Plus demand charge as follows:

First 10 kw. of demand, no charge
Excess over 10 kw. @ $1.10 per kw.

Plus reactive power charge as follows:
When the maximum reactive demand (for any month) in kilovolt amperes (kva) exceeds 60% of the kw. demand, the consumer will be billed 25¢ per kva for such excess reactive demand. (PE Pa.)
Note:

Power factor (decimal) = kw./kva
Reactive power = $\sqrt{kva^2 - kw^2}$

10.6. A certain job can be laid out and drilled by a skilled mechanic in 30 minutes time. His pay is at the rate of $2.00 per hour, with shop overhead at $1.75 per hour. A jig can be made at a cost of $200, which will do the same job in a multiple-spindle drill press in 2 minutes, including loading and unloading the jig. The machine rate for the multiple-spindle drill press is $3.40 per hour (which includes other shop overhead), and the operator gets $1.50 per hour. The jig would require repairs at $50 after drilling each 5,000 pieces.

a) What is the minimum order for these pieces that will justify building the jig, its cost to be absorbed in the one order?
b) What is the unit cost to drill 50,000 pieces? (PE Pa.)

10.7. To cut one tooth on a 13-tooth gear requires .25 minutes. It requires .50 minutes and .33 minutes to load and unload respectively from the fixture. Indexing (from one tooth to the next) is automatic. The operator's wage is $2.50 per hour. The machine overhead rate is $4.50 per hour. There is an 8% allowance for personal needs, fatigue, and delays.

a) Compute the time (decimal hours) and cost for cutting 100 gears.
b) Now assume that the operator can handle two or three machines on the same job. There would be an allowance of .20 minutes per gear for travel between machines. During the travel and the loading and unloading operations on one machine, the other one or two can run unattended. For operating economy, how many machines should be used? What is the time and cost per 100 gears in that case? (PE Pa. revised)

10.8. A cost estimate is being made for a new item that is to be produced in large quantity. A synthetic time study has been made on the

10 production operations required. The time estimates are *normal* times to which must be added *allowances* suitable for the department and character of work. The essential details are as follows:

Operation	Normal Time Minutes	Allowance	Hourly Wage Rate
GR2	.40	10%	$2.90
LA11	5.50	10	3.20
LA12	2.75	10	3.20
DR6	1.90	10	2.60
HT4	.15	15	3.50
GR7	8.25	10	3.50
TL3	4.30	10	3.00
HT6	.09	15	3.50
AS2	1.10	10	2.75
PK8	.60	10	2.50

If the loss from reworking and scrapped rejects is expected to approximate 2% in labor cost, what is the estimated direct labor cost per piece?

10.9. In the product referred to in Problem 10.8, there are two parts, one a bronze casting and the other made from cold-rolled alloy steel. Previous experience indicates that the casting should cost about 1.75 times the market price of copper. Extras for the steel should add about 75% to the base price for low-carbon cold-rolled. Salvage prices for scrap metal in good condition may be assumed at half the base price for the cast metal and one third the base for the steel. The casting weight is estimated at 7.4 pounds. The finished weight of the steel part is 1.45 pounds, an estimated 22% of the raw stock being lost in machining.

If casting rejects average 3%, and spoilage of steel parts is 1%, what is the estimated cost of direct material? Obtain the base prices from trade journals (e.g., *Iron Age*).

10.10. The average life of fluorescent lamps in a certain factory area is 4,000 hours. Statistical records have shown that the variation in life expectancy is "normal" with a standard deviation of 400 hours. The cost for lamp, labor, and work interruption for a single replacement is $3.85. There are 200 lamps in the area. If these were replaced all at once, the unit replacement cost could be reduced to $3.05 each. If they are changed at one time, it is obvious that unused life will be sacrificed in some lamps and others will have burned out before the replacement, with consequent impairment of lighting. The latter conditions depend on the replacement schedule adopted. The lights are in use 6,000 hours per year.

   a) If not more than 10% loss in light from premature burnouts can be tolerated, what would be a proper replacement schedule for all lamps in the same day? The three-shift working days are 24 hours. (Statistical tables show that the expected life for 10% failures is equal to 1.282 standard deviations below the average.)

b) Compare the annual cost of lamp maintenance by the two methods of replacement.

c) If someone suggested that the lamps be replaced regularly every 7 months (average 500 hours each), how would the annual costs compare? And, for readers familiar with statistics, what percentage of lamps could be expected to fail before replacement?

d) Assuming that an economically reasonable schedule for regular, periodic lamp replacement could be adopted, what are the likely intangible considerations that would favor or discourage such a program? Are there any conditions that might make it necessary to replace lamps individually when they become unserviceable?

10.11. Refer to Problem 9.4. The present problem is to consider the effects of deviations from the original estimates of income and costs.

a) Assume that the estimates of first costs are reliable, but that selling prices of rooms could average 5% greater or less than predicted, and that the same variation is possible in the operating cost elements (except depreciation). Under these conditions, what would be the maximum and minimum estimates for the break-even point at required return?

b) Now assume that inflation during a 3-year period has caused both room prices and operating costs (except depreciation) to increase 10% over the values estimated in Problem 9.4. What would be the effect in per cent of capacity on the break-even point at required return?

10.12. Select an industry that interests you. Examine the trade or technical publications available to you, or consult your librarian. Make a comprehensive list of the publications that would be good sources of economy data applying to projects in the selected industry. Consider the following topics:

a) Current business conditions and trends.

b) General economic indexes and long-term trends.

c) Data similar to above relating to your region (e.g., state and metropolitan area).

d) Process times in particular industrial operations.

e) Raw material costs (current, trends, indexes).

f) Labor costs (current, trends, indexes) in your industry.

g) Regional costs of electrical energy and water.

h) Costs of major operations or projects (e.g., construction, highways, excavations, and their indexes and trends).

i) Miscellaneous costs peculiarly important in your industry.

CHAPTER 11

Comparing
Alternatives

DECISION making is basically a problem of choice among alternatives. The simplest of alternatives, perhaps, is to take *no* action. Opposed to no action, or inaction, there may be several possibilities characterized by advantages and disadvantages that must be weighed by the decision maker. In private business, most government operations, and many nonprofit enterprises, the fundamental criteria for decision are economic—a matter that was stressed in the early pages of this book. Profit objectives or needs for cost control regulate management decisions.

Decisions involving present and future financial considerations should be based on recognition of pertinent factors, accumulation of needed data, and analyses that indicate the comparative economies of the attractive alternatives. Up to now, we have been concerned with methods of appraising the economy of single proposals or existing properties and activities. In this chapter and several to follow, the principles previously described will be applied to several types of comparisons.

Methods of Data Comparison

Many readers are familiar with the advantage of comparing data in columnar form, alternatives side by side, so as to show conspicuously the respective merits and disadvantages of each proposal. This type of summary is useful for personal problems, such as choice among proposed investments, household appliances, automobiles, or job opportunities. Its applications are many in organization activities.

Column-beside-column summaries are common for comparisons of financial data. They can be similarly used for intangible factors. Their effectiveness depends on the selection and arrangement of items that are to be summarized in this fashion. The decision of the analyst is influenced by the kind of problem, its complexity, and the type of person for whom the summary is intended. Following are suggested several general principles for this type of presentation:

1. The tabulation must show conspicuously the comparative factors that are probable criteria for decision.
2. The concluding tangible factors that are usually most appropriate are: net profit compared with required return, net yield compared with required yield, or operating cost plus required return. The latter applies when cost is the prime consideration.
3. The amount of investment should be stated, since capital requirement is important to any investor.
4. Certain details or groups of operating costs that are significant should be listed—e.g., to show requirements for out-of-pocket expenditures verses deferred obligations, such as depreciation.
5. It may be important to show the *quantitative advantage* of one proposal over others—advantages in capital requirement, significant operating costs, profit in excess of required return, cost plus required return, and similar items.
6. Elements of investment, operating cost, income, and profit that are not individually significant can be accumulated within totals listed in the summary.
7. Items that are quantitatively the same for the compared alternatives can be omitted in the summaries, unless they are essential for certain computations. For example, if administrative or sales overhead is unaffected by choice of alternative, it need not be included in cost comparison.

Break-even charts are particularly useful for comparing alternatives when certain factors in the study are variable. This was mentioned in Chapter 9. The principles of charting described can be extended to variables other than those previously demonstrated—e.g., to yield, payoff periods, selling prices, and other significant factors.

BREAK-EVEN ANALYSES

Among the characteristic problems in comparing alternatives is to consider the effects of variability in one or more factors that have a significant bearing on results. At this point, let us consider the comparison of two proposals involving one factor that is expected to vary within some reasonable range of possibility. At some value of the forementioned variable factor, the economy of the two proposals may be equal (no choice). We term this critical value of the variable the *break-even point*. At either side of this break-even point, one proposal or the other has the economic advantage. In the study of such alternatives, various economic factors are known or estimated, but the value of one factor is uncertain. The problem is to determine the break-even point and the critical nature of deviations from that value.

In these problems, it is useful to tabulate, column beside column, the known and unknown factors that total up to the criterion most significant for decision. The two most common types of alternatives are those that break even at operating cost plus required return and those that break even on net profit or net yield.

Proposals that Break Even at Operating Cost Plus Required Return

A condensed summary of two proposals that may break even at required return may be tabulated as follows:

	Proposal A	Proposal B
Investment......................	xxxxx	xxxxx
Expected life....................	xx	xx
Salvage value...................	xxxx	xxxx
Depreciation....................	xxxx	xxxx
Other operating cost............	xxxx	xxxx
Required return.................	xxxx	xxxx
Total operating cost + required return........	xxxx	xxxx

Any one of the contributing factors may be unknown (a variable)—for example, first cost, life, labor rate, power rate, efficiency, rate of output, required return, and the like. Probably the most common variable is the rate of operations (e.g., required annual output), making the study similar to those described in Chapter 9. One precaution is necessary for beginners. *Do not add into the total of operating cost plus required return the amount of investment.* Investment is reflected only in depreciation (or depletion) and required return; it is not an *annual* cost.

At the break-even point, the two totals of the above must be equal. If the cost relationship of the variable factor is linear, an algebraic solution, similar to that of Chapter 9, is the simplest. The following example will illustrate both algebraic and graphic methods.

Two ten-horsepower motors (A and B) are being considered for an industrial application. The study period is five years. Motor A costs $450. It has a guaranteed efficiency of 87% at rated load. Its

estimated salvage value in five years is $270. Motor B would cost
$350, but its efficiency is only 82%, and estimated five-year salvage
value is $175. Required economic yield is 20%. Electric power costs
2¢ per K.W.H. Overhead, other than depreciation, is unaffected by
choice of motor.

The motor is to drive a pump at full load but for an uncertain
number of hours (x) per year. At how many hours per year would the
two motors be equal, or under what conditions would the higher-
priced motor be justified? The exact method of computing capital
recovery and return is to be used.

PRELIMINARY CALCULATIONS

Electric power costs:
Motor A: (10)(.7457)(.02)/.87 = $.1714 per hour
Motor B: (10)(.7457)(.02)/.82 = $.1819 per hour

Depreciation plus required return:
Motor A: $D + R$ = (450–270)(.3344) + .20(270) = $114.19
Motor B: $D + R$ = (350–175)(.3344) + .20(175) = $ 93.52

COST SUMMARY

	Motor A	Motor B
First cost................	$450	$350
Power cost for x hours....$.1714$x$		$.1819$x$
Depreciation + return....$114.19		$93.52
Operating cost + return...$114.19 + $.1714$x$		$93.52 + $.1819$x$

CALCULATED BREAK-EVEN POINT

$$.0105x = 20.67$$
$$x = 1,969 \text{ hours}$$

The conclusion is that the higher-priced motor will be justified only
if the predicted demand will exceed 1,969 hours per year at full load.

The above break-even point calculation does not reveal the difference between the alternatives for various predictions of hours. Total
costs plus required returns could be computed and tabulated for the
various rates of operations, and the results compared. Another
method, often effective, is to prepare an accurate break-even chart
such as Figure 11–1. In the example, the graphs for A and B intersect
at such an acute angle that the break-even point is not accurately
indicated. But the chart does show that within an operating range
of 1,500 to 2,500 hours little is gained or lost by adopting either
proposal. It is probable, then, that intangibles would govern the
decision. As previously stated, the graphic analysis is particularly

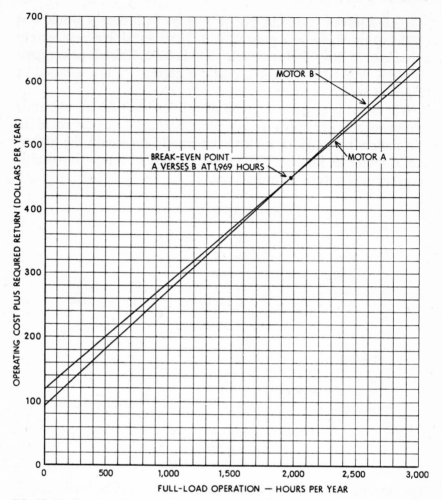

FIG. 11–1. Economy of two motors (A and B) versus hours per year of operating time at full load.

useful if the operating cost plus required return does not vary as a straight line with respect to the independent variable.

Proposals That Break Even on Profit

Profit or yield is the logical criterion for choice among alternatives that involve income as well as cost. Yield is important if investment or yield requirements differ. Required yield may not be the same for competing proposals that differ in character. The excess of profit or yield above the required amount may be the significant criterion for decision.

In addition to the variable factors encountered in the previous type of problem, a common uncertainty may be selling price. Market conditions are often difficult to forecast, and the firm's objective may be to maintain a fixed operating rate by making adjustments in the selling price of the product. Physical output is perhaps the most common variable in these problems. Variation in both price and output is considered in Chapter 14.

A tabulated summary of data comparing two alternatives of the type mentioned may appear, in general, as follows:

	Proposal A	Proposal B
Investment............................	xxxxxxx	xxxxxxx
Anticipated life......................	xx	xx
Salvage value........................	xxxxxx	xxxxxx
Depreciation..........................	xxxxxx	xxxxxx
Other operating cost..................	xxxxxx	xxxxxx
Total operating cost..................	xxxxxxx	xxxxxxx
Income...............................	xxxxxxx	xxxxxxx
Economic return......................	xxxxxx	xxxxxx
Deductions from profit...............	xxxxxx	xxxxxx
Net profit............................	xxxxxx	xxxxxx
Required net return..................	xxxxxx	xxxxxx
Profit exceeding requirement..........	xxxxxx	xxxxxx
or		
Net yield on investment..............	xx%	xx%
Required net yield...................	xx%	xx%
Yield exceeding requirement...........	xx%	xx%

As in the previous type of comparison, any of the factors that affect the final result may be uncertain and considered variable. Any of the contributing factors summarized above may be detailed as necessary. And a break-even point on profit, or profit exceeding the return requirement, may be computed or determined graphically. Let us now consider a hypothetical case.

A large company is considering the erection of a new ore-reduction plant. A low-cost plant of moderate efficiency is being compared with a high-cost setup that yields a higher percentage of refined metal. A mining company, a subsidiary, delivers ore to the reduction plant at a fixed price based on its operating cost plus required return. The market price of the refined metal, however, fluctuates widely according to market conditions. The ore-handling capacity of both proposals is intended to be the same, but the more efficient plant will produce more refined metal. The problem is to determine the market price that would justify erection of the higher-priced plant. This break-even point compared with a long-range forecast of the market would be an important criterion for decision.

Essential preliminary data, and the summary of cost, income, and profit factors are tabulated in Table 11–1. In the calculations, 2,000-pound tons are assumed for both ore and metal. Required net yield on investment (including working capital) is 10%. The present income tax rate on the company's business is 52%. It is assumed that

TABLE 11–1

ECONOMY OF TWO ORE-REDUCTION PLANTS VERSUS VARIABLE SELLING PRICES
OF REFINED METAL

Preliminary Data:	*Plant A*	*Plant B*
First cost of plant...............	$1,000,000	$1,800,000
Working capital required.........	175,000	250,000
Total investment in plant........	$1,175,000	$2,050,000
Ore-handling capacity, tons per day	200	200
Refined metal per ton of ore......	22%	26%
Value of ore delivered per ton.....	$37.50	$37.50
Selling price of metal............	unknown (x)	unknown (x)
Daily plant operating cost less depreciation.................	$2,800	$4,500
Sales expense per ton of metal sold	$15.50	$15.50
Depreciation rate................	8%	8%
Operating days per year..........	340	340
Income tax rate.................	52%	52%
Required net yield on investment..	10%	10%
Annual Results:		
Output		
Ore processed, tons............	68,000	68,000
Metal recovered, tons..........	14,960	17,680
Depreciation....................	$ 80,000	$ 144,000
Cost of ore.....................	2,550,000	2,550,000
Processing cost..................	952,000	1,530,000
Sales expense...................	231,880	274,040
Total operating cost.............	$3,813,880	$4,498,040
Cost per ton of metal............	$2.55	$2.54
Income from sales...............	$14,960x$	$17,680x$
Operating cost..................	3,813,880	4,498,040
Economic return................	$14,960x - \$3,813,880$	$\$17,680x - \$4,498,040$
Income tax.....................	$7,779x - 1,983,218$	$9,194x - 2,338,981$
Net profit......................	$\$7,181x - 1,830,662$	$\$8,486x - 2,159,059$
Required return on investment....	117,500	205,000
Profit exceeding required return...	$\$7,181x - 1,948,162$	$\$8,486x - 2,364,059$

Break-even Point:

Proposals A and B show equal profit in excess of required return when selling price of metal is $319 per ton—computed by equating the final results in the above tabulation.

investment will be maintained at the stated level by equipment replacements or additions to offset depreciation. The no-choice break-even point is given in the table. Other break-even points are also shown in Figure 11–2.

Figure 11–2 is a graphic solution of the above problem. The graphs represent profit in excess of required return, showing where

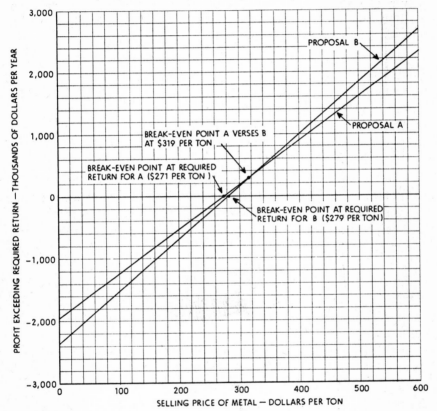

FIG. 11–2. Economy of two ore-reduction plants (A and B) versus variable selling price of refined ore.

each of the proposals break even on required return as well as the point where they break even competitively. The chart also indicates the rate at which the more efficient method gains advantage over the other at selling prices exceeding the mutual break-even figure. For plotting straight-line graphs of this type, it is necessary to compute only two points for each proposal. In this case, the points were computed and plotted for zero price and an assumed maximum of $600 per ton.

Note that the really significant break-even point between the two proposals includes the obligation for required return on investment; it is not the point at which the two break even on net profit. If it were not for the difference in investment, the break-even price would be only $252 per ton. Other break-even points may be of interest when considering the possibility of market depression. Break-even points at no gain–no loss (economic break-even points) are $255 and $254 respectively. These points were not shown in Figure 11–2. The profit shown in the figure is that *exceeding* required return, so that the break-even points at that level are also indicated—$271 and $279 respectively. Either proposal could be considered successful when market prices exceed the two figures mentioned, but it is apparent that price levels above $319 are necessary to justify the greater investment in proposal B.

SUMMARY

Economy studies often require comparison of two or more alternatives. Evaluation of the alternatives usually involves some factors that can be predicted with reasonable accuracy and others that are uncertain or variable. If the variable factors are such that optimum values can be determined and specified, the determination of the optimums is the significant problem. If a variable is unpredictable in value, a decision may depend on comparison of results that would occur within a reasonable range of values assigned to the variable factor.

In this chapter, we have been concerned with comparison of two alternatives, in one or both of which there is a variable factor that affects the comparison. One approach to this problem is to determine the condition under which the two are equal (a break-even point) and beyond which one proposal or the other is favored. The critical nature of the factor variation may also be indicated in this study. To arrive at a decision will then require a forecast of the range of values that may be expected of said variable factor.

There are, in general, two types of the problems mentioned. In one type, the study leads to comparison of operating cost plus required return. Income and profit are not directly involved. There may be variables in capital requirement, elements of operating cost, and return requirement. The rate of operations is most often the critical variable.

The second type of problem requires comparison of profit or yield on investment. When the capital or yield requirements differ among the alternatives, profit in excess of required return is an appropriate basis for comparison. Any variable affecting investment, income, cost, or profit may be encountered in this type of problem. The most common of these relate to market conditions, affecting selling price of product or service and the output or rate of operations.

A column-beside-column summary of pertinent factors is a useful device for analysis and comparison of alternatives. Significant break-even points can often be computed algebraically, particularly when the pattern of cost, income, or profit is linear with respect to the independent variable. A graphic solution may be most convenient for more complex relationships. In either case, a break-even chart will show the significant break-even points and also the rate at which the advantage of a proposal is gained or lost by change in the value of the independent variable.

Other types of problems dealing with comparison of alternatives will be considered in subsequent chapters.

PROBLEMS

11.1. Assume that you are to make an economy study of one of the following proposals. Your estimates and computations are to be summarized in a comparative tabulation of the alternatives. Make a list of the important items that would be of most interest in leading to a decision (neglecting intangibles). Similar types of cost (e.g., direct labor) may be consolidated under a single title. List the items in logical sequence.

a) Establishment of a business (a proprietorship)—an apartment house versus a retail store.
b) Choice between two production methods that have the same capacity for output but differ in equipment and operating requirements.
c) Choice between two new automobiles of different makes for commercial use.
d) A highway problem—three lanes versus four lanes of the same quality of construction and location.
e) Selection of the most economical conductor size (to be selected from several feasible alternatives) leading from entrance to a plant, where the current is metered, to a production area.

11.2. Two 100-horsepower motors are under consideration for an intermittent service. Motor A costs $1,600 and has an efficiency of 90%.

Motor B costs $1,300 and has an efficiency of 87%. If all charges for depreciation, maintenance, insurance, etc. are a total of 15% of the initial cost, and if power costs 1.1¢ per K.W.H., how many hours of full-load operation per year are necessary to justify purchase of motor A? (PE N.Y.)

11.3. It is desired to determine whether to use insulation 1 inch thick or 2 inches thick in insulating a steam pipe. The heat loss from this pipe without insulation would cost $1.50 per year per foot of pipe. A 1-inch thick insulation would eliminate 89% of the loss and would cost 40¢ per foot. A 2-inch thick insulation would eliminate 92% of the loss and would cost 85¢ per foot.

Compare the annual cost per 1,000 feet for the two thicknesses of insulation, using a life of 10 years for the insulation with no salvage value. Assume straight-line depreciation, and average interest at 6%. (PE N.Y.)

11.4. A certain sewer-pipe plant is using 350 tons of clay per day for 300 days per year. They have the choice of leasing a 40 years' supply of the clay at a royalty of 5¢ per ton, to be paid monthly as the clay is mined by underground mining; or they can buy the clay on surface land at a cash price of $125,000. The surface land will be worth $20,000 after the clay is mined. If money is worth 5%, which is the better investment and by how much? (PE Ohio)

11.5. Snow removal from streets of Central City can be accomplished either by hand loading into trucks or by machine loading. For hand loading an average snowfall in a day, 60 men at $8 each will be required. The annual cost of the shovels, including replacements and storage, is $900.

Machine loading requires a machine that would cost $40,000 and would last 10 years (without salvage value). Ten operators would be required at a wage rate of $18 per day. Fuel, oil, and repairs would amount to $100 per day. Storage cost would be $250 per year.

Assuming that capital to the municipality is worth 3%, determine the number of days per year for snow removal required to justify the purchase of the machine. Use the exact method. (PE Ohio, revised)

11.6. A standard pumping installation costs $15,000 installed and has an estimated life of 12 years. By the addition of certain auxiliary equipment, an annual saving of $200 in operating cost can be obtained, and the estimated life of the installation can be doubled. Neglecting any salvage value for either installation and with interest at 6%, what present expenditure is justified for the auxiliary equipment? (PE N.Y.)

11.7. As a plant engineer, you have received two bids on an elevator. A New York firm's bid summarizes at: first cost, $25,000; life, 20 years;

salvage value, $2,000; and maintenance, $2,200 per year. A Chicago concern's figures are: first cost, $32,000; life, 25 years; salvage value, $2,000; and maintenance, $1,800 per year. Required net yield on investment is 12%, and the anticipated income tax rate is 53%. Using a 10-year study period and average interest with continuous depreciation, compare the two proposals.

11.8. A decision is to be made concerning the installation of a slate roof or a good shingle roof for a small building. The required yield on investment is 12% (based on the exact method). The quotation on the shingle roof is $1,500; for the slate roof, $3,500. The anticipated annual maintenance costs are $350 and $100 respectively. Experience with the shingle roof indicates a life of 12 years; but the life of the slate roof is unknown. How long should the slate roof last to justify its additional cost?

11.9. One of two factory trucks is being considered for purchase. Truck A is priced at $2,400, expected life is 5 years, and annual maintenance and fuel costs are $1,500. For truck B, the price is $3,200, expected life is 5 years, and estimated maintenance and fuel costs are $1,100 per year. The expected trade-in value for both trucks is 15% of first cost. The required economic yield is 25%. The firm customarily employs the average interest method with annual straight-line depreciation. Which truck do you recommend?

11.10. Determine how much more per horsepower could be paid for a hydroelectric power plant and transmission line than for a steam plant to be run at full load for 3,000 hours per year (if the operating costs for the steam plant are .6¢ per horsepower hour, while for the hydroelectric system they are only .2¢). Assume the life in either case to be 30 years and interest to be 5%, while all other things are equal. (PE Pa.)

11.11. A manufacturer needs additional warehouse space. A brick warehouse would cost $46,000, whereas a frame and galvanized metal building could be built for $19,000. The life of the brick building is estimated at 50 years, annual maintenance cost at $400. The life of the frame building is estimated at 15 years, annual maintenance at $600. Insurance cost is $2.00 per $1,000 of first cost for the brick and $5.00 per $1,000 of first cost for the frame. Average annual taxes are 1.25% of first cost for each. Assume 20% salvage value for each building at the end of its life.

Compare the two on the basis of annual cost for a 15-year study period. Use straight-line depreciation plus average interest at 10%. (PE Pa. revised)

11.12. During a slack period, a manufacturer can sell 3,000 articles per month, which is one third of the capacity of the factory. The investment in the factory is $2,000,000, which depreciates at the rate of 5%. Other fixed expenses are $20,000 per year. Maintenance and other variable costs vary from 1% at zero output to 4% at full output. If labor and material for the article cost $1.00 and the article must be sold for only $1.20, should the factory stay in production or shut down? Disregard intangibles. (PE Pa.)

11.13.   Dies for a set of stampings cost $2,400. The stampings cost 8¢ a set, and the cost of assembly is 2½¢ a set. A die for an aluminum casting to replace the stamping assembly costs $1,600; the casting costs 11¢; and the machining cost is 3¢. At what production are the costs equal, and what is the total unit cost at this point? (PE Pa.)

11.14.   Two methods are available for recovering ore. One method recovers 75 tons per 100 tons treated at a cost of $3.00 per ton recovered. The other method recovers 80 tons per 100 tons treated at a cost of $3.25 per ton recovered.

   a) If the value of recovered ore is $6.00 per ton, which method of recovery should be used?
   b) At what value of the recovered ore would it be economical to change the method of recovery? (PE Pa.)

11.15.   Two routes, A and B, for a highway are being considered. Route A is 12 miles long and will cost $1,000,000. Route B is 14 miles long and will cost $650,000. Rebuilding of each road will be required every 15 years at a cost of $25,000 per mile. Annual maintenance costs are $500 per mile. Is the shorter route justified under the following assumption? Estimated traffic is 200 trucks and 800 passenger cars per day. Cost of gas and oil is 10¢ per mile for the trucks and 2¢ per mile for the passenger cars. Speed of traffic is 40 miles per hour. The value of an hour saved is $1.00 for a truck, and negligible for a passenger car. Money costs 4%. (PE Pa.)

11.16.   A motion-picture theater, with an average summer attendance of 1,200 admissions at an average price of 50¢, is considering the installation of air conditioning at a cost of $20,000. Air conditioning will be operated for a period of 20 weeks. By what per cent must the average daily summer attendance rise in order to justify the investment, assuming the following conditions: daily water requirement, 2,000 cubic feet at 20¢ per 100 cubic feet; taxes and insurance, 2% of first cost; annual maintenance and operations, $200; expected life of installation, 10 years; investment charges, 12%. (PE Pa.)

11.17.   Electric lamps rated at 100 watts and 110, 115, and 120 volts can be purchased for 20¢ each. When sample lamps were tested at 115 volts, the following data were obtained:

	Voltage Rating		
	110	115	120
Average watts consumed........104.6		100.0	96.0
Average life in hours............ 420		750	1340
Average lumen output per watt input.................... 18.0		17.2	15.5

Energy costs 3.5¢ per K.W.H. Determine the cost per million lumen hours for each lamp. (PE Pa.)

11.18. A company may furnish a car for the use of its salesmen, or the company may pay the salesmen for the use of their own cars at the rate of 11¢ per mile. The following estimated data apply to company-furnished cars. A car costs $2,400 and has a life of 4 years and a trade-in value of $900 at the end of that time. Monthly storage cost for the car is $3.00, and the cost of fuel, tires, and maintenance is 2.8¢ per mile. What annual mileage must a salesman travel by car for the cost of the two methods to be equal if the interest rate is 10%? (PE Pa.)

11.19. A small dairy is considering the purchase of an automatic bottling machine at a cost of $67,000 and with a bottling capacity of 1,000 quart bottles per hour. Its estimated hours of operation will be 4 per day, 365 days per year. The operating costs per hour of operation are:

Electric power, water, and supplies.................	$3.00
Machine attendant.............................	1.75
Repair and maintenance.........................	.50

The life of the machine is assumed to be 10 years, and the interest rate is 10%.

a) What is the cost (plus required return) per quart for bottling with the automatic machine? Compute required return by the exact method.

b) If it costs 1.5¢ per quart to bottle by hand, should the automatic machine be purchased?

c) How many hours will the automatic machine have to be used to pay for its entire cost (recover investment)?

d) Would the purchase of a fully automatic machine for $75,000 with a 15-year life, operating costs per hour of $3.75 (for electric power, water, and supplies), 75¢ for repair and maintenance, and no attendant be a better purchase for the dairy?

e) What is the cost (plus return) per quart with the $75,000 fully automatic machine? (PE Pa.)

11.20. A safety device to shut off the motive power in the event of an interruption of gas supply is being considered for installation on a number of continuous-type ovens used in painting and varnishing sheet steel for can bodies. The installed cost for each oven is $800. The estimated life for the device is 12 years. In the event of interrupted gas supply, damage to the product in each oven will amount to approximately $175 if the automatic cutoff is not installed. If it is installed, damage will amount to $30. The interruptions of gas supply occur, on the average, about twice in every three years. Maintenance costs for each device are estimated at $5.00 per year.

With a minimum attractive return at 10%:

a) Should the safety device be installed?

b) What are the cost figures for or against the installation of the device?

c) What price could be paid for the device to be relieved of the hazard forever? (Assume that a device would last forever.) (PE Pa.)

11.21.   Our company is considering the purchase of a two-ton, battery-type fork truck. At present, we pay our warehouse manual labor $1.80 per hour. If we buy the truck, we expect to pay a truck operator the same wages. The average warehouse trip with the fork truck involves moving a load of two tons for 100 feet and returning light for another load. In the warehouse, one man, using a hand truck, can move 500 pounds per trip, averaging 20 trips per hour. It now requires two manual truckers working 8 hours per day, 5 days per week, 52 weeks per year, to keep up with requirements.

If we buy the fork truck, it is apparent that it will not be necessary to operate it 8 hours per day. Man-hours not spent operating the truck can be used elsewhere and will not be charged against the truck. However, fixed operating costs are present whether the truck is idle or working and must be charged against the truck.

The truck salesman has prepared the following data concerning the proposed purchase.

Purchase Cost:

Truck (without tires)..........................	$4,200
One set of 4 tires.............................	200
24-volt, 350-ampere-hour battery..............	475
Charging equipment...........................	680

Yearly Operating Costs (Considered as Fixed):

Maintenance.................................	120
Insurance...................................	12
Charging current............................	48
Yearly depreciation on	
Truck....................................	6½%
Tires....................................	100%
Battery..................................	16%
Charging equipment.......................	5%

Standard-Time Data:

Pick up load................................	5 seconds
Release load................................	4 seconds
Travel loaded...............................	400 feet per minute
Travel light................................	500 feet per minute
Delay factor (a multiplier of actual time to cover acceleration, deceleration, maneuvering, etc.)	2.0

a) Compute the annual operating cost with manual trucking, for present requirements.

b) Compute the annual cost with fork truck for present requirements.

c) How many days will it take with present volume of work for the savings in operating cost (without depreciation) to pay off investment in the fork truck?

d) Assume now that required yield on investment is 24% (before income tax) based on average investment with continuous depreciation and no salvage value. Then, what is the daily tonnage requirement necessary to justify purchase of the fork truck?

e) Would you recommend the purchase of the fork truck? Why? (PE Pa. revised)

CHAPTER 12

Increment Analysis

ALTERNATIVES may be judged by comparing their over-all results or by considering in detail the *differences* between their characteristics. In fact, the study may be confined to the differences only, and the characteristics that are alike may be disregarded. Differences may be the significant criteria for decision.

In an economy study, the differences mentioned may be termed *increments* (changes) in financial factors—increments in cost, income, profit, or yield. A study that concentrates on these increments may serve one or both of the following objectives: (1) It may simplify the analysis, and (2) it may provide a more significant result than would be apparent from conventional comparisons of details and totals. In these comparisons, variable costs are most significant; fixed costs can often be neglected. To illustrate these principles, we shall demonstrate three types of problems that typify increment analysis.

Increased Output at Reduced Selling Price

A 200-room hotel anticipates only 50% occupancy during a slack season if its rates are maintained at the customary average of $10.00 per room per day. A firm planning a sales convention will reserve 60 rooms for three days if the hotel will agree to a special rate of $7.50 per room per day. Disregarding intangible considerations, should the hotel management accept this offer? Investment and operating cost data are as follows:

Net worth $1,200,000
Fixed operating cost per year . . . . $ 180,000
Variable cost per room per day . . . . $ 2.60
Required yield on investment, before interest
  and taxes 20%

If this problem were treated in the manner described in previous chapters, comparing results with and without the 60-room deal, the pertinent data could be tabulated as follows. The figures cover a three-day period only. "Reject" assumes that only 100 rooms will be occupied at $10.00 per day. "Accept" assumes 100 rooms at $10.00 per day plus 60 rooms at $7.50 per day. Fixed costs and required return are for three days, of course.

Item	Reject	Accept
Fixed operating cost	$1,480	$1,480
Variable operating cost	780	1,248
Total operating cost	$2,260	$2,728
Income	3,000	4,350
Profit (before interest and taxes)	$ 740	$1,622
Required return	1,973	1,973

A hasty conclusion might be that the offer should *not* be accepted because the required return is not earned even with the additional business. (The break-even point at required return is 155 rooms at the $10.00 rate.) Actually, there is a profit advantage (before deductions) amounting to $882—fixed obligations have to be met in either case. An increment analysis is simpler and more revealing.

For the additional 60 rooms:

Variable cost per day per room	$2.60
Income at special rate	7.50
Increment profit per room	$4.90
Total increment profit	$(4.90)(60)(3) = \$882.00$

Fixed costs and required return are not pertinent in this analysis. The increment profit is $882, which otherwise would not be realized. Hence the offer should be accepted—neglecting intangibles such as effect on other patrons, possibility of competing offers, seasonal price reduction of lesser amounts, and the like.

Increments of Investment and Profit

Assume that the forementioned hotel is in the planning stage. Figures on the 200-room hotel have been assembled. One of the promoters now proposes increasing capacity to 250 rooms. An investigation of this alternative results in the following comparison.

	200 Rooms	250 Rooms
First cost	$1,100,000	$1,400,000
Working capital	200,000	230,000
Total investment	$1,300,000	$1,630,000
Fixed operating cost per year	$ 180,000	$ 210,000
Variable operating cost per room per day	$ 2.60	$ 2.60
Forecast of average daily occupancy, rooms	170	200

The average occupancy predicted for the larger hotel is greater because it would be able to handle peak demands which the smaller establishment could not accommodate. The room rates are expected to average $10.00 per day. The income tax rate is 30% on taxable profit plus 22% on the increment over $25,000. The promoter's net yield requirement is 10%. The separate cost, income, and profit analyses for each of the proposals are as follows:

	200 Rooms	250 Rooms
Fixed operating cost	$180,000	$210,000
Variable cost at predicted occupancy	161,330	189,800
Total operating cost	$341,330	$399,800
Predicted income	620,500	730,000
Profit before income tax	$279,170	$330,200
Income tax	139,502	166,204
Net profit	$139,502	$163,996
Net yield	10.7%	10.1%

The net yield in both cases exceeds the required 10%. Consequently, the 250-room hotel might be preferred because of the greater return which seems to justify the investment.

The foregoing conclusion is in error, as will be shown by increment analysis. The following analysis is designed to reveal the advantage or disadvantage from the additional (increment) investment of $330,000.

Increment investment	$330,000
Increment fixed cost	30,000
Increment variable cost	28,470
Increment operating cost	$ 58,470
Increment income, 30 rooms at $10.00 per day	109,500
Increment profit before tax	$ 51,030
Income tax @ 52%	26,536
Increment net profit	$ 24,494
Yield on increment investment	7.4%

The income tax rate is based on the knowledge that taxable profit from the other proposal would exceed the surtax level of $25,000. Increment income tax will be discussed presently. The net yield on increment investment shows that the additional $330,000 does not meet the specified profit requirement. It shows that additional capital might be better invested in a more attractive venture. Therefore, this analysis favors the 200-room hotel.

Increased Investment to Reduce Operating Cost

Increment cost analysis can often be applied to economy problems in which income and profit are unknown; operating cost is the criterion for decision. The selection of a production process or the replacement of a machine (if optional) is a typical situation of this type. (Replacement analysis will be discussed at length in Chapter 15.) When an increase in investment is being considered, the problem, reduced to essentials, is to determine whether the savings in operating cost warrant the required capital.

To illustrate this problem by a simple case, assume that a new method involving equipment is being considered to replace an old one. A tabular comparison of the old and the new may be summarized as follows:

	Old Method	New Method
Investment..................................	$10,000	$35,000
Required yield on investment (before income tax) based on first cost..................	20%	20%
Operating cost..............................	$15,000	$ 8,000
Required return............................	2,000	7,000
Operating cost plus required return............	$17,000	$15,000

The conclusion, showing the annual advantage of $2,000, indicates that the new method should be adopted. The figures summarized above may not be as significant to some executives as the result obtained from increment analysis. In this case, the problem is to clearly justify the added investment. By increment analysis:

Increment investment..............................	$25,000
Saving in operating cost (increment cost).............	7,000
Yield on increment investment......................	28%

The yield on increment investment exceeds the required yield by 8%. The 28% figure also provides a basis for comparing this proposal with other investment prospects that compete for capital.

There are other methods of handling problems of this type, such as the payoff period previously mentioned. In this case, the above operating cost includes depreciation on equipment, and it would be more accurate to introduce time factors in the return requirement. When two alternatives are being compared, the cost elements that are the same for both can usually be neglected so that the operating cost may not include items such as floor space, power, material, indirect labor, and the like.

Income Tax in Increment Analysis

The treatment of income tax is particularly important in studies of increment cost and profit. The average tax rate experienced in the enterprise is not applicable to increment profit. The appropriate rate is the one that applies at the level of profit then attained by the taxpayer. If a corporation's taxable profit (for federal taxation) has reached the $25,000 level before increment profit is figured, then each additional amount of profit is taxed at 52% plus the effective state tax rate. When an individual without dependents already has a taxable income of $100,000, additional income up to $50,000 is taxed at 89%, which greatly exceeds his average tax rate. Both of these examples are based on 1960 tax regulations; but the principle of higher rates on higher levels of income or profit is well established. Of course, it is possible that increment profit or income will involve two or more rates of taxation.

When *required return* is a significant factor in increment analysis, the required yield *before tax* is the most convenient basis for that return computation. The formulas given in Appendix E can be used for the yield determination; but the federal tax rate must be the one that applies at the increment level of profit. To illustrate this, assume that profit prior to the increment already exceeds $25,000 and that there is no state tax. The required net yield is i, and the rate before tax is i'.

Then

$$i' = \frac{i}{1 - .52} = i/.48 \text{ (based on 1960 rates)}$$

And if there is a state tax of 6% to be figured on the federal tax base:

$$i' = \frac{i}{(1 - .52)(1 - .06/1.06)} = i/.4528 = i/.45 \text{ (rounded)}$$

Other obligations, such as interest on borrowed capital and profit-sharing bonuses must also be included in the required return, as explained in Chapter 8. (Review pages 102 to 106.)

SUMMARY

Increment analysis is often the most effective means of comparing two or more alternatives. The significant result of that analysis may be expressed in terms of cost difference, profit difference, or yield on added investment. The important considerations are: (1) What is the most significant criterion for decision?, and (2) are there fixed elements of cost that are common to the alternatives and that can be disregarded to simplify computation and to clarify results?

Any comparison of alternatives can also be made by the conventional detailing and totaling of costs, income, and profit items, as previously demonstrated. These figures can be compared, and the differences between them can be expressed as increments (advantages or disadvantages). In the problems to follow, the reader is to decide what type of computation is the simplest and the most significant as a guide to management decision.

PROBLEMS

12.1. Apply the increment method to Problem 11.3. In this case, the criterion for decision is the yield on increment investment.

12.2. Apply the increment method to Problem 11.4.

12.3. Refer to Problem 11.11. Attempt to justify the added cost of the brick warehouse by yield on increment investment.

12.4. A plant engineer had tentatively decided to use #0000 wire for a new power circuit in the plant. An electrical engineer suggested that 250,-000-cm. wire would be a better selection because of the considerable reduction in resistance losses, although the smaller wire had satisfactory capacity and voltage drop. From the viewpoint of economy, is the added cost of the larger conductor justified? Essential data are as follows:

Length of wire..............................	1,200 feet
Average load 4,000 hours per year...............	200 amperes
Wire resistance:	
#0000.....................................	.0490 ohms per 1,000 feet
250,000 cm.................................	.0425 ohms per 1,000 feet
Cost of wire:	
#0000.....................................	$735 per 1,000 feet
250,000 cm.................................	$900 per 1,000 feet
Cost of electrical energy.......................	.85¢ per K.W.H.
Straight-line depreciation......................	5% of first cost
Required yield based on average investment with continuous depreciation for 10-year study period....	12%

12.5. A machine part has a finished value of $4.80. Of this cost, 40% is material, 30% labor, 20% overhead, and 10% profit. If material goes up 25%, pay rate goes up 20%, labor production rate goes down 15%, and overhead remains the same, what is the new value to clear a profit of 10%? (PE Pa.)

12.6. A manufacturer of hi-fi loud-speakers estimates the following financial, cost, and sales prospects for the coming year:

Total investment (net worth)............................$250,000
Fixed operating cost.......................................$ 80,000
Variable operating cost at 60% capacity....................$120,000
Anticipated sales... 12,000 units
Net wholesale price each..................................$18
Plant capacity for normal operation....................... 20,000 units
Desired minimum yield on net worth before taxes........... 20%

It is apparent that the prospect for the year is not particularly good. Now, a large maker of record-playing outfits wants to incorporate this speaker in his sets, but limits the price he will pay to $12 each in a contract for 8,000 units. Should this offer be accepted? Assume that the predicted sale of 12,000 speakers at the $18 price would not be affected by the deal (neglect intangibles).

12.7. Assume that your automobile is being used partly for business and partly for pleasure. For this reason you have been keeping a careful record of transportation costs. On the basis of previous experience, your annual costs have been estimated as follows:

```
Decline in trade-in value.........................................$450
Registration and driver's license.  Not  affected.......... $15
Garage expense............................................ $60
Gasoline per mile........................................... 1.8¢
Lubrication and inspections per 1,000 miles..................... $5
Tires per 30,000 miles........................................ $90
Other variable maintenance per 1,000 miles.................... $7
Fixed maintenance (battery, waxing, etc.)..................... $50
Tolls, parking, and miscellaneous expense per 1,000 miles.............. $10
Average mileage per year.....................................12,000
```

Your family is urging you to take them on a transcontinental vacation trip this summer. The estimated mileage is 5,500, and the tour would take four full weeks.

a) Compute a reasonable estimate of transportation cost.
b) During the trip, the daily cost of food and lodging is $30; the normal expenses for food and utilities while at home is $40 per week. What is your estimate for the total cost of the trip, neglecting entertainment, purchases, and special fees?

12.8. An industrial concern is in a critical condition on account of a serious business depression. The sales forecast indicates operation at 30% capacity, which is below the break-even point. Management is to decide whether to shut down or continue to operate at a loss. The president, who is to recommend action to the board of directors, has before him the following summary of financial data:

```
Long-term debt at 5% interest..............................$ 600,000
Shareholders' equity (net worth)............................. 2,500,000
Sales forecast (30% capacity)................................ 2,100,000
Fixed operating costs........................................ 1,050,000
Variable operating costs (in proportion to sales)................. 1,560,000

Income tax rate on profit—30% (after interest) plus 22% on incre-
    ment over $25,000
Desired minimum net yield on net worth...................... 6%
```

a) First consider only the annual dollar advantage or disadvantage of continuing to operate at 30% capacity. What is your conclusion? Disregard intangibles and the possibility of liquidation of assets or sale of the enterprise.

b) Now assume that the fixed operating costs could be reduced 50% by layoffs and salary reductions of key personnel if the plant were completely shut down for a year. What is your conclusion in this case?

c) Make a list of conspicuous intangibles and state whether the factor would encourage or discourage continued operation.

12.9. A group of promoters is considering the erection of a business building on a lot that is valued at $200,000. A decision is to be made regarding the height of the building. A survey of demand indicates that tenants would be available for space up to 20 floors. If the maximum horizontal area were utilized, the space is expected to rent for $60,000 per floor per year. The minimum attractive return on investment is 8% net, based on first cost. The corporation federal income tax would be 30% on profit plus 22% on the increment of profit exceeding $25,000; and there is a state tax of 5% to be computed before the federal tax. The following preliminary cost estimates have been obtained:

n = number of stories
Construction cost = $100,000 + \$115,000n + \$5,000n^2$
Depreciation (straight-line) = $2\frac{1}{2}\%$ of construction cost
Insurance and real estate tax = 3% of first cost
Maintenance and other operating costs = $12,000 per floor
Fixed charges, miscellaneous = $20,000 per year

a) For preliminary considerations, the results are to be compared for 4, 8, 12, 16, and 20 stories (after which more exact estimates will be obtained). What is the optimum height?

b) Now assume that detailed estimates have confirmed the preliminary figures, so that the computations above (a) may be considered correct. Continue the computations to determine the exact number of stories that should be specified.

12.10. Two punch presses are being run continuously on a mass-produced product. Long pieces of strip steel are fed by hand into the press in one operation. The present annual costs and valuation apply to *each* of the two presses.

Present value	$15,000
Annual depreciation (straight-line)	2,500
Maintenance (includes die replacements)	4,500
Power	400
Other overhead	2,000
Direct labor	4,200
Fringe benefits (percentage of direct labor costs)	15%
Required yield on investment before taxes	25%

An automatic feeding device has been proposed to enable *one* operator to run both presses (two now being required). The cost of the equipment is $5,500 for *each* of the presses, and the anticipated life is 12 years with

$500 salvage value. Annual maintenance is estimated at $400 each. Make an economy study of this proposal using the average interest method.

12.11.   The Esser Chemical Company manufactures a cosmetic lotion that enjoys a national reputation. The plant capacity, however, exceeds considerably the sales forecast for the year. Financial data are as follows:

Plant capacity (6-oz. bottles in one shift)...............	8,000,000
Net worth of firm.....................................	$1,200,000
Long-term debt at 5%...............................	$ 250,000
Selling price per 100 bottles (wholesale).................	$25
Predicted sales, bottles..............................	8,000,000
Fixed operating cost.................................	$800,000
Variable cost for *one* shift at 100% capacity.............	$1,000,000
Federal income tax rate	
On all profit.......................................	30%
On profit increment exceeding $25,000................	22%
Required net yield on net worth......................	10%

Subsequent to the forementioned sales forecast, the company receives a proposal from a drugstore chain to purchase 1,500,000 bottles (to be labeled under its own trade-mark) at a special price of $16.50 per 100 bottles. This order would require a second shift with an increase of 15% in unit variable cost. It is also predicted that $50,000 additional working capital would have to be borrowed for one year at 6% interest.

a) Neglecting intangibles, should this proposal be accepted? Justify your conclusion with appropriate computations.

b) Enumerate intangibles and explain how they would affect the decision.

12.12.   A company is considering the purchase of automatic billing equipment to replace 10 clerks who cost $300 per month each. The proposed equipment will require only two operators costing $400 per month each. It is estimated that operation and maintenance of the machines will cost $100 per month. The life of the equipment is estimated at 10 years, and it will have a salvage value of 10% of its cost. Taxes and insurance (combined) on the equipment will be 3% of the original cost per year.

If straight-line depreciation is used with average interest at 24%, what is the greatest sum the company can pay for the equipment and break even? (PE Cal. revised)

12.13.   A large food-processing concern is considering the economy of operating second and third shifts in one of its plants. The night shifts are not as efficient as the regular day shift; and costs are critical because of the small profit margin on sales. The data available to the estimator are as follows:

Annual Estimates	One Shift	Two Shifts	Three Shifts
Output, pounds...............	5,000,000	9,500,000	13,700,000
Supervision and indirect labor....	$ 90,000	$145,000	$ 205,000
Direct labor..................	$400,000	$840,000	$1,300,000
Utilities.....................	$ 75,000	$165,000	$ 265,000
Variable maintenance..........	$ 45,000	$100,000	$ 160,000
Working capital...............	$120,000	$200,000	$ 280,000
Selling price per pound.........	24¢		
Fixed operating cost...........	$210,000		
Fringe benefits based on wages and salaries....................	16%		
Direct material cost per pound of finished product............	5¢		
Required yield on increment investments before taxes......	20%		

Determine the advantages or disadvantages that would result from the extra shifts.

CHAPTER 13

Present Worth
Comparison of
Alternatives

NNUAL costs or profits are the most common criteria for comparing alternatives in economy studies of continuing projects. Investments are then reflected only in depreciation and in the requirements for return or yield. There are, however, situations in which the annual estimate does not indicate fairly the economy. Time value of money has not been accounted for except in the estimates of depreciation and required return, if computed by the exact method. The program may call for a sequence of investments and predictions of cost and income that can not be estimated directly in terms of annual average. This chapter describes a procedure for evaluating programs for expenditure and income that are long in term or involve time changes in financial events.

Present Worth, a Criterion for Decision

The present worth concept and some of its applications have been discussed previously. The present worth of predicted financial events is a well-recognized criterion among engineering economists, accountants, and professional investors. To some decision makers, present worth valuations may seem obscure or unrealistic; and to them, an annual average may be more significant. An annual equivalent that takes time value into account can be derived from present worth. The present worth of a program may be looked upon in two ways: (1) appraisal of cost, or (2) appraisal of profit potential.

If the study requires appraisal of cost, the present worth may be thought of as an *endowment* (real or hypothetical) that would be required to support the program during the study period or anticipated life of the project. In this case, all scheduled expenditures are plus items, and all recoveries or items of income are negative. Then, the most favorable among alternatives is the one that requires *least* endowment, or *lowest* annual equivalent, provided the services rendered or benefits realized are equal.

If the problem is to consider *profit potentials,* the pertinent criterion is the present worth of future profits. Hence, all expenditures would be treated as negative, and the items of income would be plus factors. In this case, the most favorable alternative is the one with the *greatest* present worth or for which the *greatest* annual equivalent is indicated.

After the analyst decides whether endowment or present worth of profit is the proper criterion, it is apparent that he must follow the plus or minus designation of financial factors consistently. But there are some differences of opinion among analysts as to the appropriateness of financial items in the study and their treatment. The author believes that the simplest and most consistent answer to this problem is to *include all the actual expenditures and items of income when they occur* in the predicted time schedule. Salvage value of property at the end of the study period is to be considered an item of income, whether actual disposal is anticipated or not. The more difficult issues are the treatments of depreciation and required return, debt obligations, income taxes, yield requirement, and study period. These matters will be discussed in some detail.

First Cost, Depreciation, and Required Return

In Chapter 8, it was demonstrated that the present worth of depreciation, required return, and the residual value of a property had a combined value equal to the initial value of the property. Using the previous notation:

$$I = (D + R) \left[\frac{(1 + i)^n - 1}{i(1 + i)^n} \right] + \frac{S}{(1 + i)^n}$$

Therefore, the charge for first cost, when the expenditure takes place, will account for the present worths of subsequent depreciations, required returns, and salvage value (to be recovered at the end of the study period). A separate charge for depreciation and required return would duplicate penalties against the project. The computation may not be so simple, however, when the project is financed by borrowing. Also, it may be necessary to determine depreciation for income tax computation.

Debt Obligations

That portion of first cost which is financed by borrowing may require separate treatment in the present worth analysis. If the rates specified for required return, debt interest, and possible sinking fund are all the same (which may be true in some public or institutional projects), the first cost will represent the present worth of the combined obligations. (To verify this, note that the future worth of the sinking fund would be the principal of the loan at its date of retirement. And the present worth of that amount combined with the present worth of the interest payments would equal the initial amount of the loan.) It is more likely, however, that interest rates on the loan and on sinking funds would be different from the required yield normally specified for investments of the enterprise.

If the debt obligations mentioned above are to be treated separately, the borrowed portion of the investment should not be charged to the project at the time of borrowing but at the times that payments are due, either into a sinking fund or to the lender. It will also be necessary to evaluate the interest payments as among the periodic costs incurred by the project. The amount of periodic interest depends on the provisions of the loan. The periodic payments into a sinking fund depend on the rate of earnings anticipated in the fund. The present worth of these debt obligations can be based on the required yield applied to other costs. (Some may think it reasonable to evaluate the sinking fund payments at the interest rate earned by the fund, at least during the life of that fund.)

The termination date of a long-term debt, such as a bond issue or a mortgage, may establish an appropriate study period. If interest rates on the debt and sinking fund are equal to required yield for time value, the combined annual amount including sinking fund deposit would be equivalent to the charge for depreciation and required return on investment, as previously stated. The present worth would then equal the initial amount of the debt. If the interest rates are not the same, the present worths must be detailed as follows:

$$\text{Amount of debt} = I$$
$$\text{Required yield for present worth evaluation} = i$$
$$\text{Interest rate on debt} = r_1$$
$$\text{Rate of return on sinking fund} = r_2$$
$$\text{Periodic interest on debt} = r_1 I$$

$$\text{Sinking fund deposit} = I \left[\frac{r_2}{(1 + r_2)^n - 1} \right]$$

$$\text{Total present worth} = r_1 I \left[\frac{(1 + i)^n - 1}{i(1 + i)^n} \right]$$

$$+ I \left[\frac{r_2}{(1 + r_2)^n - 1} \right] \left[\frac{(1 + i)^n - 1}{i(1 + i)^n} \right]$$

To illustrate the effects of interest rates, consider a first cost of $1,000,000. Of this amount, the firm advances $400,000 and borrows $600,000 for a term of 10 years (the study period). At first, let us assume that the loan is at 5%, and a sinking fund must be maintained earning only 3%. Required yield on investment is 10%. Then:

```
Sinking fund deposit @ 3% = 600,000/11.46.........$  52,338
Annual interest @ 5% = (600,000)(.05)..............    30,000
Total annual obligation............................$  82,338
Present worth of above @ 10% = (82,338)(6.144).....   505,885
Initial outlay.....................................   400,000
Total present worth................................$905,885
```

Now assume that there is no sinking fund or that it earns income at the rate (i) equal to required yield, so that its future worth equals the amount of the debt. In this case:

```
Present worth of annual interest = (30,000)(6.144)....$184,120
Present worth of debt retirement = 600,000/2.594.....  231,300
Initial outlay.......................................  400,000
Total present worth..................................$815,620
```

If 10% were used for all the interest rates, it can be demonstrated that the sum of the detail present worths in both of the foregoing examples will equal $1,000,000 (the first cost). In these examples, we neglected a possible salvage value at the end of the study period. The present worth of this, which would be negative in the examples, would affect the various totals equally.

Income Taxes

The taxes on profit are critical factors in all economy studies except those that are tax free, such as public works and nonprofit enterprises. In the average large corporation, since 1950 income taxes have had the effect of reducing by 50% or more the dollar advantage or disadvantage of individual projects.

In the simpler present worth comparisons, the effect of the income tax can be included in a *gross* required yield, as described in Chapter 8. When depreciation is other than sinking fund (for tax computa-

tion), when there are debt obligations that affect the tax, and if
there is a salvage value to be accounted for, the gross required yield
is not appropriate for present worth computation. In these cases,
the present worth must be based on the *net* yield requirement, and
the income tax or tax increment must be estimated as an annual
cost.

With regard to depreciation, the annual average amount by any
method except sinking fund is the same as straight line. Therefore,
it may be appropriate to use straight-line depreciation for estimating the income taxes during the study period. That assumption
must be regarded with caution, however. When the tax accounting is
based on depreciation that is accelerated during the early life of the
property, the increase in the tax with time will affect the present
worth and the annual equivalent. As in other cost estimates, the
annual average may be accurate enough, considering the greater uncertainties in forecasting future events. Of course, any change in the
program for investment and operations would call for a time change
in the tax estimates.

When capital is borrowed, the annual interest on the debt must
be deducted as a cost for determining the taxable profit. Other deductions for tax purposes should include profit-sharing bonuses, although they may not be listed in the present worth summary.

When the income tax must be identified in the present worth summary, it appears as an item of annual cost in the studies that aim at
profit comparison. On the other hand, the project under consideration may be only a part of a large enterprise, and cost may be the
criterion for decision (the share in operating income may be unknown). In this case, the income tax may be treated on an *increment*
basis. For each series of years during which cost and income is assumed to be stable, it must be determined which of the alternatives
shows the *greatest* annual cost, including depreciation (as used in
tax accounting); then *zero* tax is assigned to this alternative during
the pertinent years. Next, the cost savings estimated for the other
alternatives are determined. The income taxes that would reduce
these savings can be termed *increment taxes* or *tax penalties* that
should be charged as annual costs to those alternatives. (See page
187.)

Profit Sharing

Profit sharing deserves treatment similar to the income tax; but
the computation depends on the character of the bonus plan. (See

page 91.) It is appropriate to include the estimated amount in the annual cost. If no computation of profit is involved in the study, the profit-sharing bonus can be treated on an *increment* basis, as suggested for the tax penalty.

Required Yield

The recommended interest rate for the present worth evaluations is the minimum yield that should be expected from the type of project under consideration (the required yield). Those who may argue that sinking funds should be evaluated (for present worth) at their rates of return should consider the fact that such funds tie up capital that might otherwise be employed with greater profit, which justifies the required yield for the present worth computation.

The applications for a *gross* required yield that includes allowances for income taxes and other deductions from economic return were mentioned previously. This gross yield is seldom appropriate for present worth comparisons. Depreciation method affects income tax and other items based on economic return. Salvage value can not be treated as taxable profit unless capital gain is involved. Any capital gain tax that is anticipated can be deducted from salvage value. Because of these complications, the required *net* yield should be used to determine present worths in most of these problems.

More than one interest rate may be necessary for computing present worth—i.e., when parts of the program deserve differing yield requirements (permanent buildings versus certain production tools, for example). This fact must be recognized when the annual equivalent is computed. Then, the present worths should be grouped according to their interest rates; and the annual equivalent for each group should be based on the interest rate used for determining its present worth.

In long-term studies that characterize present worth comparisons, should required yield be greater to compensate for risk in long-term forecasting? (See page 156.) Forecasting risk should certainly be considered in the yield requirement, or an allowance for contingencies should be substituted for it. Of course, an increase in interest rate will reduce the total present worth or hypothetical endowment to support estimated annual costs, which may seem inconsistent. It should be recognized, however, that the *annual equivalent* in this case will then include a greater required return on the investment items. Required return in this type of analysis should reflect risk, as in all business decisions that involve investment and time. In problems that deal with actual endowment, however, risk can be reflected in *low* interest rate. Here we are concerned not with required yield on investment but with the forecast of earnings.

Study Period

It is generally agreed that present worth comparisons are most appropriate for long-term projects; but the length of the study period may be a controversial issue. If present worth is the criterion for decision, it is certain that the study periods should be the same for each of the compared alternatives. If the present worths are converted to annual equivalents, the study periods of the alternatives can differ—as in the MAPI method of replacement analysis (Chapter 15).

If a project is expected to continue indefinitely (a dam or a super-highway) the study period may be treated as if it were infinite, using *capitalized cost* (to be described presently). When long-term borrowing supports the project, the termination date of the loan or loans may establish an appropriate study period.

For most commercial investors, a long depreciation life is much too long for justifying investment. Assume that a well-built business structure is expected to last 50 years or more, and depreciation (for accounting purposes) is based on that estimate. Would any investor base an earnings requirement on an investment status of 25 years hence (average value of investment)? It would be unlikely indeed. A ten-year prediction is long for most commercial projects. Longer predictions may be justified for power plants, land, certain public utilities, and other relatively stable investments. In general, the most reasonable study period is that length of time managers and investors are willing to accept to justify the project under consideration. No rule of thumb can be recommended for this specification.

With regard to salvage values, these must be based on the study period. What is the property expected to be worth at the end of that time? This estimate could be arbitrary, a future market value prediction, or a computed book value based on the predicted depreciation rate.

If the appropriate study period is longer than the expected life of some of the properties, intermediate salvage recoveries and replacements can be provided for in the program. The annual equivalent of such replacements can be combined with maintenance costs or can be stated separately as depreciation in the annual estimates.

The comparison of alternatives that deserve different study periods merits special treatment. Among the possible solutions to the problem are the following:

1. *Annual equivalents* of the present worths can be used for decision criteria. (The present worths will not be comparable otherwise.)
2. The predicted life of the short-term alternative can be used as the study period for other alternatives.
3. It can be assumed (hypothetically) that the short-term alternative can be repeated often enough to equal the life of the competing alternatives. It may be possible to adopt a study period that is a common multiple of the lives of the competitors.

The first of these suggestions is the most reasonable unless the present worth comparison is particularly required (as in actual endowment).

Perpetual Endowment

Perpetual endowment or capitalized cost, described in Chapter 2, has some practical applications in these present worth comparisons. Note that:

$$\frac{(1 + i)^n - 1}{i(1 + i)^n} = \frac{1 - (1 + i)^{-n}}{i} \rightarrow \frac{1}{i}, \text{ as } n \rightarrow \infty$$

The factor $(1/i)$ for capitalized cost simplifies present worth computation. Although infinite life is imaginary, the error in that approximation for study periods of 40 years or more is often negligible for comparing alternatives. The errors in predicting future costs and interest rates will probably exceed those of capitalized cost by a wide margin.

The use of capitalized cost for present worth is usually confined to projects for which indefinitely long life is predicted (e.g., public works), which are not to be based on monetary profit or for which actual perpetual endowment is intended (e.g., permanent scholarship funds and perpetual care of cemetery plots). In commercial enterprises, the study periods are seldom long enough to justify capitalized cost.

Significance of Results

The accuracy of the present worth summation and the annual equivalent can not exceed the accuracy of the financial factors, which can be exceedingly speculative in long-range estimates. Therefore, it would be reasonable to round the final figures. As a criterion for decision, the present worth summation is significant only to persons who understand the method, unless it is intended to represent a real endowment. The annual equivalent is more in line with the thinking of many decision makers, and it is necessary for the comparison when different study periods are used for the various alternatives.

The annual equivalent has been mentioned previously. If the meaning of this is unclear to some readers, let it be understood that it is simply an annual amount that would have a present worth equal to the summation of present worths of the various financial events scheduled in the program. Let there be a single interest rate (i) and present worths of several financial events $(P_1, P_2, P_3, \ldots P_x)$. Then, the annual equivalent (A) becomes:

$$A = \Sigma P \left[\frac{i(1 + i)^n}{(1 + i)^n - 1} \right]$$

The treatment of more than one interest rate was described on page 199.

When cost is the criterion for decision, the summation of present worths is the actual or hypothetical endowment required to support the project during the specified study period. When profit is the criterion, the summation of present worths may be more obscure in significance. Actually, that summation represents the present worth of profits and residual value of investment *in excess of required return*. The net summation could be zero, indicating that the required return was just realized. And a zero annual equivalent would be comparable with an annual estimate of net profit from which an equal required return is deducted.

If it is advisable to derive an annual equivalent for *net profit* from the present worth analysis, it would be necessary to identify separately the required return for the various periods of investment in the program, as described on page 112. The present worths of these returns could then be summed, and that amount could be deducted from the total present worths to give the present worth of the net profits.

Now let us consider the simplest type of program which starts with an expenditure for investment uncomplicated by borrowing. There are no additions or replacements during the study period, and the operating cost and income items are uniform annual amounts. In this case, the annual equivalent of the present worths would be exactly the same as the annual estimate of cost plus required return or profit less required return (required return computed by the exact method). In that situation, there is no justification for the present worth analysis. The time value of cost or profit is most significant when there are time changes in the program during the study period.

EXAMPLES OF PRESENT WORTH ANALYSES

The variety of projects that may be compared by present worth analysis has been indicated in the discussions of the critical financial factors. These principles will now be demonstrated by three hypothetical problems: a sprinkler project, a factory building program, and a public highway. The first of these cases is a simple one that could be handled equally well by the customary summary of annual costs or by increment cost analysis. The second example illustrates involvement with borrowed funds and a period of rental income. The third project illustrates a method of handling cost of travel to highway users and the capitalizing of annual costs. The first two cases, which are associated with private businesses, require income tax charges.

A Sprinkler Project

Installation of a sprinkler system is intended to reduce annual charges for insurance by $2,500. The study is to neglect intangible considerations for the present. Essential data on the sprinkler installation are:

First cost (construction)............................	$ 10,000
Life of building (assumed life of project).............	30 years
Ultimate salvage value............................	zero
Increment income tax rate.........................	50%
Required net yield on investment...................	6%
Depreciation for tax computation..................	straight line
Maintenance cost of system.......................	$100 per year

To compute the income tax penalty, the saving in annual cost must be determined. It is then assumed that taxable profit would be increased by that amount, and the income tax would be correspondingly increased.

Reduction in annual insurance premium.........		$2,500
Annual depreciation.........................	$333	
Annual maintenance.........................	100	
Annual cost of sprinkler system...............		433
Annual saving in operating cost...............		$2,067
Income tax on saving @ 50%.................		1,034

To compare the alternatives, sprinklers or none, on an endowment basis, the sprinkler system will be charged with increment income tax and the "no sprinkler" situation with the additional insurance premium. Present worths are based on 30 years at 6%. Present worth factor is 13.77. TABLE B-3

Present Worths:	Without Sprinklers	Sprinkler System
First cost	...	$10,000
Insurance penalty	$34,425	...
Annual maintenance	...	1,377
Income tax penalty	...	14,233
Total present worth	$34,425	$25,610
Advantage of sprinkler system		8,815
Annual equivalent of sprinkler advantage		640

The same result can be obtained by increment cost analysis on an annual basis. For the sprinkler system:

Depreciation plus required return by exact
  method = 10,000/13.77.....................$ 726
Maintenance...................................... 100
Increment income tax......................... 1,034
Total increment cost plus required return...........$1,860
Saving on insurance premium.................... 2,500
Net annual saving in excess of required return......$ 640

If the program involved changes in the schedule of financial events during the 30-year period, the average of annual costs would not be the same as the time-valued annual equivalent of present worths. The borrowing of capital will also change the results, as will be demonstrated in the next problem.

A Factory Building Project

A manufacturing concern considers the building of a new general-purpose plant. The problem has been reduced to a choice between two alternatives, decision to be based on economy study. The alternatives are: Plan A, to build for immediate needs and figure on expansion in 5 years; and Plan B to erect a plant that will accommodate predicted future needs, aided by the temporary leasing of extra space. The proposed programs and essential data are as follows:

	Plan A	Plan B
Construction cost now	$500,000	$800,000
Construction cost in 5 years	400,000	...
Salvage value in 15 years	400,000	400,000
Maintenance and property taxes		
First 5 years per year	19,000	32,000
Next 10 years per year	36,000	36,000
Rental income per year first 5 years	...	45,000

In both cases, one half the funds for construction will be borrowed by mortgaging the property at 5% interest, and all mortgages are to terminate 15 years from now. Thus, 15 years is the accepted study period. The increment rate for income tax is predicted at 54%, and cost for tax purposes is based on straight-line depreciation at 4% of first cost per year. Required *net* yield on investment is 10%. The two proposals are to be compared by present worth analysis (hypothetical endowment).

Before summarizing the present worth analysis, let us consider the debt obligations and the income tax situation.

Debt Obligations (Mortgage Interest and Retirement):

Plan A—The initial mortgage is $250,000 with $12,500 per year interest. The mortgage is increased by $200,000 in 5 years, which adds $10,000 to annual interest. The total $450,000 mortgage is to be retired in 15 years.

Plan B—The $400,000 mortgage, to be retired in 15 years, involves annual interest at $20,000.

Income Taxes: These are to be evaluated on an increment cost basis, since operating profits are unknown. We shall first compare the estimates of annual costs which will affect taxable profit.

> *Plan A*
>
> First 5 years:
> | | |
> |---|---:|
> | Depreciation = (.04)(500,000) | $20,000 |
> | Interest on debt | 12,500 |
> | Maintenance, etc. | 19,000 |
> | Operating cost + interest | $51,500 |
>
> Next 10 years:
> | | |
> |---|---:|
> | Depreciation = (.04)(900,000) | $36,000 |
> | Interest on debt | 22,500 |
> | Maintenance, etc. | 36,000 |
> | Operating cost + interest | $94,500 |
>
> *Plan B*
>
> First 5 years:
> | | |
> |---|---:|
> | Depreciation = (.04)(800,000) | $32,000 |
> | Interest on debt | 20,000 |
> | Maintenance, etc. | 32,000 |
> | Operating cost + interest | $84,000 |
> | Rental income | 45,000 |
> | Net operating cost + interest | $39,000 |
>
> Next 10 years:
> | | |
> |---|---:|
> | Additional maintenance | 4,000 |
> | Net operating cost + interest | $88,000 |

These estimates show the annual cost advantage for Plan B for both time periods, advantages that would be reduced by 54% income tax penalty.

Plan B
  First 5 years:
    Increment tax = (.54)(51,500 − 39,000) = $6,750 per year
  Next 10 years:
    Increment tax = (.54)(94,500 − 88,000) = $3,510 per year

Present Worth Analysis: Following is the summary of present worths based on the financial details as specified and computed above. Results are rounded to the nearest $100.

Years	Items	Plan A	Plan B
0	Initial investment by owners........$250,000		$400,000
5	Additional investment by owners....	124,100	. . .
1–15	Interest on initial mortgage.........	95,100	152,100
6–15	Interest on additional mortgage.....	38,100	. . .
15	Retirement of mortgages............	107,700	95,800
1–5	Maintenance, etc..................	72,000	121,300
6–15	Maintenance, etc..................	137,300	137,300
1–5	Rental income....................	. . .	−170,600
1–5	Income tax penalty................	. . .	25,600
6–15	Income tax penalty................	. . .	13,400
15	Salvage value of property..........	−95,800	−95,800
	Sum of present worths........	$728,500	$679,100

To illustrate the computation for items scheduled for years 6–15, consider the interest on the mortgage addition for Plan A (i.e., $10,000 per year beginning at the end of the 6th year). Two present worth factors must be used, one to evaluate the annual payments during the last 10 years, and another to convert that total to the zero year.

$$\text{Present worth} = (10,000)(6.144)/(1.611) = \$38,100$$

If the building were intended as a profit-making enterprise with substantial income, the signs of cost and income items should be reversed, and the totals would indicate *profit in excess of required return.* In the above estimate, Plan B has a definite advantage, and the annual equivalents would compare similarly. The results are close enough, however, to indicate that intangible considerations may offset the tangible advantage. Among the important intangibles are competing, immediate demands for capital and the risk of predicting future needs as to size and character of the enterprise.

It may be observed that the *combined* present worths of debt interest and mortgage retirement are less than the present worth of the initial loan, which equaled the owner's initial investment in this case. The reason is that the interest rate on the debt (5%) was less than the stipulated yield requirement (10%), on which the present worths were based. This demonstrates the advantage of borrowing (assuming, of course, that the required yield would actually be realized). Some authorities may argue that the present worths of debt obligations should be based on the debt interest rate, a procedure that would not demonstrate the advantage mentioned.

A Highway Project

The economy studies for highways, bridges, dams, and other long-life public works often make use of capitalized-cost comparisons. Such structures are expected to last indefinitely with proper maintenance and replacement of worn parts. The interest rate adopted usually equals that of the bond issues required for financing. It may be desirable to specify a higher yield to account for the cost of tax collections or the loss of taxes on an enterprise that could otherwise be privately conducted. Consider the following hypothetical highway project.

A highway intersection problem has reached the stage of comparing the economies of four alternatives:

a) Maintain the present grade crossing as is.
b) Construct an overpass (bridge) on the main highway, with no immediate access to the secondary crossroad.
c) Construct an overpass on the main highway, providing for right turns only to and from the secondary road.
d) Construct a clover-leaf intersection that provides for both right and left turns.

The economy study involves the usual considerations of investment, financing, and operating cost. Also to be considered are the tangible costs or benefits to the public, matters related to travel and trade.

The main highway now carries 1,500,000 vehicles annually in this location. Of these, 100,000 travel to or from the secondary road, the right and left turns being equally divided. The secondary road now carries 200,000 vehicles annually at this point, and half of these come from or turn onto the main road.

On the secondary road, a quarter of a mile from the intersection, is a small village. The local businessmen claim that $250,000 of their annual trade comes to the village via the main road. The profit from trade averages 5% of sales ($12,500).

Costs applicable to all of the alternatives are as follows:

Money to the state............................... 4%
Travel time averages per minute.................. 5¢
Travel distance and time averages per mile......... 15¢
Rise and fall in travel averages per foot............ .06¢

The rise and fall refer to vertical distance up or down and effects on vehicles and travel time. Costs to individuals may vary greatly from the averages given.

Costs and conditions applying to the individual proposals are given below. The depreciation mentioned relates to replacements, such as road surfacing, guardrails, and the like, which are aggregated into an annual average. Otherwise, the life of the project is assumed to be indefinitely long and suitable for valuation as capitalized cost.

Plan A: For the present grade intersection, existing traffic lights cost $2,000 per year for maintenance and depreciation. Maintenance and depreciation at the intersection is $3,000 per year. The traffic control delays the average main-road vehicle 0.3 minutes and the secondary road vehicle 1.2 minutes (due to heavy traffic on the main road).

Plan B: Construction cost is $150,000; maintenance and depreciation, $8,000 per year. Rise and fall on the main road is 5 feet; on the secondary road, 15 feet. Vehicles traveling both roads would have to detour onto an inferior road and travel an extra distance of 0.5 mile to make the turn. It is estimated that the village would lose $12,500 of their annual profit because of detoured traffic.

Plan C: Land and construction cost is $230,000; annual maintenance and depreciation, $10,000. For *right* turns (50,000 vehicles), there is no rise and fall, and distance is shortened 0.03 mile. For *left* turns (50,000 vehicles), the traveler must utilize the "right" turn at the intersection. To do this, he must reverse directions on the secondary road, which involves a 15-foot rise and fall and 0.5 mile of added distance. *Through* traffic on the main road (1,400,000 vehicles) involves a 5-foot rise and fall and on the secondary road (100,000 vehicles) a 15-foot rise and fall. On account of inconvenience in making the turn, the village estimates some loss of profit from trade ($2,500 per year).

Plan D: Land and construction cost is $350,000; maintenance and depreciation, $15,000 per year. For *through* traffic, the rise and fall is the same as proposal C. For *right* turns, there is no rise and fall, and the cutoff saves 0.06 mile. For *left* turns, the rise and fall totals 40 feet and the loop distance (extra travel) is 0.2 mile.

A column-beside-column comparison of the four alternatives is shown in Table 13–1. Annual costs are capitalized at 4%. Since it is assumed that the annual costs are uniform throughout the life of the project, the annual equivalent of the table could be duplicated by conventional increment-cost analysis with required return based on first cost. However, if there were future additions to investment or if

TABLE 13-1

COMPARISON OF FOUR PROPOSALS FOR A HIGHWAY INTERSECTION

	Plan A Grade Crossing	Plan B Bridge and No Turns	Plan C Bridge and Right Turns	Plan D Cloverleaf Interchange
Annual Costs:				
Rise and fall				
Straight through............... ...		$ 5,100	$ 5,100	$ 5,100
Left turns..................... ...		...	900	1,200
Distance and time				
Left turns..................... ...		7,500	3,750	1,500
Right turns................... ...		7,500	−225	−450
Traffic delays....................$ 34,500		...	...	...
Loss of trade.................... ...		12,500	2,500	...
Maintenance and depreciation...... 5,000		8,000	10,000	15,000
Total annual cost............$ 39,500		$ 40,600	$ 22,025	$ 22,350
Annual cost capitalized @ 4%.......$987,500		$1,015,000	$550,625	$558,750
Initial cost........................ ...		150,000	230,000	350,000
Total present worth..........$987,500		$1,165,000	$780,625	$908,750
Advantage of Plan C over Plan A.....			$206,875	
Equivalent annual advantage.........			8,275	

Note: The capitalized annual cost is the annual amount divided by the interest rate (4%). The annual equivalent is the total present worth times the interest rate.

changes in traffic and annual costs were predicted, the present worth comparison would be more significant.

PROBLEMS

13.1. For installation in a certain new building, both steel and aluminum window frames are being considered. Comparative costs are as follows:

	Steel	Aluminum
First cost, installed and painted......$32,000		$36,000
Repainting, average per year......... $700		Not required
Taxes and insurance................		2% of first cost

Assume 40-year life, no salvage value, and required yield on investment at 8%.

a) Compare the two proposals on the basis of present worth and annual equivalents.

b) Compare the two proposals by the annual cost method, using the exact method of capital recovery and required return. (PE Pa. Revised)

13.2. A growing community now requires one duct for power. It is estimated that two ducts will be required in 5 years, three ducts in 15 years, and four ducts in 25 years. The cost of installing one duct at a time is $1,700 per 1,000 feet, and the cost of installing four ducts at one time is $4,400 per 1,000 feet. With money at 6%, is it more economical to install one duct at a time as needed or to install four ducts now? (PE Pa.)

13.3. Two methods of conveying water are being studied. Method A requires a tunnel—first cost is $150,000; life, perpetual; annual operation and upkeep, $2,000. Method B requires a ditch plus a flume. First cost of the ditch is $50,000; life, perpetual; annual operation and upkeep, $2,000. First cost of the flume is $30,000; life, 10 years; salvage value, $5,000; annual operation and upkeep, $4,000. Compare the two methods for perpetual service, assuming an interest rate of 5%. (PE Pa.)

13.4. A real estate firm is considering the purchase of a large area of undeveloped land for future development and sale as suburban lots. The land is unsuited for cultivation, and the only cost for holding it is a county property tax, due at the beginning of each year, which amounts to an annual $5 per $1,000 valuation. The valuation is the price at which the property is transferred. The company's plan is to develop and promptly sell 25% of the land at 5-year intervals, beginning in 5 years. It is estimated that the net return from the sale of lots (price paid less development cost) would amount to $1,200,000.

Assume that the original land purchase would take place at the beginning of the year, and the company would be obligated for the county tax. Also assume that during the year the property is developed (e.g., the 6th year), the county tax would have to be paid on that portion, but that all the lots would be developed and sold by the end of that year. Consequently, the returns from the sale of lots are to be credited to the venture in 6, 11, 16, and 21 years. Based on these estimates, what is the maximum price that could be paid for the undeveloped land if the firm is to realize a minimum yield of 10% on its investment?

13.5. In the study of a new boiler, the capital and operating costs are being considered. The installed cost is $30,000, life is 25 years, and there is no salvage value. No maintenance is anticipated for 5 years, at which time a $500 job is anticipated. A $1,500 job is anticipated in 10 years, $2,500 in 15 years, and $3,500 in 20 years (replacement in 25 years). The fixed costs for labor, taxes, insurance, and miscellaneous overhead amount to $10,000 per year. With interest at 8%, what is the equivalent annual cost?

13.6. A certain new residential plan when finished will require a sewer system costing $65,000, if installed completely at the beginning of a 10-year period. It seems likely that all sewer demands can be met by installing the total sewer system in four parts as follows:

At the beginning, the first portion............$25,000
In three years, another portion..............$20,000
In six years, a third portion................$20,000
In ten years, the final portion..............$11,000

Assuming capital is worth 4% per year:
  a) Which plan (complete job at once or in four parts) is the most economical based on present worth?
  b) What is the annual equivalent saving in the preferred plan? (PE Pa. revised)

13.7. In the purchase of land for the construction of a manufacturing plant, the question arises regarding the desirability of purchasing certain adjoining unimproved land for possible future expansion. The land is available now for $20,000. Assume that the land will not be used for 10 years, that taxes will average 2%, and that capital is worth not less than 16%.
  a) What must be the prospective value of the land in 10 years to justify its purchase now?
  b) Assuming that capital is available for the purchase, what prominent intangibles would favor or disfavor the project? (PE Pa. revised)

13.8. Compare two types of bridges on the basis of capitalized cost at 5% interest. Bridge A has an estimated life of 25 years, initial cost, $50,-000; renewal cost, $35,000; annual maintenance, $500; additional repairs every 5 years, $2,000; and salvage value (in 25 years), $5,000. Bridge B has an estimated life of 50 years, initial cost, $75,000; renewal cost, $75,-000; annual maintenance cost, $100; additional repairs every 5 years, $1,000; and salvage value, $10,000.
  Determine the capitalized costs (perpetual endowments) and the annual equivalent. Hint: for replacements and periodic costs, other than annual, reduce to annual equivalents, as for a sinking fund. (PE Pa. revised)

13.9. A new residential district has been growing at a rate that requires an engineering study of the water supply. It has been estimated that water consumption in the area will reach 300,000, 600,000, and 900,-000 gallons per day in 10, 20, and 45 years respectively. The estimated installation costs of connecting mains with the above capacities are $55,-000, $70,000, and $120,000 respectively. The estimated life of the mains is 65 years. Assume that the installations would cost the predicted amounts at any time between now and 45 years. Note that there are four possible schedules for installation of mains, from 300,000 gallon capacity in three stages to 900,000 gallon capacity at once. Determine the best of the four schedules by comparing present worths and annual equivalents. The town borrows its capital at 4% interest. The study period is 45 years. (PE Pa. revised)

13.10. A city is considering a new bridge. Three-lane capacity is required immediately. It is predicted that six lanes will be needed in 10 years. The problem is whether to construct the six-lane bridge now to save on construction cost, or to defer the additional three lanes for 10 years. The three additional lanes would be constructed by widening the original superstructure.

Construction costs are to be financed by bonds issued at the time of construction; but the one or two bond issues would terminate 20 years from *now*. The bond interest will be 4%. However, it will be necessary to provide a sinking fund for bond retirement, and this fund is expected to earn only 3%. Other essential data follow:

Construction Costs:

Six lanes now.........................	$1,800,000
Three lanes now.......................	1,350,000
Three lanes added to first three.........	750,000

Maintenance Costs per Year:

For three lanes only...................	22,000
For six lanes.........................	30,000

Assuming a 20-year study period, which of these proposals should be adopted? Assume bond interest is the required yield.

13.11. A retail store in a certain city is owned and operated by a distributing firm with headquarters a considerable distance away. The retail store is 35 years old and, while not of fireproof construction, does have an automatic sprinkler as a means of fire protection. Operational expenses of the retail store have averaged annually: $2,310 for maintenance, $750 for fire insurance on the building, and $430 for fire insurance on the stock. Additional fire risk not covered by insurance is estimated to be $300 annually.

A plan for civic improvement indicates that the existing store will be razed in about 11 years, certainly not before 10 years have passed. A 10-year lease on another store in the city, equally suited by location and size, can be obtained at an annual rental of $5,160. Operation and maintenance for this alternative location will be $605 yearly. The yearly insurance premium on the stock will be reduced to $320. Since this is a more modern building, the estimated cost of fire risk not covered by insurance is $145 annually. At the end of 10 years, the present building will have no value, but the land is valued at $18,000. If the move is made now, the present store may be sold for $27,250 net. The cost of moving the stock to the new location would be $450.

Make a 10-year economy study comparing the two alternatives. Use present worths and annual equivalents with interest at 10%. (PE Pa. revised)

13.12. In the design of a three-story municipal office building, the question arises whether provisions should be made for the addition of two more stories at a later date. The architect makes two designs. The one which provides for this possible expansion involves an estimated first cost of $79,300. The one without this provision is estimated at $73,000.

If the former plan is adopted, it is estimated that the subsequent addition of the two stories will cost $52,000. Without the additional strength of columns and footings provided by this plan, it is likely that, for the additional stories, the necessary reconstruction and strengthening of the lower stories would cost at least $15,000.

Assume that the life of the building would be 45 years from now, with or without the additions. How soon must the additional stories be needed to justify the first cost of $79,300? There would be no change in annual operating costs or maintenance (other than depreciation). The interest rate is $3\frac{1}{2}\%$. (PE Pa. revised)

CHAPTER 14

Minimum Cost, Maximum Profit

MOST industrial economy studies relate to alternative specifications, rates of operations, or operating programs in which the decision criteria are minimum cost or maximum profit. This chapter is concerned with comparison of alternatives characterized by one or more variable and controllable factors that determine the optimum outcome.

The simplest of the forementioned problems involves *one* independent and controllable variable that is to be decided upon. The general case will respond to the usual cost or profit computations and column-beside-column comparison of appropriate alternatives, and/or graphic analysis. When cost or profit is a continuous function of the independent variable, the optimum condition can often be solved readily by calculus. When there is more than one independent variable, the solution becomes more complex; and the more difficult of these problems require higher mathematics and electronic computers perhaps.

Several typical problems involving one independent variable will be demonstrated. Three problems of the more complex type will also be described; but their solutions will not be detailed because of computations beyond the scope of this book.

Following is a broad classification of industrial economy problems that involve only one or two independent variables that determine minimum cost or maximum profit. In the list are noted the essential characteristics and the criteria for decision.

Fixed capacity, variable details of specifications, *minimum first cost* (investment)

Fixed capacity and demand, variable details of equipment, *minimum operating cost*

Fixed investment, variable rate of operations, *minimum operating cost per unit of output*

Fixed capacity and demand, variable operating schedule, *minimum operating cost*

Fixed investment, variable selling price and demand, variable rate of operations, *maximum profit*

Capacity relates to the output or service potential of a physical property. Demand refers to a product or service, which is normally expected to be in balance with the average rate of operations. *Cost* advantage may be equivalent to *profit* advantage; but, whether or not profit is pertinent or determinable, the required return on investment is an essential factor. The examples to be described do not exhaust the many possibilities for studies to maximize profit or to minimize cost. The objective here is to demonstrate the *principles* involved in the solution of such problems.

MINIMUM FIRST COST

The specification of details relating to a facility that has a stated fixed capacity is a common economy problem. It is likely that there are many optional details which make the problem a complex one. On the other hand, the alternatives may have been reduced to one critical detail, an independent controllable variable. The basis for choice is minimum first cost, the assumption being that operating cost will not be adversely affected. Examples of this situation include the spacing of supporting structures in a power line, floor beams in a building, or piers in a bridge.

A Bridge Problem

A bridge of a standard type has been used repeatedly by a state highway department. Cost estimating formulas have been developed for the superstructure, piers, and abutments in terms of span length (distance between piers) and height of piers. The situation is diagramed in Figure 14–1. In our hypothetical example, the piers are the same in height (accounted for in the formula) and are equally spaced. The cost formulas and essential data are:

L = length of bridge between abutments = 1,525 ft.

n = number of spans (optional)

$n - 1$ = number of piers

s = length of equal spans = L/n = $1,525/n$

C_a = cost of one abutment = $60s + 35,000$
C_p = cost of one pier = $75s + 70,000$
C_s = cost of superstructure for a single span
$\quad = 3.5s^2 + 400s + 5,000$

When cost is a simple function of an independent variable (n or s) as in this case, the calculus method is most reasonable for determining the optimum specification. For this purpose, n is chosen as

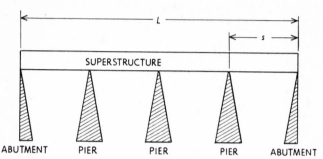

FIG. 14–1.   Diagram of a type of bridge construction.

the independent variable, and the appropriate equivalent is substituted for s in the formulas with the following results:

Two abutments = $2C_a = 2[(60)(1,525/n) + 35,000] = 183,000/n + 70,000$
Piers = $(n - 1)C_p = (n - 1)[(75)(1,525/n) + 70,000]$
$\qquad\qquad\qquad\qquad = 70,000n - 114,375/n + 44,375$
Superstructure = $n[(3.5)(1,525)^2/n^2 + (400)(1,525/n) + 5,000]$
$\qquad\qquad = 8,139,688/n + 5,000n + 610,000$
Total cost = $C = 8,208,313/n + 75,000n + 724,375$

To determine the value of n for minimum cost, it is necessary to differentiate the cost equation and equate to zero thus:

$$dC/dn = 0 = -8,208,313/n^2 + 75,000$$
$$n = \sqrt{8,208,313/75,000} = 10.46 \text{ (10 or 11 spans)}$$

The formula for C can now be used to determine the difference between 10 and 11 spans and also to estimate the cost penalty for deviations from the optimum n (which may be dictated by other considerations).

The General Case

The foregoing problem represented an ideal situation. Spans were equal in length, piers were equal in height and footing, and abutments were equal. More often, those details would vary; and the total cost could not be represented by a continuous function readily solvable by calculus. This limitation applies to many practical problems in the minimizing of cost or maximizing of profit. In the general case, dealing with one or perhaps two variables, a tabular comparison of cost or profit or a graphic solution is often appropriate.

The tabular or graphic method is based on the assignment of several alternative values to the independent variable. At the beginning, the analyst may either have no idea about the range of values that should be compared or he may have experience with similar situations that will indicate reasonable possibilities. In the first situation, it is suggested that three alternatives be chosen to start with—an extreme but possible high value, an extreme but possible low value, and one midway between. The total costs resulting from these assumptions can then be plotted (e.g., cost versus number of spans), and a tentative graph can be drawn through these points. This graph will indicate the cost trend which will serve as a guide for selection of additional alternatives. The computations and plotting of five or six alternatives, selected by this method, will probably be sufficient to identify the optimum value.

Consider the bridge problem again. Let us assume that the analyst is unable to employ the calculus method previously demonstrated

TABLE 14–1

ESTIMATED COST OF A BRIDGE
(See Page 216 for Essential Data and Cost Formulas.)

Number of spans, n	4	7	10	8	12	11
Span length, s	381.3	217.9	152.5	190.6	127.1	138.6
Number of piers, $n-1$	3	6	9	7	11	10
Cost						
Abutments:						
$60s$ ....$	22,878 $	13,074 $	9,150 $	11,436 $	7,626 $	8,316
$+35,000$....	57,878	48,074	44,150	46,436	42,626	43,316
$\times 2$........	115,756	96,148	88,300	92,872	85,252	86,632
Piers:						
$75s$........	28,598	16,343	11,438	14,295	9,533	10,395
$+70,000$....	98,598	86,343	81,438	84,295	79,533	80,395
$\times(n-1)$.....	295,794	518,058	732,942	590,065	874,863	803,950
Superstructure:						
s^2.........	145,389.7	47,480.4	23,256.0	36,328.4	16,154.4	19,210.0
$\times 3.5$........	508,864	166,181	81,397	127,149	56,540	67,235
$400s$.......	152,520	87,160	61,000	76,240	50,840	55,440
	5,000	5,000	5,000	5,000	5,000	5,000
Cost per span...$	666,384 $	258,341 $	147,397 $	208,389 $	112,380 $	127,675
$\times n$.......	2,665,536	1,808,387	1,473,970	1,667,112	1,348,560	1,404,425
Total cost	$3,077,086	$2,422,593	$2,295,219	$2,350,049	$2,308,675	$2,295,007

and that he has had no experience with this design to indicate the probable outcome of the study. For preliminary trial, the alternatives selected for the number of spans (n) are 4, 7, and 10. The tabulated results are shown in Table 14–1, and costs are plotted in Figure 14–2.

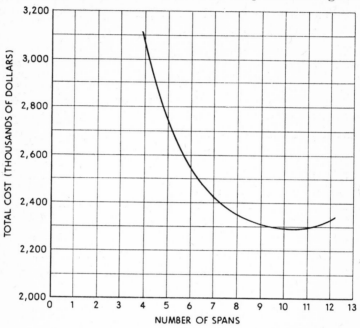

FIG. 14–2.   Cost of a certain type of bridge of specified length versus number of spans.

The tentative graph (not shown in the figure) indicates that the minimum cost will occur in the region of $n = 10$. Therefore, costs are computed and plotted for two additional values of n (8 and 12). Now, the minimum cost appears to be between 10 and 11. Computation for $n = 11$ shows an advantage for 11 spans of about $200, a negligible amount. The final graph in this region is quite flat, which shows that the cost penalties for 9 and 12 spans are also unimportant. This indication of cost differences and trends is one of the advantages of graphic analysis—important because the final decision is likely to be influenced by considerations in addition to theoretical economy.

MINIMUM OPERATING COST

Minimum operating cost is usually analogous to maximum profit. If the objective of economy study is to determine the conditions that will produce minimum cost, the effect of income taxes can be neglected because the taxes will not alter the minimum point. On the other hand, the *amount* of cost advantage or saving may be significant. Then, the income tax penalty on cost difference must be introduced into the comparison. Alternative amounts of investment, however, must always be recognized by a charge for the use of capital (required return). When investments are the same for all the alternatives, required return need not be included. Charges that are the same for all alternatives will not affect determination of optimum point.

The comments above apply to cost on a term basis (e.g., annual). When unit costs (per piece, per ton, etc.) are significant, the costs that are fixed on a time basis must always be included in the study. Such costs are not fixed per unit of output because the unit amount is in inverse proportion to the output. This will be illustrated in the following example.

Fixed Investment, Variable Rate of Operations

The relationships between elements of cost and rate of operations were discussed in Chapter 9. When variable cost increases in direct proportion to output, the unit cost will decline indefinitely. In many situations, however, the *slope* of the variable cost line varies with efficiency, changes in labor rates, changes in methods, maintenance requirements, and the like. As a result, unit cost may reach a minimum value before potential capacity of the facilities is utilized. About the best example of this is power-generating equipment. The principle applies to most machinery. Another typical case is the manufacturing plant which may incur lowered efficiency and higher labor cost when operating with night shifts or overtime. A hypothetical situation like this will be used to demonstrate the type of study.

Assume that a certain plant has a normal day-shift capacity of 100,000 units of product per month. A second shift, operated up to full time, will increase production up to 80,000 more units. The incremental potential for a third shift is 70,000 units. A cost comparison for several operating rates is tabulated below.

Units produced per month.	100,000	140,000	180,000	215,000	250,000
Operating cost per month:					
Fixed................	$ 75,000	$ 75,000	$ 75,000	$ 75,000	$ 75,000
Variable.............	200,000	305,000	410,000	507,000	604,000
Total...............	$275,000	$380,000	$485,000	$582,000	$679,000
Unit cost.............	$2.750	$2.714	$2.694	$2.707	$2.716

The comparison indicates that the lowest unit cost is obtained with two shifts operating full time. But in the operating range between 140,000 and 250,000 units, the cost difference does not exceed 1%.

Unit cost is an important criterion for decision in minimum cost problems only when the degree of plant utilization is a vital factor or when unit cost controls selling price. In the usual profit-making enterprise, annual cost and annual profit are most significant. The selling price is important. Assuming in the example that the profit margin is reasonable, operation at maximum capacity would be much more profitable than a two-shift operation, although the unit cost is greater. The effect of selling price and income will be discussed in a sequent section.

Fixed Capacity and Demand, Variable Investment

A common objective of economy study is to determine which of several alternative facilities will accomplish the same output or service at the lowest annual operating cost, including adequate return on investment. In some problems of this type the alternatives are characterized by one independent, controllable, variable factor. Familiar examples of this situation are thickness of heat insulation, size of pipe or conduit for gas or liquid, number of effects in an evaporating system, and size of electrical conductors. In these examples, the increase in size (and investment) reduces operating losses, but that gain tends to be offset by the cost of capital recovery, return on investment, property taxes, and like charges. Consider the following typical problem.

A new direct-current conductor is to serve an electrochemical process. The distance from power plant to installation is considerable. An economy study is to determine the optimum size of the copper conductor. Essential data are:

L = length of conductor to and from installation = 1,000 feet
I = average current, 24 hours, 365 days = 2,000 amperes
Cost of energy = 1.5¢ per K.W.H.
Cost of copper wire = 70¢ per pound
Salvage value of copper = 20¢ per pound
Expected life of installation = 20 years
Required net yield on investment = 10%
A = size of conductor in units of 1,000 circular mils (the optimum to be determined)

The basic formulas and cost derivations in terms of A are as follows:

Weight of conductor $= .003024LA = 3.024A$
Cost of conductor $= (.70)(3.024A) = 2.117A$
Ultimate salvage value $= (.20)(3.024A) = .6048A$
Depreciation $+$ required return (exact method) $= .2382A$
Resistance of conductor $= R = .0108L/A = 10.8/A$
Power loss (kw.) $= I^2R/1,000 = (2,000)^2(10.8)/(1,000A)$
Cost of energy loss per year $= (.015)(24)(365)(2,000)^2(10.8)/(1,000A)$
$$= 5,676,480/A$$
Annual cost $+$ required return $= .2382A + 5,676,480/A$

The optimum value of A is determined by differentiating the cost equation and equating it to zero.

$$dC/dA = 0 = .2382 - 5,676,480/A^2$$

and

$$A = 4,880$$

The optimum conductor size (4,880,000 circular mils) is equivalent to a diameter of 2.21 inches. The safe current capacity is approximately double the required 2,000 amperes. A conductor of this size could be a combination of several smaller wires or bars, if desired for convenience in installation.

The solution of this and similar problems illustrates a principle known as Kelvin's Law, which states that the condition for maximum economy of an electrical conductor is the size at which the carrying charges for investment exactly equal the cost of energy losses.

It should be recognized that additional cost factors may complicate the solution of such a problem. In this case, there are costs of installation, supports, fittings, etc., and commercial sizes of copper wires or bars. The general case can be analyzed readily by the tabular and graphic methods previously described.

ECONOMY OF LOT SIZE

The problem of lot size is common in industries that have a continuing need for some product to be provided intermittently in batches or job lots. The problem arises when the capacity to produce markedly exceeds the demand for the particular product. Consider the user of a special screw. He may need 100,000 a year, but his automatic screw machine could, if desired, turn out ten times as much. (Obviously the machine is justified only because it is also needed for other work.) If the screws were purchased, the supplier could deliver the 100,000 in a relatively short time because of capacity to produce many such orders.

If the demand for the forementioned product is highly irregular and uncertain, and if no supply is needed for contingencies, the only practical policy is to produce or purchase when orders are received. On the other hand, the demand may be reasonably predicted. Then the economy problem is this: In what lot sizes or time intervals is it best to schedule the purchase or manufacture? All of the forecasted, annual quantity could be produced at one time. At the other extreme, the item could be scheduled daily, so as to take care of the demand for each day, one day at a time. In the first instance, the production cost or purchase price would be most economical because the order-starting costs (preparation, planning, and tool setups) would be required only once a year. However, the year would start with a large inventory, which means working capital and storage cost. In the second instance, the starting costs would be repeated every day, and the inventory would be minimum or negligible. Between these extremes is a schedule that provides the lowest annual cost.

The unusual feature of this problem, one that has not been demonstrated previously, is the variability of working capital, represented by inventory. Comparing results on an annual basis, we are interested in the *average* amount of capital tied up in inventory. Inventory is expected to go up and down with income and outgo of material. The average quantity must be estimated. Its value, when associated with manufacturing, is most commonly appraised on the basis of *factory cost*. General administrative and sales expenses are usually disregarded. Factory cost includes factory overhead. The valuation aspect of the problem will be discussed presently. Let us consider the quantity situation first.

An ideal inventory situation is a uniform series of periodic cycles of income and outgo such as that represented by Figure 14–3. Actual conditions may vary from the ideal regularity to an extremely irregular pattern of build-ups and shrinkages which may not be predictable. In the figure, the minimum inventory is presumed to be an allowance for contingencies, an amount that depends on the risk and cost of possible shortages. The annual average obviously depends on the magnitude of fluctuations; and that average is reduced with increasing frequency of cycles.

The storage factor depends on storage practice. Usually there are two possible alternatives for accommodating stored inventory: (1) A space of sufficient capacity may be *reserved* for any maximum quan-

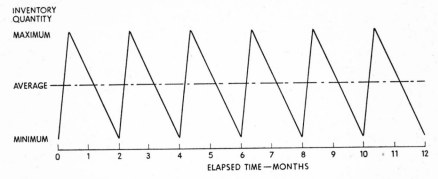

FIG. 14–3. Inventory cycles for regular periods of supply and continuous uniform rate of consumption.

tity of the item that can be anticipated; and (2) a general location may be reserved that could be occupied by several products so that the item in question will monopolize only that portion temporarily required by its quantity. In the first case, the charge for space is that required by *maximum* inventory, with an allowance for possible excesses. In the second case, *average* inventory is the proper basis for the charge.

The more difficult problem in inventory analysis is the appraisal of its average value, the basis for figuring required return on working capital. There are several accounting practices used for valuing inventory in financial statements—purchase cost, "last-in, first-out," factory cost, present market value, and the like. The most reasonable valuation for economy study is the one that most truly represents the capital tied up in the inventory. For products that have been worked upon by the plant, *factory cost* would be a reasonable basis. That cost usually includes the cost of maintaining storage facilities and related insurance and taxes. For purchased goods, the annual cost should include the purchase price plus the costs of handling the material, storage, and purchasing overhead—all of which may be considered equivalent to factory cost. It should be understood that factory cost can be replaced by some other designation (e.g., "cost of goods sold") if the inventory is not connected with the manufacturing industry. The basis for valuing the inventory is a *unit cost* derived from the annual total cost divided by the annual quantity.

An exception to the previous practice is called for by the situation where inventory is stored in a separate establishment (a warehouse, for example), so that storage cost would not be considered a part of factory overhead. Then, the storage cost would not be included in the valuation of inventory, but it would be added to the annual cost and could be subjected to an interest charge. Whether or not the storage cost is treated in this manner makes little difference in the economy of lot size.

If seasonal variations in demand were anticipated, it is possible to assume varying intervals between lots, or varying lot sizes, the object being to reduce average inventory and storage costs. This may require analyses of lot sizes or production intervals for periods shorter than a year, quarterly perhaps; but the most significant criterion is the annual result.

Annual factory cost (or that of shorter term) includes the overhead of producing and of service departments. When overhead is being charged, care must be exercised to deduct storage and starting costs that are computed separately in the analysis. The forementioned overhead may be fixed (may not vary with lot size), but it is essential for the valuation of inventory in most cases.

The required net yield on working capital should be the same as would be specified for other investments of similar risk in the enterprise. To avoid computation of increment income tax and other deductions from gross profit, it is most convenient to apply a gross yield requirement. The gross yield can include interest on borrowed capital, but it need not be affected by general administrative and expense rates unless it is known that these costs will vary with inventory.

The usual criterion for decision is annual cost plus required return. If a shorter time period is more appropriate, the yield requirement should be correspondingly reduced. *Unit* cost plus required return may be of interest in relation to prices and profit margins, but their computation is unnecessary for determining the most economical schedule. It should be borne in mind that the total cost of *one* lot is not a significant criterion; the entire program must be evaluated.

The General Case

The computations that lead to cost plus required return follow a sequence that depends on the treatment of storage cost and inventory valuation. We shall use the term *factory cost* with the understanding that a different but equivalent term may be appropriate. The analysis usually starts with the following data and assumed alternatives:

Annual demand (goods to be purchased, made, or sold)
Lot size (quantity per lot)
Lots per year
Interval between lots (months, weeks, or days)

If factory cost is the basis for inventory valuation:

Production cost per year (material, direct labor, and overhead, except
    the following items)
Starting costs per year (planning, ordering, tool setups)
Annual cost of storage (space, handling, insurance, and property taxes)
Total factory cost
Unit cost of product (factory cost ÷ annual quantity)
Cost of average inventory (based on above unit cost)
Required return (interest) on average inventory
Annual factory cost plus required return

If the item is purchased:

Annual cost of goods as purchased
Overhead except storage (purchasing, transportation, unloading, etc.—
    can be a fixed annual cost)
Annual cost of storage (as above)
Total factory cost, etc. (as above)

If inventory valuation is not to include storage, omit that item from factory cost and proceed as follows:

Annual factory cost
Unit cost of product (factory cost ÷ annual quantity)
Cost of average inventory (based on above unit cost)
Annual cost of storage
Required return on cost of inventory and storage
Total of annual factory cost, storage cost, and required return

The selection of lot sizes or schedules for comparison can be a burdensome cut-and-try proposition. Note the procedure suggested on page 217. The plotting of a graph (e.g., annual cost versus lot size) helps determine the optimum point and indicates the critical or uncritical nature of the schedule.

In a graph of cost plus required return (versus lot size, lots per year, or time interval between lots) the curve is usually rather flat near the optimum region. (See Figure 14–4.) This provides considerable latitude for decisions affected by considerations other than theoretical cost. Attention is invited particularly to the specification of intervals between lots (months, weeks, or days). The interval may be made convenient for scheduling production, but a more important advantage is that the periodic quantities can then be varied somewhat to conform with fluctuating demand. In the author's experience, the cost of deviating from uniformly repeated quantities may be relatively insignificant. A fixed lot size with variable timing is another practical possibility. Accurate determination of the best schedule for fluctuating demand is mathematically complex and beyond the scope of this discussion.

A Special Case

For scheduling manufacture, the simplest situation for analysis of lot-size economy is the following:

Uniform rate of demand (rate of withdrawals from inventory)
Uniform rate of production during production periods
Fixed cost *per unit of output,* except for starting and storage costs

This is an ideal situation, of course, particularly as to rate of demand. Inventory withdrawals that fluctuate daily can be averaged for estimating maximum and average inventory. And if demands and costs change markedly from the forecast, the schedule can be restudied and revised.

To demonstrate the solution of this problem, the following notations will be used:

a = annual demand (quantity to be produced)
w = working days per year
n = lots per year
q = lot size = a/n
t = days between lots = w/n
d = daily demand = a/w
r = daily rate of production (during production period)
g = daily accumulation of inventory = $r - d$

e = days to produce a lot = q/r
m = minimum inventory (for contingencies)
M = maximum inventory = $m + eg$
L = average inventory = $(m + M)/2 = m + eg/2$
p = unit cost of production (includes overhead except costs of starting and storage)
h = starting cost per lot (planning, setups, etc.)
s = annual cost of storage per unit of product
F = annual factory cost
c = unit factory cost
i = required gross yield on working capital

A tabular comparison of alternative lot sizes would entail computation of maximum and minimum inventories for each lot size as noted above. It is necessary to specify whether storage space is to be provided for maximum or average inventory. Now, if we assume that inventory valuation can be based on inclusion of storage cost in factory overhead, the following sequence is required:

Annual production cost = ap
Annual starting cost   = hn
Annual storage cost   = sM or sL
Annual factory cost   = F = sum of above
Unit factory cost = c = F/a
Cost of average inventory = cL
Required return (interest) = icL
Annual cost + required return = $F + icL$

For purchased goods, certain modifications in the above details may be pertinent. If deliveries from the supplier are made in one shipment per lot regardless of lot size, the maximum inventory becomes $(m + q)$. The item for starting cost (hn) would be omitted because it would be reflected in a *variable* purchase price (p), which depends on lot size. But overhead, other than storage cost, should be included either in the purchase cost or as a separate charge. Storage cost and other details would be computed as above.

Formula for Special Case

As in similar minimum cost problems, a formula for the optimum condition can be developed by calculus if the costs can be expressed as a continuous function of the independent variable. For the ideal situation previously described, a simple practical formula can be derived if certain minor factors are neglected. The minimum inventory (m) will be assumed to be zero because it will not seriously affect the optimum schedule. Substituting elemental values in the previous cost tabulation and assuming that storage facilities are to be provided for maximum inventory, the annual cost plus required return (C) becomes:

$$C = ap + hn + a(1 - d/r)(2s + ip)/2n + hi(1 - d/r)/2$$
$$+ ais(1 - d/r)^2/2n^2$$

If storage charges are to be based on average inventory, the factor ($2s + ip$) becomes ($s + ip$).

It is practical to simplify derivation of optimum schedule by deletion of the last two terms in the above formula. Both of these terms are relatively small values in most situations, and the first of them is fixed with respect to schedule. The following additional notation will also be used:

N = optimum number of lots per year
Q = optimum lot size
T = optimum time interval between lots (working days)
B = a factor in the following economy formulas

When storage space is reserved for *maximum* inventory:

$$B = a(2s + ip)(1 - d/r)/2$$

When storage charges are based on *average* inventory:

$$B = a(s + ip)(1 - d/r)/2$$

In both cases:

$$C = ap + hn + B/n$$

At minimum C:

$$dC/dn = 0 = h - B/n^2, \text{ and } n = \sqrt{B/h}$$

The optimum schedule may then be expressed as follows:

$$N = \sqrt{B/h}, \text{ or } Q = a/N = a\sqrt{h/B}, \text{ or } T = w\sqrt{h/B}$$

The above simplified formula for cost plus required return (C) is useful for determining the penalty for deviations from the optimum schedule. The total, however, will be somewhat less than what would be obtained by detailing the costs, on account of the minor factors that were neglected in deriving the formula. Note that the optimum schedule, according to the formula, is realized when $hn = B/n$, which can be verified by substituting for n the value $\sqrt{B/h}$. There are other formulas for optimum lot size, based on different assumptions as to storage charges and evaluation of inventory.

Example of a Lot-Size Problem

To illustrate the tabular method and formula, consider a hypothetical situation. A manufacturer requires a large quantity of brass bushings for a mass-produced product. The bushings are made by an automatic screw machine, which is also used for other parts. Demand is expected to be uniform and continuous. Pertinent data are as follows:

Annual demand (a) = 175,000
Working days per year (w) = 250
Production rate (r) = 3,500 per day
Production cost less starting cost and storage (p) = \$55 per 1,000
Starting cost (setup, etc.) = h = \$125 per lot
Storage cost (s) = \$1.50 per 1,000 bushings per year, based on reserving
    space for maximum inventory
Minimum inventory for contingencies (L) = 10,000
Required yield on working capital (i) = 25%, which includes allowance
    for insurance and taxes

Table 14–2 shows the tabulation of given and computed data in the sequence previously described. Figure 14–4, annual cost plus required return versus lots per year, indicates that the optimum schedule is approximately 3 lots per year.

The solution by the formula is:

$$B = (175,000)(1 - 700/3,500)(.0030 + .01375)/2 = 1,173$$
$$N = \sqrt{1,173/125} = 3.06 \text{ lots per year}$$

This agrees with the tabular method as closely as can be observed in the graph (Figure 14–4). Note that the graph shows the penalties

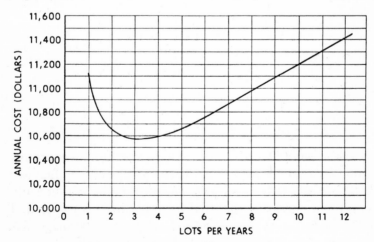

FIG. 14–4. Graphic solution of a lot-size problem—annual cost versus lots per year.

TABLE 14–2

ANNUAL COST PLUS REQUIRED RETURN FOR SEVERAL PRODUCTION SCHEDULES*

Lot size	175,000	87,500	58,333	43,750	29,167	14,584
Lots per year	1	2	3	4	6	12

Inventory

Production

Rate per day	3,500					
Demand per day	700					
Accumulate per day	2,800†					
Days per lot	50	25	16.67	12.5	8.33	4.17
Maximum accumulation	140,000	70,000	46,667	35,000	23,333	11,667
Minimum inventory	10,000‡					
Maximum inventory	150,000	80,000	56,667	45,000	33,333	21,667
Average inventory	80,000	45,000	33,333	27,500	21,667	15,833

Annual Costs

Production cost	$ 9,625	$9,625	$9,625	$9,625	$9,625	$9,625
Setup, etc.	125	250	375	500	750	1,500
Storage§	225	120	85	68	50	33
Factory cost	$ 9,975	$ 9,995	$10,085	$10,193	$10,425	$11,158
Required return‖	1,140	643	480	401	322	252
Factory cost + required return	$11,115	$10,638	$10,565	$10,594	$10,747	$11,410
Cost per 1,000	$57.00	$57.11	$57.63	$58.25	$59.57	$63.76
Cost of average inventory¶	$4,560	$2,570	$1,921	$1,602	$1,291	$1,010

* For details of problem, see page 229.
† Accumulation rate during production is the same for any schedule.
‡ Minimum inventory (for contingencies) is the same for any schedule.
§ Storage charge is based on reserving space for maximum inventory.
‖ Required return based on cost of average inventory.
¶ Average inventory value is based on unit factory cost.

for deviations from the optimum schedule; and the relative importance of these cost increments is also indicated by the tabulated figures.

The practical schedule may be different from the theoretical best for several reasons. The formula result is a good criterion. The tabulated figures and the graph indicate cost trends, which contribute to decision.

OPTIMUM SELLING PRICES AND SALES EFFORT

Up to this point it has been recognized that annual operating cost is related to rate of operations when investment or facilities are fixed. There are two conditions affecting dollar volume of sales (income) and operating cost that have not been considered. These critical factors are *selling price* and *sales effort*. Management decisions concerning these factors affect profit; and the usual business objective is to maximize that profit.

Variable Selling Price

The natural relationship between selling price and the quantity of a product that may be sold was discussed in Chapter 7. In most business enterprises, there is some latitude for pricing. The price range may be narrow for the single producer who must conform with market conditions beyond his control. It may be considerable for the large operator or the monopolistic enterprise. Price differences of competing products can be reflected in trade discounts, quantity pricing, quality differences, and accessory intangibles. Under conditions that are strictly comparable, however, it may be assumed that the quantity sold will increase with decline in unit selling price. Even if competitors should meet the price changes instituted by individuals within the industry, the market for the industry's products will be affected.

The complexities of prices and markets are specialties of the professional economist and market researcher. With or without this professional assistance, the individual seller must make price decisions. To illustrate the possibilities of economy study, we shall consider a hypothetical enterprise for which estimates have been made as to the sales potential at various selling prices.

The market forecast has indicated the following price-quantity relationship:

Unit Selling Price	*Sales Potential (Units of Product)*
$ 8	900,000 (maximum capacity)
9	600,000
10	300,000

Within these limits, this price-quantity relationship may be expressed as a straight-line formula $(q = ap + b)$. To determine the values of a and b, substitute two pairs of prices (p) and quantities (q) and solve the simultaneous equations.

$$900,000 = 8a + b$$
$$300,000 = 10a + b$$

Then, $a = -300,000$ and $b = 3,300,000$; and the formula becomes:

$$q = 3,300,000 - 300,000p$$

Income from sales in terms of selling price is:

$$I = pq = 3,300,000p - 300,000p^2$$

To *maximize profit*, the difference between income and operating cost must now be considered. The estimated fixed cost is $1,730,000, and the variable cost is $5.34 per unit of output or sale. Then, the cost formula is:

$$C = 5.34q + 1,730,000$$

This equation may be written in terms of p, based on the price-quantity formula.

$$C = 19,352,000 - 1,602,000p$$

Then,

$$\text{Profit } (P) = I - C = -300,000p^2 + 4,902,000p - 19,352,000$$

The above formula can be used to determine profit (before income tax) for various alternative selling prices (p). To determine the optimum directly, differentiate the equation and solve for the zero value thus:

$$dP/dp = -600,000p + 4,902,000 = 0, \text{ and } p = 8.17$$

At the $8.17 selling price, quantity $(q) = 849,000$ units.

We shall not analyze the profit situation further because our objective was solely to determine the price and quantity to yield maximum profit. The same result could be obtained by tabular comparison of alternative prices (and quantities) and graphic analysis. This is represented in Figure 14–5. In this example, the optimum rate of operations is slightly less than maximum capacity; but the result is about the same in the price range from $8.33 to $8.00 (from 800,000 to 900,000 units of output or sale).

Economy of Sales Effort

In the previous example, variable operating cost was assumed to be a straight line. Part of this variable cost was variable sales expense. That *variable* sales expense is in direct proportion to quantity sold is, of course, an ideal condition. Sales commissions could be in direct proportion to quantity sold. But the effects of salaried effort, promotion, advertising, and the like are subject to diminishing returns. The economy of sales effort is a most significant problem in sales management. Maximum profit is the criterion.

If the unit selling price is fixed, and if the quantity sold depends on sales effort, then income versus output will be straight-line, and the operating cost line will curve upward (assuming no change in other cost characteristics). Under these conditions, the procedure

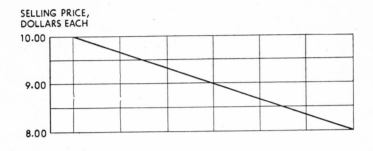

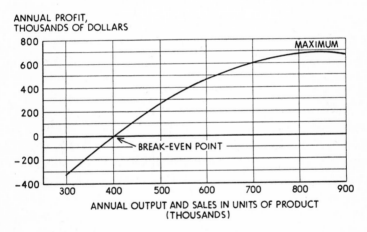

FIG. 14–5. Annual profit versus selling price and corresponding quantity of product produced and sold.

for determining optimum sales effort is similar to the preceding one. There must be a forecast of quantity sold related to expenditures for sales effort. Such a forecast is highly speculative in most practical businesses; but it is necessary if decisions are to be made for expenditures such as advertising and other promotion.

A more typical problem in sales strategy is to estimate the best combination of price structure and sales effort—a problem that is resolved by business judgment more often than not. A cut-and-try mathematical method is to determine the optimum sales effort for each of several alternative selling prices. The cost of sales effort related to quantity sold will not be the same for all price alternatives. Higher prices will require greater effort for equal quantity. The best of the optimums will correspond with the best combination of price, sales effort, and rate of operations.

Competition

Competition is a complicating factor in the strategy of pricing and sales effort. A local service station reduces the price of gasoline to obtain more business. Competitors immediately follow suit. A gasoline "war" ensues. Although the local trade may increase for all, profit from sales may decline. Then, the competitors end their "war" and prices revert to near the original levels.

In an actual case a few years ago, a manufacturer brought out a new paper punch that was superior to competing products then on the market. The device was offered at the same price as the competitors'. Quality advantage was equivalent to price advantage. Consequently, the competing firms reduced their prices. The new hunch was, unfortunately, too high in cost to permit price reduction. Its quality advantage was not obvious enough or sufficiently publicized to stimulate the required quantity of sales.

Ordinarily, decisions that relate to competitors' actions or reactions are matters of human judgment—the game of trade. On the other hand, it may be possible to rate the alternative moves of competitors in terms of numerical probability. Then, the price-sales effort strategy can be based on the maximum probability of success (i.e., profit).

The theories of probability relating to simple games of chance (e.g., coin tossing, dice, and cards) have long been known. In the 1940's, Van Neuman and Morgenstern developed additional techniques known as the *theory of games* to cover more complex situations. These techniques have already been used extensively in military tactics and strategy. They are also applicable to business competition. The method depends on ability to forecast possible alternatives, to estimate their probabilities, and to derive from these the optimum chance or profit potential. Theory of games is an advanced mathematical subject. The reader is referred to current literature on game theory and operations research.

LINEAR PROGRAMING

Linear programing is essentially a procedure for determining a "product mix" or schedule for a variety of products so as to produce maximum profit in a situation where market conditions, capacity of facilities, and availability of material sources are limited or fixed. The concept can be broadened to include services and internal operations as well as physical products that are to be sold. The term *linear* means that the relationships of the variables are straight line in character. Nonlinear characteristics are possible, but they add to the complexities of mathematical solution.

The following, relatively simple example of linear programing is condensed from a hypothetical case study published by the Esso Standard Oil Company.[1]

A Refinery Problem

The blending section of a refinery has available five streams (sources) of unblended gasoline that may be combined into various grades of a finished product. To produce two grades (M and N) of aviation gasoline with a required vapor pressure, it is possible to use a combination of four preliminary blends (A,B,C,D) obtained from the forementioned sources. These preliminary blends have different octane ratings and different production costs. The object of economy study is to determine the combination of preliminary blends that will yield the maximum profit.

The following notation is to be used in the tabulations of data and formulas:

M = a desired product (Grade 100/130)
N = a desired product (Grade 115/145)
PN = performance number (a measure of octane quality) controlled by blending
A,B,C,D = preliminary blends available
X_A,X_B,X_C,X_D = quantities not used out of amounts available
X_M,X_N = quantities not made (amounts less than demand)
X_P,X_Q,X_R,X_S = "slack" variables used in computations
Z = profit in cents per day
Cost = cost of preliminary blends in cents per gallon
Price = refinery price of finished product in cents per gallon
Avail = available quantity of preliminary blends in barrels per day (may or may not be used)
Req'd = requirement (demand) for finished product in barrels per day (may or may not be met but can not be exceeded)

The specifications, refinery (selling) prices, and requirements are as follows:

---

[1] Adapted from Gifford H. Symonds, *Linear Programming* (Esso Standard Oil Co., 1955), chap. 4. (Now out of print.)

Product Grade	PN–Lean	PN–Rich	Price	Req'd
M......100/130	100	130	16¢	2,000
N......115/145	115	145	18	2,000

The octane ratings for both lean and rich mixtures constitute the *PN* specification, expressed as 100/130 or 115/145. Higher octane values are permissible but would represent a "giveaway" of quality exceeding specifications.

The quality, costs, and availability of the preliminary blends are:

Component	PN–Lean	PN–Rich	Cost	Avail
A.........120	155	16¢	1,000
B.........110	145	15	1,000
C.........100	115	14	1,000
D......... 90	125	13	1,000

The linear equations are developed from the foregoing data. The formulas for quantity (barrels per day) are:

For blend M: $A_M + B_M + C_M + D_M + X_M = 2{,}000 = M$
For blend N: $A_N + B_N + C_N + D_N + X_N = 2{,}000 = N$
For component A: $A_M + A_N + X_A = 1{,}000$
For component B: $B_M + B_N + X_B = 1{,}000$
For component C: $C_M + C_N + X_C = 1{,}000$
For component D: $D_M + D_N + X_D = 1{,}000$

The quality relationships are expressed as inequalities to allow for possible amounts that exceed specifications.

For M lean: $120A_M + 110B_M + 100C_M + 90D_M \geq 100(M - X_M)$
For M rich: $155A_M + 145B_M + 115C_M + 125D_M \geq 130(M - X_M)$
For N lean: $120A_N + 110B_N + 100C_N + 90D_N \geq 115(N - X_N)$
For N rich: $155A_N + 145B_N + 115C_N + 125D_N \geq 145(N - X_N)$

In the right sides of these inequalities, we shall substitute the values for M and N (from the previous linear equations). Then, we shall simplify the results and introduce "slack variables" (X_P etc.) to convert the inequalities to equations (equalities) as follows:

$$-2A_M - B_M \qquad\quad + D_M + X_P = 0$$
$$-5A_M - 3B_M + 3C_M + D_M + X_Q = 0$$
$$- A_N + B_N + 3C_N + 5D_N + X_R = 0$$
$$- A_N \qquad\quad + 3C_N + 2D_N + X_S = 0$$

The equation for profit (Z in cents per day) is derived from the previous price (income) and cost data for blends (M and N) and components (A,B,C,D), with the following result:

$$Z = 2A_N + B_M + 3B_N + 2C_M + 4C_N + 3D_M + 5D_N$$

Note that there is no profit on A_M (blend M, component A) because the unit price and cost are equal.

Now we have eleven simultaneous equations and nine variables, excluding slack variables. Within the specified limits, the combinations are infinite.

To determine the combination that yields the maximum profit (maximum Z) is a problem in matrix algebra which will not be demonstrated here. The author of the original problem required eleven trials (Simplex tableaux), with the following result:

Component	Blend M	Blend N	Avail	Not used
A.............	0	1,000	1,000	0
B.............	750	250	1,000	0
C.............	500	250	1,000	250
D.............	750	0	1,000	250
Made.............	2,000	1,500		
Demand...........	2,000	2,000		
Not made.........	0	500		

The maximum profit in this case is $3,255 per day. The requirement for grade 100/130 is met, and blends A and B are used to capacity. It is not economical, however, to meet all the requirements (demand) for grade 115/145. The portions of blends C and D that are not used would be available for lower-grade gasoline.

This example illustrates a situation that typifies linear programing. The mathematical techniques are recent developments. There is a considerable body of literature on the subject. (For several suggestions, see the Bibliography in the back of this book, under Operations Research.)

ECONOMY OF WAITING TIME

Economy of *waiting time* is another problem in the minimizing of cost or the maximizing of profit. It is essentially a problem of determining an optimum combination of facilities and schedules for desired products or services. The mathematical techniques for solving this problem are often known as *queueing theory*.

Queueing is a term that applied originally to the long lines (queues) of persons waiting for service, as at cafeterias and ticket windows, and in dispensing supplies to disaster victims. The same idea applies in industrial and business operations to machines, workers, materials, and customers—any situation in which supply and demand are not uniform and continuous.

Advantages of waiting may be obvious. Facilities could ideally be provided with just sufficient capacity to care for the long-term (annual) average requirement—maximum economy in the use of fixed assets and personnel. If the sequence of production or service operations could not be made continuous, it would be possible to schedule individual operations or lots for maximum working economy—hence waiting between some operations. And during the ups and downs of demand for a finished product or service, customers would wait their turns.

Disadvantages of waiting are also potent. The amount of business may be affected by promptness of service. If inventory is built up ahead of time to ensure prompt deliveries of goods or transfers from one operation to the next, there are charges for storage and working capital (as in the lot-size problem). Elimination of waiting time means that adequate inventories would have to accumulate ahead of demand, or that facilities would have to be provided to accommodate peak demand.

The simplest of these problems is that of manufacturing management, when the capacity of facilities is fixed and schedules must be planned for specified products and operations. This is a multiple problem of lot size and timing, and maximum over-all economy is the objective. Time between lots and operations is *waiting time*. Raw materials, work in process, and finished goods wait for consumption. The complexity of the problem is in proportion to the number of variables involved.

The problem becomes more complex when customers' needs and reactions relate to waiting time. In the most favorable situation, customers' demands may be uniform and continuous. (The supplying of parts for automobile production or bakery operations are examples.) In other cases, the time required to meet a customer's occasional demand may be a vital factor in the sale. Many of us will give up going to a good show because of the long line at the ticket window. We may abandon our favorite cafeteria for the same reason. Obviously, it is extravagant to provide for immediate service at peak demand periods; but trade is lost when waits are costly to customers. For a quantitative solution of the problem, it is necessary to forecast the peaks and valleys in demand and to estimate the probability of lost business related to waiting time.

Again, we must refer the reader to literature on operations research. The potential gains in operating economy may well justify the talent and time required for mathematical analyses of these problems.

PROBLEMS

14.1. A certain cross-country transmission line is being designed. The spacing and requisite size of the supporting structures are now under consideration. For the load conditions and terrain, the cost (c) of each support related to length of span in feet (S) between supports may be estimated by the formula:

$$c = 2,500 + .004S^2$$

The other costs are independent of span length and need not be considered here.

Determine the optimum span length that should be specified. For readers unfamiliar with calculus, it is suggested that some arbitrary length of line (e.g., 5,000 feet or one mile) be chosen for comparison. Then, several span lengths between 200 feet and 1,500 feet can be tried for comparative total costs. A graph will then reveal the minimum-cost point. Assume that supports are to be equally spaced and that the actual length of the line is many miles.

14.2. An elevated highway in a large city is to be supported by bridge-like structures, which we shall term *piers*, for a distance of two miles. Although underpasses and interchanges will dictate the character of supports at several points, it is assumed that the most economical spacing of piers will be adopted for the uninterrupted stretches. In the following formulas, the cost of a single pier is designated C_p, that of a span between piers is C_s, and the span length in feet is S. These formulas were worked out for a particular highway, traffic density, elevation, and other average conditions anticipated.

$$C_p = 15,000 + 125S$$
$$C_s = 10,000 + 600S + 1.5S^2$$

For estimating purposes, assume an equal number of spans and piers in a very long total distance (e.g., 10,000 feet) disregarding the possible fractional span or pier. Determine the optimum span length.

14.3. For a broaching operation, the most economical grinding and replacement schedule for the broaching tool (a rather expensive item) is being considered. The broach is to be reground when its performance results in excessive scrap, and it must be replaced after five regrinds on account of dimensional limits in its design. Determine the appropriate schedule in hours based on the following pertinent data:

```
Cost of new broaching tool............        $250
Cost of each regrind.................         35
Rate of wear.......................... .0002 inch per hour
Cost of rejects in production increases at the rate of 25¢ per
    hour for each .0001 inch wear in the broach.
```

14.4. A large cold-storage room is being designed for a long-term project that requires a 20-year study period. The thickness of insulation is being considered. The following estimates of heat transfer for several thicknesses have been developed based on a 1,000-square foot unit of wall area and an average inside-outside temperature difference of 40° F.

Insulation, Inches	Heat Loss, B.T.U. per Hour
3	4,440
4	3,400
5	2,840
6	2,360
7	2,020
8	1,760

The cost of heat removal is estimated at .60¢ per 1,000 B.T.U., and the estimate for insulation is $125 per 1,000 square feet per inch thickness installed. The required yield on investment is 20% based on the exact method without salvage value. Assuming continuous operation throughout the year, which of the six listed thicknesses should be specified?

14.5. An automatic machine for metering and packaging a product was conservatively designed for an output of 700 units per hour. It was found possible to double this speed without failure of parts or process, but at a sacrifice of quality, other operating cost, and machine life. In order to decide on the most economical operating rate, the following estimates have been accumulated:

First cost of equipment............................	$78,000
* Estimated life of equipment operating 2,000 hours per year at rated speed........................	15 years
Salvage value at end of useful life....................	$3,000
Fixed overhead (other than depreciation)............	$10,400
Direct labor for a 2,000-hour year...................	$6,000
* Variable maintenance for 2,000 hours at rated speed..	$3,000
* Annual cost of power for 2,000 hours at rated speed...	$300
* Annual output, 2,000 hours at rated speed less .50% probable rejects...............................	1,400,000
Direct material cost per unit processed..............	6¢
* Anticipated cost of interruptions due to temporary failures of equipment (time to be recovered by overtime work)................................	$50 per year
Required yield on investment based on average interest and continuous depreciation....................	20%

The items designated by (*) are affected by operating rate according to the following theoretical estimates. Depreciation (straight line) will increase with the square of the speed. Annual output will increase directly with the speed, of course; but the percentage of rejects will increase with the square of the speed. Power cost will increase little more than directly with speed. Variable maintenance (wear) and interruptions of service are expected to increase with the square of the speed.

The criterion for decision in this case is the unit cost plus required return for acceptable output. It is assumed that the machine will be run 2,000 hours per year, interrupted operation being made up by overtime work. It is also assumed that double rated speed is the maximum to be considered. Determine, within the nearest 100 units per hour, the operating rate that should be adopted.

14.6. In connection with a water-supply project for a small city, the specification of pipe size is the immediate problem. The water source, a lake, is 200 feet below the surface of the reservoir and two miles from it. Demand on the lakeside pumping station is expected to average 3 cubic feet per second, for 6,000 hours per year. The economy study requires consideration of investment in pipe and the cost of pumping against friction head, both of which depend on pipe size. A pipe length of 1,000 feet is to be used for cost comparisons. Under these conditions, the following formula and data apply to the problem.

Friction head $(h) = 5.67/d^5$, in which d is the inside diameter of the pipe and both d and h are measured in *feet*.

Pumping cost = 1.5¢ per H.P. hour, neglecting fixed charges.

Cost of cast iron pipe = 20¢ per pound.

Life of installation = 40 years, no salvage value.

Required yield on investment = 5%, based on exact method.

The following data apply to a certain standard type of pipe and to a range of sizes that may be practical for the installation. In this list, the diameters are in *inches*.

Nominal Size, Inches	Average Inside Diameter, Inches	Average Weight Pounds per Foot
8	8.23	37.0
10	10.22	49.1
12	12.24	63.7
14	14.28	78.8
16	16.32	95.2

14.7. A price schedule is being considered for a certain company's products. It is intended to publish a price catalog that will be stable for the coming year. There is considerable latitude in the price that may be assigned to one of the company's most important items, and the sales potential will depend on that price. A market research organization predicts the following simple price-quantity relationship: 150,000 units @ $42; 100,000 @ $50; and 50,000 @ $58. It is assumed that the variable selling expense will be in direct proportion to quantity sold. The over-all operating costs (including sales expense) are expected to be as follows:

Fixed annual operating cost.................$800,000
Variable cost per unit of output and sale....... $38

Determine the optimum price and sales quota by: (*a*) the calculus method, and (*b*) the graphic method. (Suggestions: Draw a graph, price versus quantity, from which annual income at various quantities can be estimated. Draw a carefully scaled break-even chart based on five annual quantities from 50,000 to 150,000.)

If it is found possible to sell more than predicted at the optimum price, should sales be accepted beyond that quota?

14.8. The advertising budget for a nationally distributed product is being subjected to market analysis and economy study. The product's selling price is fixed by market conditions, and the quantity sold will depend mostly on sales effort represented by advertising and promotion. The results of such effort are highly speculative, of course; but the financial planning must depend on prediction of some sort. Following is the predicted relationship between expenditure for advertising and promotion and sales volume:

Sales, Pounds	Advertising and Promotion Required
16,000,000	...
40,000,000	$ 180,000
60,000,000	350,000
80,000,000	550,000
100,000,000	800,000
120,000,000	1,200,000

Other operating data are:

Fixed operating cost per year..................	$1,000,000
Variable cost other than advertising and promotion, per pound of product:	
For day-shift operation..................	9.3¢
For first night shift....................	10.3¢
For second night shift..................	11.3¢
Capacity output for each shift per year.........40,000,000 pounds	
Selling price, estimated average................ 12.5¢ per pound	

Based on the above estimates:
  a) What are the optimum quotas for advertising and promotion expenditures and for sales?
  b) What is your recommendation if the variable costs other than advertising and promotion can be reduced 10%?
  c) What is the result of a 5% increase in the above variable costs?
  d) If it is found possible to increase sales and output beyond the established quota without increasing the budget for advertising and promotion, should the increase be allowed?

14.9. A manufacturer of electrical appliances wishes to determine the most economical lot size for a knurled brass terminal nut that is used in large quantities. The essential data are:

Anticipated annual requirement......................5,400,000
Working days per year................................ 250
Production rate per day on automatic screw machine...... 200,000
Prime cost per 1,000 plus normal overhead.............. $3.50
Starting cost per lot.................................... $250
Storage cost per 1,000 nuts per year (for maximum inventory)... 10¢
Required yield on working capital..................... 24%

a) Determine the optimum lot size by the tabular-graphic method.

b) Confirm the above result by use of a formula.

c) Based on the theoretical optimum, what practical production interval without serious cost penalty would you recommend?

14.10. The cost of manufacturing a part (including direct labor, direct material, and overhead) is $2.25. The setup cost for manufacture is $20 per lot, which covers planning, machine setup, and other preparatory costs. Storage charge per piece for one year is 25¢ based on average inventory. Insurance and taxes on the value of average inventory are 5%. The plant has a working schedule of 250 days per year. Manufacturing capacity for the part is 500 per day. The demand for the part has been 75,000 per year. Management desires a minimum net yield of 10% on capital. The effective income tax rate is 55%.

Determine the most economical lot size and production interval in terms of 5-day weeks using: (*a*) the tabular-graphic method; (*b*) an appropriate formula. (PE Pa. revised)

14.11. A certain machined part is made from forgings that are furnished by a local supplier at the following price schedule:

For the first 100 forgings.....................$2.25 each
For each additional unit.......................$1.75 each

These forgings are to be finished at a standard cost for direct labor and overhead amounting to $2.10 each. The starting cost (planning, setups, etc.) for each lot is estimated at $60. There are no accommodations for storing the raw forgings; only the quantity needed for each lot of finished parts is ordered at one time; and they are to be delivered to the factory floor as required for daily production. The surplus of finished parts, however, is to be stored; and the cost of such storage is 35¢ each per year based on accommodating maximum inventory. Other essential data are:

Estimated demand per year for finished parts........6,000
Working days per year............................. 250
Rate of production per day of finished parts........ 80
Required net yield on working capital.............. 12%
Effective income tax rate......................... 52%
Insurance and property tax on value of average inventory... 3%

Determine the optimum lot size and production interval to the nearest number of 5-day weeks: (*a*) using the tabular-graphic method; (*b*) by formula.

14.12. Consider the situation described in Problem 14.11. Assume that a production interval in weeks has been adopted according to the original data. Now, after several months have elapsed, the estimated daily demand has dropped to an average of 15 finished parts per day. Determine the cost penalty on an annual basis for continuing the forementioned schedule, with appropriate reduction in lot size, of course. Hint: Compare actual annual cost plus required return for the reduced quantity with the result of the most economical schedule for that quantity.

14.13. A certain chemical compound is purchased for use as a raw material in a manufacturing plant. The clerical and accounting costs involved in making a purchase are $21 per purchase order regardless of the size of the lot purchased. It is expected that 3,000 gallons of this compound will be consumed at a fairly uniform rate during a year of 300 working days. The material is purchased and stored in 50-gallon drums. Its purchase price per gallon, including freight, is $3.30. Annual storage costs are estimated at $3.00 per drum, based on average inventory. Annual carrying charges (interest, insurance, etc.) are estimated at 16% on the value of average inventory. To assure continuous operation, at least 200 gallons should be maintained on hand at all times as an emergency stock. What is the most economical size of lot to purchase, assuming that each lot is delivered in one shipment. (PE N.Y. revised)

14.14. An economy study is to determine the most economical lot size for purchasing an item on which the quotation is as follows:

> For a minimum order of 1,000 units............$3.00 each
> For each additional unit over 1,000.............$2.40 each

Each order would be delivered to the purchaser at a rate of 200 units per day during the production period. The essential data concerning the purchaser (who uses the item in an assembled product) are as follows:

Estimated annual requirements..............	15,000
Working days per year.....................	250
Cost of processing each purchase order........	$50
Annual storage cost to accommodate maximum inventory...........................	60¢ per unit
Interest, insurance, and taxes on value of average inventory.........................	25%

Determine the desirable purchase-lot size and interval between orders, assuming that the item will be purchased in multiples of 100 units.

CHAPTER 15

Replacement Economy

E QUIPMENT may have to be replaced because it is worn out or inadequate—it will no longer do the work. In this case, the problem of decision is that of choice among competing replacements. The comparison of alternatives can then be conducted by methods that have been previously described. Pertinent factors include first cost, required yield on investment, depreciation, output, operating cost, and possible differences in income and profit potentials. Intangibles, to be discussed at the end of this chapter, are also important.

In this chapter, we are concerned with the possibility of replacement of equipment that can continue in its present service. This problem recurs constantly in all progressive enterprises. New machines or new methods that have an operating advantage over previous types become available. Industrial progress, higher costs, and competition make continual demands on management to replace the old by the newer and more productive. Increasing maintenance costs and quality problems connected with the present installation may be contributing factors.

The optional replacement of present equipment involves economic considerations that are peculiar to this type of problem. It is necessary to determine the possible advantages of one or more new alternatives (*challengers*) with the present setup (which may be termed the *defender*). Several methods of doing this are employed by engineers and managers. Some methods are simple and direct but fail to recognize several important economic factors. Others are more complicated and not commonly understood, but do more accurately predict economic advantage or disadvantage. No single method is commonly accepted or equally good for all industrial situations. The industrial engineer should be familiar with the several methods to be discussed here; and he should be in a position to adopt a good procedure that is suitable for his particular enterprise. As in other economy studies, it is necessary to present data and conclusions that are clearly understood by and conform to the policies of the executive responsible for decision.

To demonstrate and compare several methods of replacement analysis, let us assume a hypothetical situation that typifies the problem. Thirty-six gear generators of an old type are now in use. They have been completely written off to zero book value but are judged to be serviceable for at least four more years. It is proposed to replace these machines with thirteen modern automatic machines that will handle the same volume of work. The company has adopted straight-line depreciation for tax purposes, and a 50% tax rate presently applies to increments of profit. Preliminary data on defender and challenger are as follows:

	Defender	*Challenger*
First cost installed.........	...	$290,000
Present salvage value.......	$31,000	...
Expected life in years.......	4	10
Ultimate salvage value......	$9,000	$29,000

The figures given above are for the battery of machines—they are not unit values. At first, it will be assumed that defender or challenger will be operated at 100% capacity and that their outputs will be equal. Under these conditions, it will be observed that all methods of analysis will favor the challenger, but the quantitative results will vary considerably.

Bookkeeping Criteria

Conventional accounting records in the company's books may appear to provide the most obvious and simplest comparisons of performance. Thus, we may compare the present record of cost with the predicted result of replacement. The cost summary may be like this:

	Defender	*Challenger*
Direct labor..................	$ 95,000	$ 31,600
Direct material.............	13,000	13,000
Overhead...................	190,000	63,200
Factory cost................	$298,000	$107,800
Saving.....................		$190,200

The overhead rate (200% based on labor cost) is a somewhat arbitrary standard that applies to the large shop in which the subject machines are only a part.

The figures presented above have serious limitations. In fact, the overhead item is definitely misleading. If a machine-hour rate were used, the comparison would be more realistic, but that type of overhead may deviate from the firm's accounting practice. And, in any conventional type of accounting, there could be no depreciation charge against the defender. Depreciation from the accounting viewpoint does not always agree with the concept that is most appropriate for economy studies. With the exception of depreciation, details of overhead are not usually identified with individual machines or operations within a department. To reveal the true cost effect of a replacement in conventional accounting records is a difficult problem. Any executive acting on the limited information given above would, of course, relate the apparent savings to the investment required and would recognize the income tax penalty.

Capital gain or *loss* is one result of replacement that must be recognized by the accountant. This depends on the book value and actual salvage value of the defender at the time of sale. There is no capital gain or loss in accounting if the replaced equipment is relegated to lower-class work in the same outfit. For economy study, however, disposal of the defender is usually assumed to take place. In our example then:

```
Proposed salvage will realize............$31,000
Book value at that time................  ...
Capital gain..........................$31,000
```

A net capital gain in the total of a year's transactions is subject to federal income tax (25% in 1960). However, if the salvage value is actually a trade-in allowance on the new equipment, there is no capital gain or loss for tax purposes. To simplify the present example, no tax on capital gain is anticipated.

Capital gain or loss is seldom a deciding factor in a replacement study. Large capital gains or losses that may result from extensive changes in a plant may have a serious effect on the book value of the firm's assets, a matter of interest to those concerned with the company's financial standing. This problem is beyond the scope of this chapter.

Savings in Out-of-Pocket Operating Cost

All methods of replacement analysis recommended by engineering economists start with a detailed comparison of those operating costs which are immediate or direct—in contrast with the indirect or deferred costs such as distributed items of overhead and depreciation. The direct and immediate costs may be designated "out-of-pocket operating costs." To determine savings per year or per unit of output makes it *unnecessary to include any cost item that is unaffected by replacement*. Typical out-of-pocket costs are: labor, material, fringe benefits for labor, supervisory expense, maintenance, power, floor space (if in competitive demand), insurance, property taxes, and the like. The gear generator alternatives compare like this:

Operating Costs:	Defender	Challenger
Direct labor	$ 95,000	$31,600
Indirect labor	13,200	4,400
Fringe benefits	14,200	4,700
Maintenance	4,000	600
Floor space	2,000	700
Power	1,100	550
Taxes and insurance	1,250	11,100
Total	$130,750	$53,650
Savings realized by replacement		$77,100

From this point on, methods of analysis differ in their treatment of investment, required return or interest, depreciation, and time factors. The significance of the different results involves appreciation of these factors and their treatment.

Payoff Period

The simplest and most common method of appraising the significance of out-of-pocket savings is to determine how many years of such savings will be required to pay for the capital outlay. The capital required, increment investment, is usually assumed to be the difference between the salvage value of the defender and the installed cost of the challenger. In the gear generator case, the result is:

First cost of challenger	$290,000
Salvage value of defender	31,000
Increment investment	$259,000
Annual savings	$ 77,100
Payoff period in years	3.36

The payoff period calculation may be modified by inclusion of the increment in depreciation and income taxes which has the effect of reducing the savings and increasing the payoff period. Another consideration that may arise is change in productive capacity that would affect income from sales. In that case, it would be necessary to determine annual profit advantage as the basis for the payoff period. Deviations from predicted output requirements have a serious effect on the payoff period, a situation that also applies to other methods of replacement analysis. This will be discussed further in a concluding section of this chapter.

The payoff period is easy to understand, but it has conspicuous limitations. It is customary for management to establish a *maximum* payoff period, which must not be exceeded if the project is to merit consideration. It may be argued that this maximum can be based on capital recovery and return requirements and would naturally include income tax considerations. In practice, however, the maximum is established arbitrarily for large categories of facilities (for example, two years for all production machines) and without regard for differences between individual equipment items. This policy often so penalizes the challenger that more is demanded than from any other type of investment with similar risk. The payoff period appraisal has been abandoned by many progressive establishments.

Concepts of Operating Advantage and Required Return

In several chapters, comparisons of alternatives have been based on operating cost plus required return. With important modifications, the methods described previously can be applied to replacement analysis.

In replacement studies, we should disregard the depreciation rate and book value of the defender that were applicable up to the time of replacement. The book value may be more or less than disposal value. It is zero book value in the gear generator example. For comparison with a challenger, a realistic valuation of the defender is the *present* salvage value, which represents the capital that would be available for other uses if the asset is disposed of. In that sense, it is the capital actually tied up in the defender if it should be retained. This salvage value can be nil or negative—removal may cost more than the scrap is worth.

If the defender requires extensive reconditioning, beyond normal maintenance, to remain in service, the cost of reconditioning should be considered a part of the investment in the defender. If it is anticipated that a tax on capital gain will result from disposal of the defender, the amount of that tax should be deducted from the salvage value. It should be emphasized that *capital loss is a sunk cost* (water over the dam) which should be disregarded by the analyst. Sunk costs can not be retrieved by failure to realize advantage from improvements. Of course, capital gain or loss must be recorded in the accounting records.

Up-to-date appraisal of investment in the defender must usually be paralleled by a new estimate of the asset's useful life and ultimate salvage value. This provides a depreciation figure that may bear no relation to the depreciation charged in accounting. In some methods of replacement analysis (MAPI, for example), the first year's depreciation is the estimated loss of salvage value during that year without regard to remaining life and ultimate salvage estimates.

The study period, mentioned in previous chapters, can be an important decision in replacement analysis. Whether or not the study should cover the life that would be used in depreciation accounting is a controversial issue among engineering economists. There are good reasons for restricting the study to the estimated life of the defender, since replacement would be mandatory after that time. Another consideration is that capital budgets are often established on an annual basis so that replacement projects could be reconsidered year after year. The relatively short payoff periods usually called for by management also indicate the practical desirability of short study periods. It will be observed that the quantitative differences in the methods to be demonstrated are affected considerably by the study period that is adopted.

In the demonstrations of techniques that follow, the investment and out-of-pocket operating costs are the same as previously tabulated. The required economic yield is 20%, or a net of 10% after income tax. It is to be understood that operating cost items that are the same for both defender and challenger have been omitted from the cost summaries. The results of the demonstrated methods are not strictly comparable because of differences in study periods and the fact that the MAPI Chart is based on the borrowing of 25% of the required capital at 3% interest.

Studies Based on Straight-Line Depreciation and Return on Initial Investment

This type of analysis is essentially a comparison of immediate results. The comparison summarizes as follows:

	Defender	Challenger
Investment..............................	$ 31,000	$290,000
Depreciation..............................	$ 5,500	$ 26,100
Other operating costs......................	130,750	53,650
Required economic return at 20%...........	6,200	58,000
Operating cost + required return............	$142,450	$137,750
Challenger's advantage before tax............		$ 4,700
Income tax penalty at 50%.................		2,350
Challenger's advantage after tax.............		$ 2,350

Bear in mind that the "advantage" of the challenger is not profit advantage; it is more than that. In this case, the advantage is the amount *in excess of the stipulated return requirement.* The same result will be obtained by determining the saving in operating cost (depreciation included), deducting the 50% tax penalty, and comparing with the required net return at 10% on the increment of investment.

The principal criticism of the demonstrated method is the short study period which neglects time factors except as reflected in depreciation. Although the immediate result is often the reasonable criterion for decision, a forecast of several years is justified in this example. And properties such as buildings and built-in equipment would certainly deserve long-range prediction. The type of analysis demonstrated above is often less favorable to replacement than most other methods. In that sense, the indications are the most conservative.

Studies Based on Straight-Line Depreciation and Average Interest

In the following demonstration of the average-interest method, continuous (not periodic) depreciation will be assumed, and the study periods for defender and challenger will be the anticipated lives used in calculating depreciations. The comparison now appears as follows:

	Defender	Challenger
Investment..............................	$ 31,000	$290,000
Depreciation..............................	$ 5,500	$ 26,100
Other operating costs......................	130,750	53,650
Required economic return at 20%...........	4,000	31,900
Operating cost + required return............	$140,250	$111,650
Challenger's advantage before tax............		$ 28,600
Income tax penalty at 50%.................		14,300
Challenger's advantage after tax.............		$ 14,300

As in the previous case, the challenger's advantage is the profit increment in excess of required return. The required return is now based on the average investment during the life period. There would be some logic in reducing the study period to the life expectancy of the defender (four years). In that case, the average investment in the challenger will be greatly increased; and if we assume the same rate of depreciation, the after-tax advantage will be reduced to $7,470. Although required return is now modified by capital recovery during the study period, there is still no accounting for time value of money or time changes in operating advantage.

Yield Comparisons

Yield as a criterion for replacement decision is similar to a payoff period calculation that includes depreciation. The yield, however, can apply to the immediate increment in investment or to the average increment. In the latter case, the same study period should be used for both challenger and defender. The yield can be compared with a required yield representing the *minimum* that would justify replacement. In the example, required net yield (after income tax) is 10%.

	Defender	Challenger
Based on immediate investment:		
Initial investment	$ 31,000	$290,000
Increment investment		259,000
Depreciation	$ 5,500	$ 26,100
Other operating costs	130,750	53,650
Total operating cost	$136,250	$ 79,750
Challenger's advantage before tax		$ 56,500
Income tax increase		28,250
Challenger's advantage after tax		$ 28,250
Yield on increment investment		10.9%
Based on average investment (4 years):		
Average investment	$ 20,000	$237,800
Average increment investment		$217,800
Challenger's advantage after tax		$ 28,250
Yield on average increment investment		13.0%

The average investments are based on continuous straight-line depreciation for four years.

When a required yield is specified, it is important to state whether it applies to current investment or to the average for an extended study period. The greater risk in forecasting the future justifies the higher yield requirement. And, of course, a yield requirement should specify whether it is before tax and other deductions from profit (economic yield) or is the net amount.

The limitations in the yield derivations are those inherent in the two procedures previously described. The results are essentially the same. Yield, however, is often considered a more significant criterion for investment than is a statement of dollar advantage.

The Exact Method

In the "exact" method, time value of depreciation and required return are accounted for. When the two values are combined $(D + R)$, the result is the same for any method of depreciation. If it is necessary to identify depreciation separately, the customary amount (straight line, for example) can be deducted from the calculated $D + R$ to determine required return. For formulas and derivations, see Chapter 8.

In a time value calculation, the study period (n in the formulas) is critical, especially at high interest rates. Therefore, it seems most reasonable to adopt equal study periods for both challenger and defender and to assign a realistic short-term salvage value to the challenger. In our gear generator example, the study period will be four years, and the challenger's salvage at the end of that period will be based on the previously computed depreciation rate. The required return is the time-computed value (by the exact method) less straight-line depreciation. The interest rate is the net required yield (10%). Results are as follows:

	Defender	*Challenger*
Initial investment	$ 31,000	$290,000
Salvage value in 4 years	9,000	185,600
Operating cost less depreciation	$130,750	$ 53,650
Depreciation	5,500	26,100
Total operating cost	$136,250	$ 79,750
Income tax increase		28,250
Required return	2,341	25,398
Total cost + required return	$138,591	$133,398
Challenger's advantage		$ 5,193

The challenger's advantage (net after income tax) is, of course, the amount in excess of required return. The increment income tax charged to the challenger is 50% of the challenger's saving in total operating cost.

MAPI Method

The MAPI (Machinery and Allied Products Institute) method is considered by many to be the most accurate procedure for appraising the economy of equipment replacement. Like the other methods previously demonstrated, it develops results that must be properly interpreted by the executive. The procedure was introduced in 1949 as the result of a program conducted by the Institute's research director, George Terborgh. Mr. Terborgh's book, *Dynamic Equipment Policy*, 1949, describes the somewhat complex theory that should be appreciated by users of the system. The latest MAPI manual, *Business Investment Policy*, 1958, is an essential guide for practical applications. These references must be studied by persons interested in the method. The following discussion is necessarily limited.

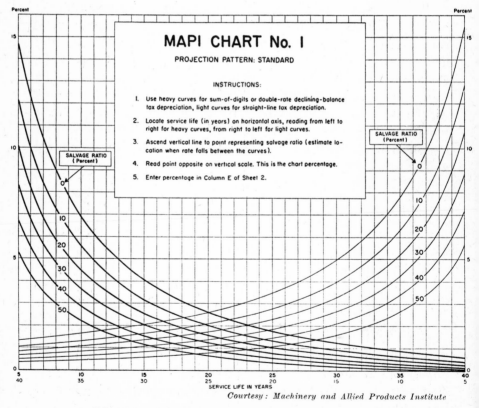

Courtesy: Machinery and Allied Products Institute

FIG. 15–1.   One of the MAPI charts for replacement analysis.

The MAPI procedure is essentially a conventional comparison of the next year's costs with a time-valued adjustment to account for the challenger's depreciation and anticipated decline in operating advantage during its life. In the simplified method, the adjustment is a percentage of the challenger's first cost. This percentage is read from a graph (the MAPI chart) according to the anticipated life and salvage ratio (ratio of salvage value over first cost). There are three of these charts to accommodate different aging characteristics. The chart most commonly used is shown in Figure 15–1. The chart readings are compromises, however, in that they are based on certain assumptions. It is assumed that the interest rate (for time value) is 10%, that the income tax rate is 50%, and that 25% of the capital is to be borrowed at 3%. It is also assumed that the rate of decline in operating advantage is an average within a considerable range of possibility. Correction factors are listed in the manual for tax rates other than 50%.

The MAPI manual recommends a set of forms for summarizing the essential data and calculations. In the demonstration of the gear generator case, we show a condensed tabulation that suits this problem. (See Table 15–1.)

To many executives, the disadvantage of the MAPI method is the study that is required for comprehension and for checking the MAPI charts against anticipated conditions in the industry. Otherwise, the charts must be accepted on faith. Mr. Terborgh states that the chart assumptions are not critical. However, special sets of graphs can be prepared to conform with unusual conditions; but the required calculations are complex and extensive.

Endowment Method

The principles of comparing alternatives by the endowment method were discussed at length in Chapter 13. The present worth of the financial events that take place during the study period represents a hypothetical endowment that would be required to support the project. The aggregated present worth can be converted to an annual equivalent, the average annual amount that could be supported by the endowment. This provides a figure that is comparable to those obtained by other analytical methods.

In applying this method to a replacement study, certain conditions should be mentioned that also apply to other types of projects. The method is most appropriate for long-term studies. The interest

TABLE 15-1

SUMMARY, REPLACEMENT STUDY OF GEAR GENERATORS

Required Investment

1. Installed cost of project (challenger).....................$290,000
2. Disposal value of assets to be retired (defender)........... 31,000
3. Net investment required...................................$259,000

Next-Year Advantage from Project

	Increase	Decrease
4. Direct labor.......................................		$63,400
5. Indirect labor.....................................		8,800
6. Fringe benefits....................................		9,500
7. Maintenance..		3,400
8. Floor space..		1,300
9. Power..		550
10. Taxes and insurance on property...................	$9,850	
11. Totals..	$9,850	$86,950
12. Next-year operating advantage.....................		77,100
13. Next-year capital consumption avoided by project (defender's depreciation)....................		5,500
14. Total next-year advantage (item 12 + 13).........		$82,600
15. Income tax (50% of item 14)......................		41,300
16. Net advantage after income tax...................		$41,300

Computation of Urgency Rating

17. MAPI chart reading (for 10-year life and 10% salvage ratio)... 6.35%
18. MAPI chart allowance for project (item 1 × 17)............$18,415
19. Available for return on investment (item 16–18)...........$22,885
20. Urgency rating (item 19 ÷ 3)............................ 8.84%

Notes:

Items 4 to 10. Differences in itemized costs listed on page 248.

Item 13. This depreciation is the best estimate for the coming year and need not agree with estimates for years to follow or with accounting practice.

Item 14. Observe that no allowance is made as yet for challenger's depreciation or required return.

Item 20. This figure is actually the net yield on the increment investment. It is a figure that rates this project in comparison with competing demands for capital. Since the amount is less than the previously specified required yield (10%), the project would probably be deferred.

rate used in the time value calculations should be the required net yield (after income taxes and other deductions from economic return), so that required return is thereby included in the endowment. The study period must be the same for both defender and challenger unless the annual equivalents are to be used for decision. The financial events evaluated should be confined to the expenditures actually anticipated. Consequently, depreciation is taken care of in the initial investment and in the present worth of hypothetical replacements at their net future costs. Ordinarily, the endowment represents cost. If income items are included in the study, they would be opposite in sign to the expenditures. Salvage values at the end of the study period are credits (negative costs). Remember that the annual

equivalent of the total endowment requires a time value calculation; it is not the endowment divided by the number of years.

The gear generator case is not particularly suited to the endowment method, as would be a building or a bridge; but it will be used
for demonstration here to compare with the other procedures. In
order to demonstrate a study period that is prolonged and equal for
defender and challenger, it is assumed that the defender can be
replaced periodically by equipment equal to the original in value, at
a replacement cost of $22,000 net. The study period is 20 years,
which is the least common multiple of the lives of the contenders.
The challenger is to be replaced at ten-year intervals at a net cost of
$261,000. The annual operating costs (less depreciation) are the
figures previously used. The annual charge of $28,250 against the
challenger for tax increase is based on annual operating cost saving
including straight-line depreciation. The interest rate is 10%. Summarized results are:

Present worths	Defender	Challenger
Initial investment	$ 31,000	$ 290,000
Replacement in 4 years	15,026	
Replacement in 8 years	10,263	
Replacement in 10 years		100,616
Replacement in 12 years	7,009	
Replacement in 16 years	4,787	
Salvage value in 20 years	−1,337	−4,309
Annual operating costs less depreciation	1,113,206	456,776
Annual income tax increment		240,521
Total endowment	$1,179,954	$1,083,604
Challenger's endowment advantage		96,350
Challenger's annual advantage		11,319

It should be understood that the annual equivalent advantage is
an amount in excess of required return and capital recovery, as in
the exact method. If capital were borrowed, that amount would be
deducted from the first cost of the challenger; and the challenger
would be charged with annual interest on the loan and payments on
principal when due. The income tax penalty would then be somewhat reduced by the interest charge, which affects the taxable profit.
Without borrowing, the same annual advantage would be obtained,
in this case, by the exact method using study periods equal to the
lives of defender and challenger.

The principal limitation of this method is the uncertainty of long-
term forecasting. And there is no allowance for probable decline in
the challenger's future operating advantage as in the MAPI procedure.

Comparisons Based on Output

Up to now, the defender and the challenger were assumed to handle the same volume of work. It has also been assumed that the required output was a definite fixed amount. Neither of these stipulations may fit the actual situation. The challenger may have greater potential which can be utilized; there may be a market for greater output. And it is possible that replacement would involve reduced capacity to accommodate less demand for product. But, more often, the output requirement is highly speculative and within a considerable range of possibility indicated by a market forecast. Let us consider the first of these situations. Variable output will be discussed presently.

Assume that the challenger has greater capacity and that its potential can be utilized. If total operating cost and required return were used as the sole criterion for decision, the challenger may appear at an unreasonable disadvantage. The best criterion is the change in profit (in relation to investment) that will result from replacement, a determination that depends on output that is assumed to be sold. If the profit attributed to a particular process or piece of equipment is difficult to determine, a sufficient indicator for management may be the unit cost plus required return. These two determinations deserve further explanation and illustration.

In a typical replacement problem, comparison of profit and yield on increment investment requires the introduction of income—specifically, that portion of total income from sales that can be allotted to the particular process or machine. This allocation of income may be exceedingly difficult or necessarily arbitrary. Of course, if outputs of defender and challenger were equal, the change in operating cost adjusted for tax increment would represent change in profit. Assuming that income can be estimated per unit of output, the summarized analysis may take the following form:

1. Operating cost for defender and challenger at predicted outputs.
2. Apportioned incomes based on outputs.
3. Economic returns from defender and challenger.
4. Gain (or loss) in economic return due to replacement.
5. Increment in income tax or other deductions from profit.
6. Net gain (or loss) from replacement.
7. Yield on increment investment.
8. Compare with required yield.

As an alternative, the net gain or loss can be compared with required return. Required return or yield can be computed by methods previously described. The MAPI procedure provides for inclusion of increment income by including it in the next-year's operating advantage. An increase in income may more than offset increase in cost.

Another possibility that is somewhat unusual is the condition in which the challenger's capacity is a multiple of the defender's. In that case, it could be assumed that the defender's capacity could be made equal to the challenger's by the purchase and installation of additional old equipment valued the same as the original defender (a hypothetical assumption). Then, the procedures previously described will serve for comparison, without the inclusion of income estimates which would be equal.

To illustrate the profit comparison, let us refer to the gear generator replacement again. Assume that only one of the old machines is to be replaced by the automatic and that full capacity output is predicted. Although these machines accommodate a considerable range of work, the income and output potentials will be based on the one most typical of the products encountered. Income apportionments are difficult because other machines and operations contribute to production; and there are overhead costs that relate to volume of output. In this case, the same percentage of selling price applies to both contenders. The average-interest method with straight-line depreciation and four-year study period will be used. Without detailing the costs, the essential data and calculated results are as follows:

	Defender	Challenger
Initial investment	$ 860	$22,300
Salvage value in 4 years	$ 250	$14,272
Average investment	$ 555	$18,286
Average increment investment		$17,731
Output at 100% capacity, units	5,000	14,000
Income apportioned	$4,000	$11,200
Depreciation	$ 153	$ 2,007
Other operating cost	3,630	4,125
Total operating cost	$3,783	$ 6,132
Income	4,000	11,200
Economic return	$ 217	$ 5,068
Income tax at 50%	109	2,534
Net profit	$ 108	$ 2,534
Gain from replacement		$ 2,426
Yield on average increment investment		13.7%
Required yield on average investment		10%

In the example, it is apparent that total operating cost would be unfair to the challenger, particularly if required return were included. It is also evident that the apportionment of income is critical. Higher unit prices will favor the contender with greater output, and there is a price situation at which two such alternatives would be equal. Variable price situations will be discussed presently.

Now consider the foregoing example without assumed apportionment of income. To some managers, a comparison of unit costs plus required return may be sufficient. More significant perhaps is the unit operating cost saving applied to the *greater* output, an amount that can be compared with required return. Neither of these procedures will reflect the price and income conditions. However, the two methods will be demonstrated using the data tabulated above. The required return is based on average investment for the four-year study period.

Comparison of Unit Cost + Required Return	*Defender*	*Challenger*
Output at 100% capacity.	5,000	14,000
Total operating cost.	$3,783	$ 6,132
Required return at 20% (before tax).	111	3,657
Operating cost + required return.	$3,894	$ 9,789
Unit operating cost + required return.	77.9¢	69.9¢

Comparison of Savings versus Required Return		
Total operating cost.	$3,783	$ 6,132
Unit operating cost.	75.7¢	43.8¢
Saving in unit cost.		31.9¢
Saving on 14,000 pieces.		$ 4,466
Income tax increase.		2,233
Net saving on 14,000 pieces (after tax).		$ 2,233
Required net return at 10% (after tax).		1,773
or		
Net yield on increment investment.		12.6%

Break-Even Chart Applications

Uncertainty of required output is a common risk in the forementioned types of replacement study. Market forecasts may indicate a considerable range in demand. On the other hand, it may be assumed that output can be maintained at a fixed level, and the market forecast may indicate a price range or pattern that would be required to dispose of that fixed output. These and other possible variables complicate replacement study. Of course, studies can be made such as have been described for various sets of conditions. Tabular comparisons like these can become cumbersome. And if more than one independent variable is involved, the studies may require complex mathematical procedures to determine break-even point, cost, and profit patterns.

The break-even chart is a useful device for a study dealing with one independent variable. The independent variable may be any item that affects the result, such as investment cost of replacement, labor cost, output demand, and selling price. The appropriate dependent variable may be: operating cost plus required return, challenger's advantage (designated in some way), profit, yield, payoff period, unit cost, and the like.

Figure 15–2 is a break-even chart that applies to the multiple gear generator replacement under variable output requirements. Operating cost plus required return is plotted against output in terms of per cent capacity. Required return is figured by the exact method (see tabulation, page 253). Operating costs at zero output (fixed costs) were not previously mentioned. They are summarized below. The income tax increment is negative at zero output, being 50% of the defender's advantage in operating cost. The essential data for chart construction follow.

For the Defender	*At Zero Output*	*At 100% Capacity*
Total operating cost....................	$19,400	$136,250
Required return........................	2,341	2,341
Total operating cost + required return.....	$21,741	$138,591
For the Challenger		
Total operating cost....................	$45,780	$ 79,750
Income tax increment...................	−13,190	+28,250
Required return........................	25,398	25,398
Total operating cost + tax + required return	$57,988	$133,398

In the chart, the broken line indicates for the challenger the operating cost plus the income tax increment, which is negative below the no-gain no-loss break-even point. The calculated break-even points (confirmed by the chart) are 31.8% at no-gain no-loss, and 87.4% at required return. Evidently, the replacement is not justified unless production above 87.4% of capacity is a good speculation.

Intangibles

As in other management decisions, replacement problems have intangible aspects that may have sufficient weight to control the decision. Many intangibles encountered in replacement projects are similar in character to those involved in the selection of fixed properties in any substantial enterprise.

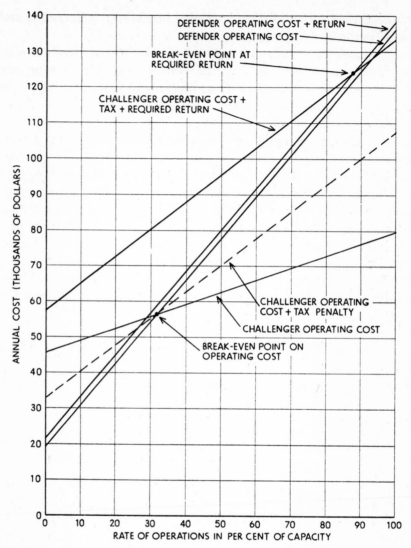

FIG. 15–2. Economy of machine replacement—annual operating cost plus required return for defender and challenger versus rate of operations.

Intangibles in replacement analysis may include: competing needs for capital, future uncertainties in market and costs, possibilities of product change, financial condition of the business, attitudes and limitations of personnel, labor shortage or surplus, ethical and social problems, and like factors. Intangibles are notably reflected in two of the quantitative factors used in the procedures that have been demonstrated, the study period and the required yield on investment.

The considerations involved in the selection of study period and specification of required yield have been discussed in this chapter and previous ones. Attention is invited again to the intangibles. The two quantitative factors mentioned above may be related. The risks of forecasting the future can be reflected by increasing the yield requirement according to the remoteness of events. Risk is a conspicuous element in required yield or payoff period. Other intangibles in required yield include competing needs for capital, demands for return by potential investors, needs for borrowing, returns expected from similar ventures in the enterprise, business forecasts, and policies that may impose limitations on profit.

A feature of the typical replacement problem is that it can be reconsidered year after year until replacement becomes mandatory. This tends to encourage decisions based on the next-year's results, and underrates the long-term effects of replacement. Even the MAPI method arrives at a next-year's advantage, but it is modified by the MAPI chart percentage which is an adjustment covering the life of the challenger. Except for projects that are obviously long term (such as buildings, power plants, and bridges), management policies usually dictate short-term studies for replacements. Unless the life of the project is known to be short, risk (future uncertainty) is the most important intangible affecting the study period.

PROBLEMS

15.1. A bulldozer used in a power plant for leveling and tamping in its outside coal storage yard cost $16,000 initially and has been in use for three years. When purchased, its estimated life was four years. A decision must be made at once whether to trade in the present bulldozer for a similar unit of the same initial cost or whether to keep the old unit for another year.

The following information was obtained from company records for the first three years and by estimate for the fourth year.

	1st year	2d year	3d year	4th year
First cost..............................	$16,000	...	...	...
Depreciation (straight line).............	4,000	$4,000	$4,000	$4,000
Trade-in value........................	...	...	5,000	3,000
Operating cost........................	8,000	8,300	8,800	9.300
Repairs..............................	640	1,280	2,400	2,720
Losses from breakdowns and interruptions....................	960	3,200	6,400	7,200

Assuming that a 15% return is required to justify purchase, should a new unit be purchased or should the old one be retained? (PE N.J.)

15.2.   A three-story loft building is to be converted into or replaced by a storage warehouse. The alternatives are to strengthen the existing structure at a cost of $12,000, or to replace it by a new building at a cost of $65,000. The present salvage value of the old building is $9,000. The strengthening is assumed to be satisfactory for ten years, at which time the salvage value of the strengthened building will be $12,000. The new building will have a life of 35 years and a salvage value of $25,000. Maintenance, upkeep, etc. for the old building is $9,800 per year; the same items for the new building will cost $8,500 per year. All costs not mentioned are the same for both projects.

Assume interest at 15% (based on the exact method) using a ten-year study period and straight-line depreciation. Would it be cheaper to build a new building or to strengthen the old one? (PE Pa. revised)

15.3.   An industrial concern obtains its water from a system of wells. They are using a six-inch, single-stage, centrifugal pump that is in good condition. The pump was purchased three years ago for $1,350 and has a present book value of $1,005. Owing to improvements in design, the present demand for this type of pump is so small that its present sale's value is only $500. It is estimated that the pump could serve for seven more years, at which time the trade-in value would be $200. An improved pump of the same type can now be purchased for $1,700 and will have an estimated life of ten years with a trade-in value of $200 at the end of that time.

The pumping demand is 225 cubic feet per minute against a head of 200 feet. The old pump has an efficiency of 75% at that load. The new pump's efficiency is 81% at the same output. The motor driving the pump in either case operates at an efficiency of 85%. Power costs 1.5¢ per K.W.H. The demand is for 4,000 hours per year.

Assuming that the required yield on investments of this type is 12% based on the average interest method, is the purchase of the improved pump justified? (PE Ohio revised)

15.4.   A manufacturer purchased a machine five years ago for $65,000 expecting it to serve 12 years and to have a salvage value of $2,000. The annual operating cost (other than depreciation) has averaged $15,000. It is now anticipated that the machine will serve another six years with the same ultimate salvage value. A new machine can be purchased now for $85,000, with a trade-in allowance of $25,000 on the old machine. It is estimated that it would have a life of 12 years with $3,000 salvage value. Its operating cost (excluding depreciation) is expected to be $9,000 per year. Property taxes and insurance are at 2% based on first cost. Required return on investment is at 10% net. The increment income tax rate is 55%.

Determine the advantage or disadvantage of the replacement, based on a six-year study period and time value. Assume that the value of the new machine in six years would be the straight-line book value. (PE Pa. revised)

15.5.   A privately owned automobile five years old now has a trade-in value of $900, which is expected to decline to $720 next year, $575 the following year, and $460 at the end of the third year. A new car would cost $3,000, and its depreciations for three years are estimated at $700, $450, and $370. In addition to depreciation and neglecting costs that would be the same for the old or new car, the following annual cost estimates apply to the next three years. These costs are based on 10,000 miles per year and the anticipated major replacements (such as tires) and repairs.

	Year 1	Year 2	Year 3
Old Car:			
Gasoline	$250	$260	$270
Repairs, etc.	270	210	370
Insurance	55	50	45
New Car:			
Gasoline	$225	$225	$230
Repairs, etc.	75	120	205
Insurance	75	75	70

Determine whether or not to replace the car, using interest on an average annual car valuation at 6% and a three-year study period. What intangible considerations would ordinarily affect such a decision?

15.6.   To undertake production of a new product, an inventor purchased a simple machine that required much hand labor. The machine cost $4,400 and was estimated to have a useful life of five years, at the end of which there would be no salvage value. Annual operating costs exclusive of depreciation and interest were $2,600. Now, at the end of the first year, the inventor is urged to purchase a semiautomatic machine for $6,200, which could match the production of the first machine and which would have an annual operating cost of $800, exclusive of depreciation and interest. Trade-in value of the first machine is $1,600. The new machine is estimated to have a life of four years and no salvage value.

Using an interest rate of 8%, calculate the difference in equivalent annual cost for the two machines, and state which machine should be used for the next four years. (PE N.Y.)

15.7.   Fourteen years ago a 1200-kw. steam-electric plant was constructed at a cost of $220 per kilowatt. Annual operating expenses have been $43,100 to produce the annual demand of 5,400,000 K.W.H. It is estimated that the same amount of operating expenses and demand for current will continue. The original estimate of a 20-year life with a 5% salvage value is still expected to be correct.

The company is contemplating the replacement of the old steam plant with a new diesel plant. The old plant can be sold now for $75,000. The new diesel plant will cost $245 per kilowatt to construct. The diesel plant will have a life of 25 years with a salvage value of 10% at that time; and it will cost $23,000 annually to operate. Annual property taxes and insurance will be 2.3% of first cost of either plant.

Using an interest rate of 12% with the exact method, determine whether the company is financially justified in replacing the old steam plant now. (PE N.Y. revised)

15.8.   In a manufacturing plant producing engine parts, the industrial engineer is considering replacing a ten-year-old lathe with a new one of special type. Orders are expected to continue the same as now, which keep the old lathe busy the full year of 2,000 hours. Any labor saved by the new tool can readily be used elsewhere in the plant. The effective wage scale for the operator of either lathe is $2.40 per hour. Production on the present lathe for an average piece has been 60 pieces per hour. On the new lathe, the production rate is estimated at 90 pieces per hour, which reduces the direct labor costs about 33.3%.

Spoilage on the present lathe has been about 3%. It is believed that the new lathe will reduce this to about 1%. For the purpose of economy study, the cost of spoilage is to be estimated as a percentage of direct labor plus direct material costs with no allowance for indirect manufacturing expense. Annual direct material cost for these parts is $30,000 at present.

The annual cost of maintenance and repairs is estimated at $200 for the old lathe and $60 for the new one; supplies at $100 for the old lathe and $50 for the new; and power costs at $120 and $80 respectively. Property taxes and insurance average 3% of first costs. Other annual costs (excepting depreciation) are unaffected by the choice of lathes.

The original cost of the old lathe was $8,000. It has been depreciated on the books at $350 per year, but its present resale value is only $3,500. It now is estimated that its future worth will decline at $500 per year. The new lathe will cost $12,000 installed and is expected to depreciate to $2,000 salvage value in 15 years.

If a study period of five years and average interest at 20% is used, what is the advantage of replacement? (PE Pa. revised)

15.9.   It is proposed to replace two old-style machines with one new high-speed machine that has 50% greater capacity than the old combination. The two old machines are now being run full time for one shift (2,000 hours per year). At the same output, the one new machine would require only 1,333 hours, and its operator would be used for other work at other times. Following are the essential data concerning investments and operating costs:

	Defender (2 Machines)	Challenger (1 Machine)
Cost installed	$20,000	$50,000
Original life estimate in years	15	...
*Original salvage estimate	$ 2,000	...
Present age in years	12	...
*Present value estimate	$ 4,000	...
Present life estimate in years	4	15
*Present estimate of ultimate salvage value	$ 1,000	$ 5,000
*Estimated removal cost	$400	$300
Direct labor rate including fringe benefits:		
Regular day shift per hour per machine	$3.00	$3.00
Night shift per hour per machine	$3.50	$3.50
Electric power per hour per machine	10¢	15¢
Variable maintenance per hour per machine	25¢	75¢
Fixed maintenance per year	$600	$400
Floor space per year	$300	$225

The salvage value estimates (*) are resale or trade-in values and do not include removal costs. Costs that are not listed above are unaffected by replacement. The required economic yield on this type of investment is 22%, based on a four-year study period, continuous depreciation, and average interest. *Each* of the old machines requires an operator at the rates mentioned.

a) Determine the advantage or disadvantage of the challenger if the present rate of production is continued.

b) Now, assume that demand actually increases 50%, which can be be handled by the challenger in one shift, but which will require one of the old machines to run during a night shift. Compare the two alternatives under these conditions.

c) Draw a break-even chart comparing defender and challenger and determine the hours of annual demand at which the choice is equal. If necessary, the hours can be extended up to three shifts (6,000 hours per year).

15.10. Reconsider Problem 15.9 at the 50% increase in annual demand by the following methods of analysis:

a) Payoff period required to recover investment based on out-of-pocket savings in operating cost.

b) MAPI method using the chart, Figure 15–1, and assuming straight-line depreciation. List the chart assumptions that differ from the conditions stated in Problem 15.9, and state how these will affect the "urgency rating."

15.11. A certain construction company is now using steel wheelbarrows with steel-tired wheels. Wheelbarrows with pneumatic tires and aluminum bodies can be purchased for $45 each. It is possible that men operating the new unit will not only carry a greater load but will also quicken their pace.

The steel units now in use were purchased three years ago at a cost of $20 each. They can now be disposed of at $5.00 each; but if continued in use, they should serve for two more years, when they could be salvaged at $1.25 each. From the records, it is found that the wheelbarrows have been in operation an average of 300 hours per year at a labor cost of $1.50 per hour. The new units have an expected life of five years and an ultimate salvage value of $8.00 each. Required return on investment in equipment is at a rate of 15% based on the exact method.

Compute the following:

a) The number of hours of actual operation per year at which the choice is equal.

b) The percentage increase in output per hour that would justify the purchase of the new units as compared with 300 hours per year for the old units. (PE Pa. revised)

15.12.   An automated production line is proposed to replace a more conventional work station and conveyor setup for the fitting of parts and the assembling of a product. The book value of the present equipment is $10,000; but dismantling would cost at least $600, and the actual scrap value would not exceed that amount. The automatic equipment would cost $150,000 installed. Its expected life is ten years to an ultimate salvage value of $15,000. Annual operating costs for the defender and challenger have been estimated for the present output of 75,000 assemblies per year, neglecting costs unaffected by the change.

	Defender	Challenger
Direct labor and fringe benefits	$42,500	$6,875
Floor space	1,200	600
Power	500	1,100
Variable maintenance	450	750
Fixed maintenance	700	850
Insurance and property tax	300	4,500

The foregoing estimates are based on 75,000 assemblies per year which require 250 eight-hour days for the old equipment. The automatic equipment would handle the same output in 250 five-hour days. If demand reached the potential output of the challenger, it would be necessary to extend the old setup at a cost of $9,000, an investment with zero salvage value in five years. Labor, power, and variable maintenance are assumed to be in direct proportion to annual output for both systems. The extension of the old system would add 50% to area, fixed maintenance, insurance and property tax. Required yield on investment is 24% (before income tax), based on a five-year study period and the exact method.

    a) Determine the advantage or disadvantage of the challenger at the present output.

    b) Determine the above at the eight-hour-day potential of the challenger versus the old setup extended.

    c) Make a break-even chart representing the entire range of output up to the 2,000-hour capacity of the challenger. Indicate the demand, in assemblies per year, at which the two systems would be equal in economy.

15.13. A company maintains a fleet of light delivery and pick-up trucks that average 22,000 miles each per year. An economy study is being made to determine the age, up to a maximum of five years, at which trade-in should be negotiated. The standard for comparison is a new truck that now costs $2,500. The estimated depreciation rates on a declining balance basis are 25% the first year, and 20% per year thereafter, which is assumed to approximate the trade-in values. The following operating costs have been experienced and are expected to continue.

Average fuel consumption, miles per gallon	14
Average cost of fuel per gallon	29¢
Lubrication and inspection per 1,000 miles	$3.50
Tires every 30,000 miles	$90
Batteries every two years	$25
Brake linings every 25,000 miles	$35
Engine overhaul at 50,000 miles	$100
General overhaul at 100,000 miles	$150
Miscellaneous maintenance:	
1st year	$50
2d	$100
3d	$150
4th	$200
5th	$250
Miscellaneous other variable costs per mile	1¢
Miscellaneous yearly fixed costs other than depreciation	$85

Assume that any of the major expenses or replacements noted above would take place during the year indicated by mileage.

The criterion for decision is the age in full years at which the time-valued, equivalent annual cost (or cost per mile) is the lowest. Use the present worth (endowment) method with required yield at 20%, before income tax allowance.

CHAPTER 16

Ownership and Financing

THE economy study of a complete enterprise must take into consideration the financing problem and the interests of financial participants. Proposals for major investments within any enterprise may involve similar considerations.

The assets of a business are contributed to and shared by three groups of participants, whose interests are listed as liabilities in the balance sheet. These are:

1. Commercial creditors and others to whom the firm has short-term obligations—obligations identified as *current liabilities.*
2. Long-term lenders whose loans are not currently due for settlement —obligations represented by outstanding bond issues, mortgages, and other long-term debt.
3. Owners (proprietor, partners, or stockholders)—the legal possessors of the enterprise, whose shares are represented by the *net worth* of the business.

In banks and insurance companies, there are major liabilities to depositors and policyholders. And there may be reserves for retirement funds and similar long-term obligations. But, in general, the financial structures of industrial enterprises are indicated by the items classified above.

Participation in financing and ownership is tied in with the operating obligations, the division of proceeds from operations or from liquidation, and the sharing of risks in the venture. Creditors or lenders of funds are "outsiders." They participate in the proceeds of operations by collection of interest on debt, amounts that are due whether profit to owners is realized or not. The rights of owners to profit or division of assets are subordinate to those of the lenders and other creditors, whose claims must be met first. Individually or collectively, and directly or indirectly, the owners are responsible for operations. In the control of operations, the owners are, or may be represented by, top management—except under unfavorable conditions that may call for interference by creditors or government.

Ownership

Every enterprise starts with some individual or group who may be termed promoters. From their viewpoint, the following factors have a bearing on the form of ownership and type of financing:

Amount of capital required.
Availability of capital and sources.
Cost of obtaining capital.
Effects of financing on immediate and ultimate profit.
Risks to financial stability and income.
Risks to ownership and control.
Operating responsibility desired.
Demands for share in ownership or control by those whose funds or talents are desired.
Ambition for growth.
Marketability of interests, or ease in effecting complete or partial withdrawal from the business.

These objectives can be satisfied in varying degrees by the different forms of ownership and financing to be described presently.

Among industrial enterprises, the principal forms of ownership are proprietorship, partnership, and corporation. Cooperatives will be neglected in our discussion because they are numerically minor and are chiefly devoted to buying and selling operations. In manufacturing and other private enterprises of large size, the corporation is the prevailing type. However, manufacturing organizations often start as proprietorships or partnerships. Thousands of small businesses are in this class.

PROPRIETORSHIP AND PARTNERSHIP

Proprietorship

Proprietorship (more exactly, *single* proprietorship) means the ownership of a business by a single individual who possesses, as personal property, all the assets of the enterprise. Liabilities of the enterprise are personal liabilities. The proprietor is personally responsible for operations although he may employ managers and others as his agents.

Advantages of proprietorship are as follows:

1. *It is simplest and least costly to initiate and manage.* To start a business under this form, it is unnecessary to go through legal formalities, except possible licensing and observance of government regulations regarding employees, operating conditions, trade, and taxation.
2. *It is relatively free from government regulations,* which pervade the financing, external relations, and management of corporations.
3. *It has a tax advantage.* Profit is taxed only as personal income; there is no additional tax on the business itself, as in corporations.
4. *It is relatively easy to terminate or change in character.* Except for possible contract obligations or loan conditions (e.g., mortgage on property), change is simply a personal affair of the proprietor.

The conspicuous disadvantages or limitations of proprietorship are:

1. *Availability of capital is limited* by the resources and credit of one person.
2. *A proprietor's liability is not limited* to investment in the business. Within the limits prescribed by bankruptcy laws, all the proprietor's personal property is subject to claims of creditors. If a person has several businesses operated as proprietorships, their financial securities are inseparable.
3. *The proprietor can not delegate ultimate responsibility for management.* His managers are responsible to him only as employees or agents.
4. *The life of a proprietorship is limited* to the period of ownership or life of the proprietor. The business can be sold or willed to heirs; but the original proprietorship then ceases to exist.
5. *The business may be difficult to dispose of,* wholly or in part.
6. *It may be difficult to employ good managers and professional talent* because they would be influenced by the forementioned disadvantages. Also, they may desire participation in ownership.

Partnership

Partnership means the ownership of an enterprise by two or more persons who share in financing and/or operations in a manner which may be classed as multiple proprietorship. The situation is a mutual agreement among the partners. The individual contributions of capital, sharing of operating responsibility, and sharing of profits may be unequal. At one extreme, one person may furnish all the initial capital (as a "silent" partner) and the other may do the managing.

Agreements as to shares in financing, operations, profits, proceeds from liquidation, and dissolving of partnership or additions to its membership can be verbal and informal. Such agreements are exceedingly risky because of misunderstandings and dependence on memory. Formal contracts are much better. Otherwise, the formation of a partnership is little more difficult than the single proprietorship.

Limited partnership is a type in which the *financial liability* and responsibility for operations of some partners is limited by agreement. State laws vary, but, in all cases, it is necessary that at least one of the partners must have unlimited liability and responsibility for operations. This type of ownership is rare in production or construction industries and is most often encountered in professional and service enterprises.

The advantages and disadvantages of partnership, particularly the common type, are much the same as proprietorship with several important differences. These are:

1. *Partnership provides for pooling of diverse talents.* A person with capital may be teamed with a good manager. Specialists in finance, sales, engineering, and production could combine in one venture. This feature accounts for the origin of most partnerships.
2. *Personal financial risk is maximum* in the common partnership. Except among limited partners, each partner is liabile to creditors to the full extent of personal resources, as in proprietorship. But the hazard is greatest for the partner with the most property because he can be called upon to settle for obligations of the firm, obligations created by other partners.
3. *It can be difficult to withdraw or sell part interest.* This involves a change in the partnership which would have to be agreed upon by the other partners. Their partnership contract, however, may call for the purchase of a withdrawing partner's interest if the others have resources for it.
4. *The death or withdrawal of one partner dissolves a common partnership.* The business must be re-established as a new partnership or proprietorship, and the final settlement can be difficult.
5. *Disagreements between partners are not uncommon.* Disputes leading to separation by a partner can be particularly difficult if there is no market for his share in the business.

THE CORPORATION

Among United States industries devoted to mineral extraction, manufacturing, and construction, more than 95 per cent (measured by assets) are incorporated. There are more than 400 firms with assets greater than $50,000,000. And at the other extreme, more than 40,000 corporations have assets less than $50,000, showing that corporations are not limited by size. In addition to these classes of enterprise, some government activities (e.g., Reconstruction Finance Corporation) and many nonprofit institutions (colleges, hospitals, and foundations) are incorporated.

The corporation is in the legal sense an individual (a legal entity) apart from its owners and managers. It exists by charter granted by a government. Commercial corporations are chartered by a state in accordance with its laws and fee requirements, which vary considerably among the states. The corporation may continue to exist without regard to changes in ownership or management at the option of those who have controlling interest and as long as the business can continue in operation. Contracts, business transactions, financial accounts, profits and losses, employment responsibilities, and the like are charged to the corporate body, not to individual participants.

The corporation as a form of organization dates back to Greco-Roman times. The earliest corporations were used for governmental and religious activities, and later for trade. Its dominance in American industry came about after the Civil War as a result of the great growth and complexity of modern enterprises. Certain advantages in incorporation have also appealed to the organizers of very small establishments.

Let us consider the economic advantages and disadvantages of incorporation in general, disregarding the differences in state regulations.

1. *It is possible to raise capital from many sources and in unlimited amounts,* depending only on the prospects of the enterprise and the reputations and policies of the promoters and managers.
2. *Liability of individual participants in ownership is, in most cases, limited to* their investments in the enterprise. Par value of the stock can be the liability if the stockholder paid in less than that amount; and in a few cases (some bank stocks, for example) the stockholder can lose his investment plus an assessment of the par value of his stock. Limited liability, however, is one of the principal attractions of incorporation.
3. *The corporation's life is not limited to the stockholding tenure of individuals,* as previously stated. Witness the long lives of many prominent corporations that have survived several generations of owners and management bodies.
4. *It is relatively easy to acquire shares in ownership or to dispose of interests in a firm,* wholly or in part. This depends only on the avail-

ability of stock or the market for it, except for possible legal restrictions. The activity of the stock exchanges illustrates this.

5. *It is relatively easy for the corporation with good reputation and/or prospects to employ competent talent* for management and technology, whether or not participation in ownership is desired. Some of the highest salaried executives in industry own exceedingly small percentages of the stock issued by their companies.

Among the disadvantages of incorporation, which may encourage the use of proprietorship or partnership for the initiation of small business, are the following:

1. *Corporations are subject to extensive government regulations and fees for incorporation.* Such regulations apply to organization, operations, financing, distribution of profits and surpluses, transfers of ownership, dissolution, and taxation. All this requires the aid of legal counsel from the beginning and throughout the life of the enterprise.

2. *Owners (stockholders) of corporations are doubly taxed.* The corporation's profits and capital gains are subject to income taxes. And the profits distributed to owners as dividends or the gains realized by owners from sale of shares are subject to personal income taxes. On the other hand, the profits of proprietorships or partnerships are taxed only once, as personal income of the participants.

3. *The responsibility of individual owners and their voices in controlling operations or financial transactions are much diluted or nil*, depending on the dispersion of ownership and consequent remoteness from management. Actual control rests with the person or group that owns or obtains voting proxies on the majority of shares. The dominant individual may own only a small percentage of the stock; or the top-management group may solicit and obtain proxies for voting control.

4. *Corporations may acquire too much power* by virtue of size or concentrations of control by financial groups. This is particularly true of parent companies that own or control several subsidiary corporations, or holding companies that may similarly control many firms in which they have financial interest. This economic and social problem has given rise to the federal legislation (e.g., the Sherman Antitrust Act) aimed at control of corporations.

Organization and Financing

In this chapter, we shall neglect much of the detail regarding the process of incorporation, structure of organization, and corporate functions of management officials. We are concerned here with matters that relate more directly to the economy of the incorporated enterprise. The owners of the corporation are the stockholders. They periodically elect a group of directors, whose primary function is to protect and promote the interests of the owners. The directors may meet and act only at infrequent intervals, or they may participate actively in management. But, in general, their functions include election of officers and top managers and the making of major decisions regarding financing, distribution of proceeds, guiding policies, and operating problems of critical importance. The day-to-day operating decisions usually rest with the officers and other chief executives. The legally responsible head of the corporation is the chairman of the board of directors. The head of the operating organization is the president, who is responsible to the directors.

On page 271, reference was made to a number of considerations that influence the promoters in deciding on the type of ownership and financing. These same factors apply, of course, to the incorporated enterprise at its beginning or during its life. The corporation charter will specify the types of stock, the authorized number of shares, and the par values or amounts initially paid in. The charter will not dictate the timing and manner of distributing the shares to be sold, or the borrowing of funds. Government regulations may control some of these matters, however; and the company's bylaws may require stockholder voting for some financial decisions, such as the issuing of stocks and bonds. We shall now describe the two principal types of stock. The borrowing of funds, which also applies to proprietorships and partnerships, will be discussed later.

The ownership of a corporation is divided into shares of stock, which are issued to the holder in certificate form representing any number of shares in any unit of value (par value) or at no stated value. Each certificate names the owner, and the record of ownership is carefully maintained by the secretary or treasurer of the corporation. Shares may be transferred readily to others by grant or sale, but the transfer of ownership must be officially recorded by the corporation and a new certificate must be issued to the new owner to establish the owner's rights. The corporation can sell stock not yet issued but authorized by the charter, and it can purchase its own stock or that of other corporations.

Common Stock

The principal ownership is represented by *common stock,* and this is the only type issued by most corporations. There are some special types of common stock with limited privileges. The ordinary common stock controls the corporation through its voting rights (one vote per share). All stockholders can vote by mail, at officially announced meetings, and on various important issues previously mentioned. In corporations with many stockholders, most of the voting is done by proxies, voting rights assigned by absent stockholders to those who are expected to attend the meetings. Proxies are most often solicited by top management individuals or groups. Proxy solicitations typify the occasional struggles for control of a corporation or the settlement of controversial issues that require stockholders' decision.

Although the value of common stock in the balance sheet is usually stated at par or an amount that was initially paid in per share, the actual book value or equity of the common stock includes the surplus (principally the profits retained in the business). *It is by increase in equity that a common stockholder realizes potential gain from corporation profits that are not paid out as dividends.*

Of those who contribute to the financing of a corporation, the common stockholders incur the greatest risk and enjoy the greatest potential profit. The value of stock may multiply many times with the firm's growth and favorable prospects. Or the stock may become worthless in event of serious decline in the fortunes of the enterprise. The market value of common stocks fluctuates more widely than other types of securities. Such fluctuations can be the result of market manipulations or supply and demand situations beyond the control of management and others seriously interested in the corporation. Market conditions are important to the stockholder. He pays the market price for his stock—except at the beginning of the corporation and under some other special conditions. To realize capital gain from the increased value of his holdings, he must usually sell his stock at a market price.

Although the rewards to the common stockholder may be great in dividends and increase in stock value, his portion is last when it comes to rights to profit and the proceeds from the sale or dissolution of the enterprise. All creditors and preferred stockholders must be satisfied first. In bankruptcy, common stockholders can be wiped out while the claims of the others may be completely or partially satisfied. But the common stockholders have rights to the surplus of profit or proceeds beyond the claims mentioned, a surplus which may be very great.

Dividends are *declared* (made payable to stockholders) by the board of directors—usually a periodic procedure. Part of the profit available for dividends, perhaps all of it, may be withheld in order to build up surplus for expansion or financial security. Some concerns maintain a fixed dividend rate year after year; and it may be necessary to pay such dividends out of accummulated surplus if the profit for the period is insufficient. Stock may be issued as dividends in lieu of cash if the firm has need for capital.

Preferred Stock

Preferred stock is a financing device that enables those who promote or control a corporation to obtain more capital without the risks of borrowing or loss of control. Preferred is a nonvoting stock, and its returns are limited. (There may be a voting privilege if dividends are not paid or some other emergencies arise.) In order to make such an investment attractive, certain prior rights are specified —hence the name *preferred*. There is always a fixed dividend percentage based on a par value and due before common stock dividends can be declared. There is always a fixed redemption value (par or more) when the stock is recalled or its specified life terminates. Its right to share in the disposal of assets (up to redemption value) is prior to that of common stock. In addition to these essential features, the preferred dividend right may be *cumulative*. That is, the dividend right, if not satisfied in any year, adds onto that of the next; and the payments to common stockholders must be correspondingly deferred. Another possible feature is a right to share in profits that exceed a stated amount. Such a liberal type of stock may be known as "6%, cumulative, participating preferred."

Returns and Yields on Stock

Returns to stockholders consist of dividend payments and gain (or loss) in value of holdings. Dividends are taxable income in the year received. Ordinarily, the capital gain is taxable only when the stock is sold, although some accounting systems show periodic capital gains based on current book or market values (gains which are then taxable).

The term *yield* applied to stock can be variously interpreted. Stocktraders speak of yield as the percentage of dividends related to market value of the stock, neglecting the possible appreciation of value of the stock. Actually, the *yield* should be based on the entire gain from the investment, as it is in bond valuation. (See page 63.)

The layman may think of yield based on the price he paid for the stock many years before. A much more realistic basis is the current market value, since that represents the capital he *now* has tied up in the stock investment. For the purpose of economy study, let us define yield on stock as the combined amount of dividends and increase in equity over the book value (which includes surplus in the case of common stock).

Required yield and return to stockholders are equivalent to the required net yield or profit from the corporation's activities. The required return on preferred stock is, of course, the specified dividend. The required return on common stock may be defined as the minimum return that the stockholders (or prospective ones) require to justify their investment. Of course, the common stock purchaser *hopes* that the actual return will exceed the required minimum.

BORROWED FUNDS

When a business or institution anticipates that the yield on the capital it employs will exceed the interest rate on borrowed money, borrowing is the cheapest form of financing. Borrowing may be induced by emergencies; and short-term borrowing is a common practice as an operating convenience. Most successful enterprises employ some borrowed capital. Most of a bank's capital is from lenders (depositors). Many government projects are financed by bond issues.

Although attractive profit can be realized on borrowed capital, there are corresponding risks that should limit the amount borrowed. Interest and payments on principal have priority over payments to stockholders. And, if the debt is secured by property, as in a mortgage, the unsatisfied lender can claim settlement by acquisition or proceeds from its forced sale. Any unsatisfied lender can force a company into bankruptcy and liquidation of assets if the borrower can't raise money to care for the claims. For the firm to maintain credit standing, current liabilities should not be allowed to exceed the amount of working capital (current assets) which can be readily converted into cash. Long-term debts become current liabilities when payments on those debts are due within the fiscal year.

The following, simple case illustrates the potential gains and risks in borrowing. Mr. John Doe has $100,000 to establish a small machine shop as proprietor. Doe's reputation and business prospects appear to be excellent, which encourages the local bank to offer another $100,000 to double the size of the enterprise. The terms of the proposed loan are mortgage security, 5% interest, and annual payments on principal (amortization of loan) at $10,000. To compare the alternatives (to borrow or not), Mr. Doe considers the outcome for a good year and a poor one. In the good year, it is assumed that profit before interest and income tax would be 20% on the total investment. The poor year is assumed to yield only 3%. The summarized results are:

	Without Borrowing	*With Borrowing*
Mr. Doe's investment	$100,000	$100,000
Bank's investment (loan)	. . .	100,000
Total investment	$100,000	$200,000
Good Year:		
Profit before interest and income tax	20,000	40,000
Interest on debt	. . .	5,000
Federal income tax	3,532	10,800
Net profit	$ 16,468	$ 24,200
Poor Year:		
Profit before interest and income tax	3,000	6,000
Interest on debt	. . .	5,000
Income tax	305	. . .
Net profit	$ 2,695	$ 1,000

In the good year, Doe's profit is increased almost 50% by borrowing; but the net is reduced greatly in the poor year. Then, the required $10,000 annual payment on the principal of the debt would cause Mr. Doe to lose his business (and other private property) at the end of the poor year, unless he could raise funds or persuade the bank to defer its claim. The reader is reminded that reduction of debt by the borrower, even if forced, is an *investment* on his part. It increases his equity in the enterprise.

Debt Retirement Programs

The interest on debt is, in one sense, a fixed cost to a corporation or to those who own the enterprise. In another sense, interest is the financier's share in the proceeds of the enterprise, a cut out of economic return. The timing and amount of interest is, of course, fixed by the terms of the loan.

All formal types of loans must also specify a termination date, except for the rare perpetual bonds issued by some governments. And, in a good many loans, the amortization or retirement must be accomplished by partial payments on the principal at specified inter-vals—a common practice in the financing of automobiles, home furnishings, and mortgages on real estate. The final settlement on a loan need not be specified at its face value. Some bonds specify a premium price for bond retirement. Some industrial bonds provide a stock exchange privilege, the current value of which depends on the market price of the stock at that time. The settlement on fed-eral savings bonds depends on age, now limited to twenty years for some of the issues. These obligations for debt retirement on the part of the borrower are as mandatory as are the interest requirements.

Any sound financial planning requires consideration of require-ments for debt retirement. Let us consider several alternatives:

1. There is no advance planning to retire debt. It is assumed that means can be found to meet the obligation when the time comes.
2. A sinking fund may be established. It will accumulate from peri-odic deposits sufficient to provide the required total when the termi-nation date arrives.
3. Provision is to be made for reductions of the debt according to a program specifying time schedule and amounts.
4. Provision is to be made for a fixed periodic payment to the lender to include both interest and amortization of debt, an amount exactly sufficient to retire the debt at the end of its specified life.

The first of the debt retirement plans (if it can be called a *plan*) characterizes most commercial short-term borrowing, borrowing to meet emergencies, and government operations. If funds are avail-able when the time comes, the debt can be paid. If the borrower needs working capital and his credit is good, money can be borrowed to pay debts that are due, or the loan can be extended or renewed. The risks in this situation have been mentioned. Banks and other financial institutions are sometimes induced to extend or renew unsatisfied loans when the borrower is unable to pay, if there seems reasonable prospect of recovery. No business lender, however, could be expected to throw away good money after bad.

The *sinking fund* is often employed by local governments and in-stitutions. It can be a legal or contractural requirement. In business operations, the sinking fund could be justified only to protect an ex-ceedingly vital debt obligation or property requirement. Because sinking funds (like trust funds) must be invested in conservative, safe securities, their earnings are usually less than the borrower would make by using the capital in his enterprise. In any case, if the interest rate on the debt were greater than the yield on a sinking fund, it would pay to amortize the debt rather than to accumulate the fund.

Sinking funds are usually accumulated by fixed periodic deposits in amounts that depend on the life of the obligation and the anticipated rate of return on the invested fund. The formula for determining the periodic amount was developed on page 16. The periodic deposit can be revised, of course, with changes in the earning rate on the fund.

A program for debt reduction can be specified with any desired timing and schedule of payments. Some examples of this practice were previously mentioned. Even a bond issue can be planned so that certain groups of bonds will be scheduled for retirement at various specified dates until the entire issue is taken care of. Perhaps the simplest program of debt reduction is to amortize the debt by uniform periodic payments equivalent to straight-line depreciation. Another important type of program will be described presently.

From the lender's viewpoint, the purpose of periodic reduction of the loan is to reduce the risk occasioned by decline in the value of security, such as mortgaged property, or possible decline in the fortunes of the borrower. From the borrower's viewpoint, one advantage of such a program is to spread the payments over a period of time, which may be easier than lump-sum settlement of the full amount. As a business policy, however, amortization of debt may provide an outlet for surplus earnings, may improve credit, and makes possible a potential for future borrowing at a time when the capital can be more profitably used in the business. Possible changes in current interest rates and business conditions are further inducements for shortening the terms of long-term loans.

Fixed Periodic Payment on Principal and Interest

One method of periodic debt reduction, of special interest in certain economy studies, is to schedule a *uniform periodic payment* that covers both interest and amortization. This is now common practice for home financing, installment-plan buying, and personal loans. It is possible for business borrowing, in modified form perhaps. In the simplest of these plans, the debt is reduced beginning with the first periodic payment in any odd amount that may be dictated by the portion due for interest. In this case, the interest portion declines as the debt is reduced and the portion paid on the principal increases with each payment. Keep in mind that the sum of the two is a fixed amount.

For the formula development, the following notation will apply:

P = initial amount of the debt (the principal)

$P_1, P_2, P_3, \ldots P_n$ = amounts paid on principal at end of periods

n = life of debt in terms of interest periods

i = interest rate per period

$I_1, I_2, I_3 \ldots I_n$ = amounts of periodic interest

D = fixed periodic payment (to be determined)

f = fraction of principal amortization due at end of first period

The fixed periodic payment may be expressed in terms applicable to the first period, thus:

$$D = I_1 + P_1 = iP + fP$$

The value of D can be solved if we can determine the factor f. For this purpose, consider the amounts of interest and amortization for the entire succession of periodic payments.

Period	Amounts of Interest and Amortization
1	$I_1 = iP$, and $P_1 = fP = fP(1 + i)^0$
2	$I_2 = i(P - fP)$, and $P_2 = fP + ifP = fP(1 + i)$
	(Note that the total of the two amounts must be maintained at the initial fixed value.)
3	$I_3 = i(P - 2fP - ifP)$
	$P_3 = fP + 2ifP + i^2fP = fP(1 + i)^2$
4	$I_4 = i(P - 3fP - 3ifP - i^2fP)$
	$P_4 = fP + 3ifP + 3i^2fP + i^3fP = fP(1 + i)^3$

Considering only the payments on principal, it becomes apparent that:

$$P_n = fP(1 + i)^{n-1}$$

The sum of all payments on principal must equal the debt. Therefore:

$$P = \Sigma P_{1-n} = fP[1 + (1 + i) + (1 + i)^2 \cdots \cdots + (1 + i)^{n-1}]$$

As demonstrated on page 16, the terms within the bracket can be simplified so that:

$$P = fP\left[\frac{(1 + i)^n - 1}{i}\right] \text{ and } f = \left[\frac{i}{(1 + i)^n - 1}\right]$$

It must be understood that the factor (f) applies to the *first period* amortization only, and the fixed periodic amount (D) is thereby determined. Combining the two amounts, we have:

$$D = iP + P \frac{i}{(1+i)^n - 1} = P \frac{i(1+i)^n}{(1+i)^n - 1}$$

For very small interest rates (as for monthly payments) remember that a useful approximation for $(1 + i)^n$ is e^{in}, when interest tables are not available for the computation.

The relationship developed above is the equivalent of other time-value relationships that have been previously discussed. From the lender's viewpoint, the fixed periodic payment is equivalent to capital recovery plus required return by the exact method. In another sense, it is the *periodic* equivalent of a present worth, that of combined interest and amortization payments; and that present worth is the initial loan or principal.

For installment buying and personal loans, a fixed monthly payment to cover interest and amortization is usually specified. The difference between the total to be paid and the initial debt is often assumed to indicate the interest rate; and if the amount is figured as simple interest on the principal (as may be implied by the lender), the percentage is entirely misleading. In such a transaction, one should determine the annual equivalent of interest that is actually being paid (i in the above formula). Consider the following example.

There is $2,000 due on an automobile, and the charge for financing is a nominal 6%, or $240 for 24 months. The monthly payment to cover the total of $2,240 is $93.33, starting with the end of the first month. What is the annual interest rate actually being charged? In this case:

$$93.33 = 2,000 \frac{i(1+i)^{24}}{(1+i)^{24} - 1} \quad \text{and} \quad \frac{(1+i)^{24} - 1}{i(1+i)^{24}} = 21.43$$

Interpolation in Table B-3 for $n = 24$ shows that $i = .0093$ (.93%). The equivalent annual rate is 11.7%. For terms as short as in this example, one can assume that the effective interest rate is approximately double the nominal figure, because the average loan is about half the initial amount due to amortization.

Having determined the fixed periodic payment, it may be of interest to determine the separate amounts of interest and amortization for any period (m). Reference to the above formula development indicates that:

$$P_m = fP(1 + i)^{m-1} = P \left[\frac{i(1+i)^{m-1}}{(1+i)^n - 1} \right] \quad \text{and} \quad I_m = D - P_m$$

This breakdown is important because the interest on debt is a cost, deductable for tax purposes; but the payment on principal is an investment (increases the borrower's equity in his enterprise).

The borrower or lender may also wish to check up on or predict the unamortized amount of the debt after payment has been made at the end of any period (m). Referring again to the formula development, it is apparent that:

$$\Sigma P_{1-m} = fP \left[\frac{(1 + i)^m - 1}{i} \right] = P \left[\frac{(1 + i)^m - 1}{(1 + i)^n - 1} \right]$$

and the remaining amount of debt is:

$$P - \Sigma P_{1-m} = P \left[\frac{(1 + i)^n - (1 + i)^m}{(1 + i)^n - 1} \right]$$

The concept of fixed periodic settlement of obligations on debt can also apply when the debt retirement program differs from that assumed above. For example, payments on the principal may be deferred for some time; or the amounts paid on the principal may have to be in units of substantial size, such as multiples of $1,000 (as for bond issues). In such cases, the residue from the fixed periodic amount (D) that can not be paid on the debt is assumed to be retained in a fund that can be used for the next payments. If said fund earns income at the same rate as the debt interest, the value of D will be exactly the same as that calculated by the previously developed formula. If the income on the retained fund is not at the debt interest rate, the adopted value of D will have to be determined by cut and try with the forementioned formula as a starting point. This requires a period-by-period tabulation in which the following column headings are useful:

1. Payment period (1 to n).
2. Unamortized balance of debt before payment for the period.
3. Interest due on unamortized balance.
4. Amount designated for amortization (fixed periodic amount less above interest).
5. Amount previously accumulated for amortization but not expended (includes interest or earnings on retained fund).
6. Total now available for debt amortization (sum of the two previous items).
7. Portion of debt which can now be retired.
8. Balance of retirement fund to be retained for future periods.

At the end of the nth period, Item 6 should exactly equal Item 2. If this tabulation and computations are started by using the value of D derived by formula, the items mentioned will not balance. It is suggested that D (the fixed periodic amount) be then corrected by an amount equal to half the unbalance divided by n. By similar trial and error, D can be adjusted until Items 6 and 2 do balance at the end of n periods. Some error in the balance should be allowed because of limitations in the estimates of earnings on deposited funds and the rounding of dollar amounts. In actual practice, any such error could be easily taken care of in the final payment on the debt.

FINANCIAL STRUCTURES

No general rules dictate the best financial structure for business enterprises. The character of the enterprise, its origin and subsequent history, the personal interests of individuals involved, rate of growth and prospects, business conditions, and many other factors affect the financing decisions. Many large companies, in evolution from proprietorships to complex corporate structures, have used all the financing devices previously described.

Financial structures of companies and institutions are shown in their balance sheets. The classified liabilities, mentioned at the beginning of this chapter, reveal the financing setup. Average structures are shown in Table 16–1, based on corporation income tax returns for the year July, 1956 to June, 1957. The dollars are the totals for five major industrial groups and United States industry as a whole (with some exceptions). The average conditions within each group are indicated by the percentages in the parentheses.

Analyses of financial statements are a specialty beyond the scope of this book. There are, however, several indications in Table 16–1 that are of immediate interest. The table shows that, for all the industrial groups, the long-term debt is only 29.2% as large as the shareholders' equity; but the ratio is considerably higher (68.8%) among the public utilities.

As to the shareholders' equity, the table shows that preferred stock averages only 5.35% of the total. Possible differences in types of common stock are not indicated; but, in general, it should be understood that the surplus is part of the common stockholders' equity. Note that the average net worth is 59.8% of the total liabilities or assets. Working capital ratios, derived from the same source, were tabulated in Table 3–1, page 35.

TABLE 16.1

FINANCIAL STRUCTURE OF INDUSTRIAL CORPORATIONS IN THE UNITED STATES, JULY, 1956 TO JUNE, 1957

(DOLLARS EXPRESSED IN MILLIONS)

Industry Group	All Industry*	Extractive	Construction	Total Manufacturing	Public Utilities	Total Trade
Number of firms	374,420	5,243	28,375	87,700	21,596	179,917
Total assets	$406,011	$10,409	$ 8,642	$203,801	$106,175	$ 64,574
Average per firm	$ 1.084	$ 1.985	$ .304	$ 2.324	$ 4.916	$ .359
Current & miscellaneous liabilities	$ 92,833 (22.9)†	$ 2,014 (19.4)	$ 4,476 (51.8)	$ 46,690 (22.9)	$ 13,007 (12.3)	$ 23,111 (35.8)
Long-term debt	70,708 (17.4)	1,022 (9.8)	532 (6.2)	23,624 (11.6)	37,995 (35.8)	5,378 (8.3)
Shareholders' equity:						
Preferred stock	12,848 (3.2)	207 (2.0)	101 (1.2)	5,883 (2.9)	4,865 (4.6)	1,587 (2.5)
Common stock‡	77,290 (19.0)	1,646 (15.8)	1,093 (12.7)	36,088 (17.7)	25,494 (24.0)	10,817 (16.8)
Surplus	152,332 (37.6)	5,520 (53.1)	2,440 (28.2)	91,516 (44.9)	24,814 (23.4)	23,681 (36.7)
Total equity	$242,470 (59.8)	$ 7,373 (70.9)	$ 3,634 (42.1)	$133,487 (65.5)	$ 55,173 (52.0)	$ 36,085 (56.0)
Total liabilities	$406,011	$10,409	$ 8,642	$203,801	$106,175	$ 64,574

* Includes agriculture and service industries; excludes banking, insurance, real estate, and lending firms.
† Percentage of assets or total liabilities in parenthesis.
‡ Common stock stated at par or nominal value.

SOURCE: *Statistics of Income, Corporation Income Tax Returns, July, 1956–June, 1957* (U.S. Treasury Department, Internal Revenue Service, 1959).

The data tabulated for 1956–57 are that of a very good business year. In event of depression, the average percentages for current and long-term liabilities could increase and surplus could decline, reducing the shareholders' equity.

The financial statement of the individual concern shows the *book value* of the stock (stockholders' equity). The value of preferred stock is the par value; that of common stock includes the surplus. Periodic increases in surplus are most often the amount of periodic earnings that are retained in the business. Such increases in surplus are part of the returns to the common stockholders, returns that are not actually realized until the stock is sold. It should be understood that stock is not sold at book value. The market value (the selling price) is certainly influenced by book value, but it is affected greatly by intangibles such as *anticipated* growth and stock market conditions.

DISTRIBUTION OF EARNINGS

The sharing of proceeds of a business varies with financial structure, rate of operations, and profit accomplishment. This has been mentioned in our discussions relating to profit, forms of ownership, and financing. In the distribution of earnings, we may also include possible profit sharing by employees, a portion that can be treated as a cost for income tax purposes.

The shares and priority of participants in the economic return of an enterprise are indicated in Figure 16–1, a break-even chart. In the situation represented by the chart, note the following sequence of obligations:

1. Interest on debt—due whether or not profit is realized.
2. Profit-sharing bonuses (an amount that varies with the individual profit-sharing plan).
3. Income taxes—based on profit after interest and bonuses.
4. Preferred stock dividends, which may be cumulative.
5. Required return to common stockholders.

For computing the various break-even points, it can be assumed that the y intercept of the cost-plus line is the sum of fixed operating cost and other obligations including taxes at the profit level indicated by the break-even situation. For this calculation then, the cost-plus line is parallel with (has the same slope as) the operating-cost line. (See sample calculations on page 134.)

Although it is satisfactory for computing the break-even point, the forementioned cost-plus line does not correctly indicate the amount of profit above or below required return at other rates of operations. The reason for this is that the slope of the cost-plus line changes with the percentage of income tax and bonus obligations, a condition that is illustrated in Figure 16–1. Of course, the equations for operating

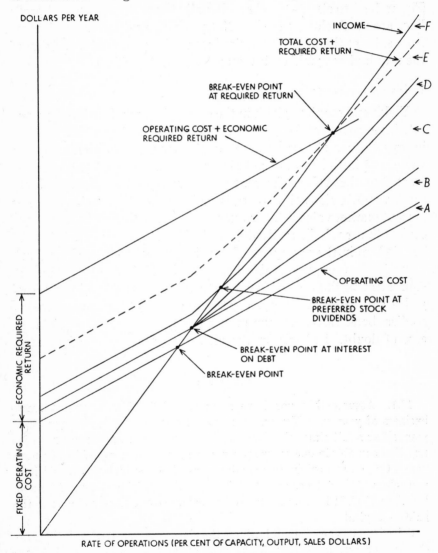

FIG. 16–1. A break-even chart for an incorporated enterprise. A = interest on debt, B = profit-sharing bonuses, C = income tax, D = preferred stock dividends, E = common stockholders' required return, F = profit exceeding required return.

cost plus required return can be determined beginning at the points where changes in rates occur; but it is simpler to draw a chart, as shown, for graphic estimates. Otherwise, it may be desirable to prepare a column-beside-column tabulation of data for various rates of operations, as demonstrated in Table 9–1, page 132.

The relative proportions of costs and profits are exaggerated in Figure 16–1 to clarify the chart. Usually the cost, income, and profit lines are much closer together. Net profit as a percentage of income from sales at the point of required return is most often a fraction of the required net *yield* on investment. (See page 135.)

Yields on Investments

Yields and required yields in the enterprise are related to the separate investments of the various participants. There are four possible interpretations of "investment" in the appraisal of yield: (1) par value, (2) initial amount paid in or loaned, (3) book value, or (4) present market value. These amounts may differ considerably. From the investor's viewpoint, there is good reason for considering that present market value is the investment because that is the amount of capital that could be realized and used for other purposes if it were not tied up in the enterprise. From the company's viewpoint, book value is the more reasonable basis. Book value and par value are equivalent in the case of loans and preferred stock, and the actual yields will equal the required percentages. And for most economy studies, book values are the proper basis for estimates of yield. In case of doubt, the basis for the yield percentage should be stated.

PROBLEMS

16.1. Assume that you have accumulated $20,000 to start a small business of your own. You want to control this business and engage in it yourself as a full-time job. You can start in a limited way as sole proprietor. You can obtain one or two partners whose interest would be less than yours. Or you can originate a small corporation in which you would hold more than 50% of the common stock, and the organizing expense would be less than $500. It is also possible to borrow up to one third as much as the paid-in capital.

Select some type of small business that interests you (e.g., printing stationery and greeting cards). Make a list of the pros and cons of the three types of organization, with special reference to the type of business proposed.

16.2. To illustrate the income tax penalty imposed on corporations in the United States and their owners, let us assume conditions existing in 1960. A businessman and his wife have acquired all the stock in a $1,000,- 000 corporation. This business is the sole source of their income. The businessman has retired early (before 65 years), and he has delegated general management to an employee of the corporation. The corporation's taxable profit for the year is $175,000, all of which will be paid as dividends because of adequate surplus. The corporation's federal income tax is at 30% plus 22% on the profit increment above $25,000. The personal income (of man and wife) derived from the business would be taxed at an effective rate of 50.4%.

Determine the net return and yield on investment ($1,000,000) received by the owners of the business.

Now assume that the business is a partnership of husband and wife, rather than a corporation. In this case, the personal income-tax rate is 64%. Determine the net return and yield on investment. Compare this with the previous result.

16.3. With reference to Problem 16.2, assume now that the owners (husband and wife) are very wealthy people whose taxable income outside of this business already exceeds $400,000. In this case, increment income is taxed at 91% (the maximum). As in the previous problem, compare the net returns and yields that would be realized from investment in the corporation and partnership.

16.4. A new factory costs $1,000,000 (borrowed capital). The cost is to be paid off in five equal, yearly payments, each payment combining an amortization installment and interest at 4% on the previously unpaid balance of the debt. What should be the amount of each payment? (PE Ohio)

16.5. The terms of a $10,000 mortgage call for ten yearly installments that will amortize the mortgage and pay 5% interest on the unpaid balance. What is the unpaid balance of the mortgage after the fifth payment is made? (PE Pa.)

16.6. An arrangement is made to purchase a home with the aid of a 20-year, $15,000 mortgage. The mortgage, held by an insurance company, specifies a uniform monthly payment to cover amortization and interest at 5%.

   a) What is the required monthly payment?
   b) What is the effective annual interest rate?
   c) What is the unamortized balance of the mortgage at the end of ten years after the periodic payment is made?

16.7. A well-established firm wishes to expand its operations. Cash is required to go ahead with the proposed program. If a $1,500,000 issue of

3%, 20-year bonds can be sold at 96; with miscellaneous expense in handling the bonds, $15,000 at the outset; and subsequent administrative expense, $1,500 annually for the 20-year program; what will be the actual interest rate paid for the money? (PE Pa. revised)

16.8.   A municipality wishes to raise funds for improvements by issuing $5\frac{1}{2}\%$ bonds. There is $20,000 available per year for interest payments and retirement of bonds at 110. What may be the amount of the bond issue if all the bonds are to be retired in 20 years? Assume that amortization money would go into a sinking fund earning the same rate as the bond interest. (PE Pa. revised)

16.9.   A municipality proposes the purchase of an existing privately owned electric utility by issuing bonds bearing 4% interest. It is proposed that the bonds be callable in any year but that all must be retired at the end of 30 years. The bankers who have been asked to purchase the issue require that the net income of the utility shall be at least 130% of the yearly cost of amortization and interest on the debt. The bank agrees to pay 4% interest on odd amounts paid in for amortization but not used to retire individual bonds.

If the yearly earnings of the utility are estimated to be $75,000, what is the maximum price that can be paid for it? (PE Pa. revised)

16.10.   Many loan companies advertise small loans which are to be paid back in uniform monthly installments, for example:

Amount	Payments Per Month	Months
$500	$86	6
400	36	12
1,200	58	24
800	27	36

In each of these examples, what would be the apparent annual rate of simple interest on the principal (the initial amount of the loan), and what would be the actual effective annual interest rate?

16.11.   A bank offers personal loans to finance automobile purchases. The stated interest rate is 6%, meaning that the borrower pays $60 for a one-year loan of $1,000. But the terms of such a loan call for a monthly payment of $88.33 to cover both interest and amortization. What is the effective interest rate actually paid by the borrower?

16.12.   A prominent chain-store catalog listed the following terms on two of its items:

a) For an appliance priced at $220: $10 down and $10.50 per month for 24 months.

b) For house-heating equipment priced at $600: no down payment and $20.50 per month for 36 months.

In each of these cases, what is the apparent annual rate for simple interest based on the initial unpaid amount, and what is the actual effective rate?

16.13. A city plans to finance an extension of its sewer system by a bond issue of $28,000,000. The bonds are to be callable (to be retired) as follows: $5,000,000 in 5 years; $5,000,000 in 10 years; $7,500,000 in 15 years; and the balance in 20 years. The bonds will pay 4½% interest, and a sinking fund must be maintained to finance the scheduled retirements. The financing plan calls for fixed annual payments to a cooperating bank to take care of interest, sinking fund, and amortization. Determine the annual amount under the following conditions:

a) Sinking fund expected to earn the same rate of return as the bond interest.

b) Sinking fund expected to earn 3%.

16.14. Assume it is possible for the "owner" of an enterprise to furnish all of the necessary capital or to borrow any amount up to 80% of the total. The interest rate on borrowed capital is 5%.

Compute the owner's yield (on his share of the total investment) when 0%, 20%, 40%, 60%, and 80% of the total capital is borrowed and under each of the following operating conditions:

a) Economic yield (on total investment) = 10%
b) Economic yield = 5%
c) Economic yield = 3%

From the above computations, draw a set of comparative graphs on one set of coordinates to show owner's yield versus per cent of capital borrowed. What is the significance of these results as to the advantage or disadvantage of borrowing?

16.15. The financial summary of a certain corporation shows the following significant details:

Long-term debt at 4½% interest.	$ 600,000
Shareholders' equity:	
Preferred stock, 6% $100 par.	500,000
Common stock at par value.	1,000,000
Surplus.	960,000
Receipts (income) for the year.	5,500,000
Operating cost for the year.	4,740,000

The operating cost does not include certain demands on economic return. The income tax rates are: 5% to the state on the same base as the federal tax, and a federal tax of 25% plus 22% on the profit increment above $30,000. There is a profit-sharing plan that specifies a bonus of 20% out of profit before income taxes based on any amount exceeding $100,000. And, of course, the interest on debt must be cared for.

a) Compute the distribution of economic return to each of the financial contributors.

b) If the amount of retained net earnings each year is to equal the dividends on common stock, what is the dividend rate (%) based on book value as indicated in the financial statement? What is the actual yield on common stock?

c) If the market value of common stock is $1\frac{1}{2}$ times book value, what are the dividend rate and theoretical yield on that basis?

16.16. Assume that the conditions of Problem 16.15 represent 90% capacity operation, and that the fixed operating cost is $1,200,000. Variable costs and income vary approximately with rate of operations. Compute the following in terms of sales dollars and percentage of capacity:

a) Break-even point at interest on debt.

b) Break-even point at payment of dividends on preferred stock. (The effective tax rate at this point is 35.3%, and there is no profit-sharing bonus.)

c) Break-even point for 10% yield on common based on book value and including retained earnings. (The effective income tax rate at this point is 48.0%.)

16.17. The Murray Manufacturing Company has made the following net earnings in six successive years:

1960	$25,000	1963	$12,000
1961	15,000	1964	30,000
1962	5,000	1965	42,000

There are 2,000 shares of common stock and 1,000 shares of $100 par value preferred stock. The preferred stock is a 6% cumulative participating type. The participating feature calls for an extra dividend when the dividend on common in any year exceeds $8.00 per share. At the participating level of dividends, one third of the amount available will be paid to the preferred stockholders (i.e., each share of common and preferred will participate equally).

To safeguard the business and to provide for expansion, 30% of the net earnings are to be retained in the business; 70% of the net is then to be paid out as dividends. No dividends, preferred or common, are to be paid out of previously accumulated surplus.

For the total six-year period, determine the following:

a) How much the preferred stockholder receives per share?

b) How much in dividends the common stockholder receives per share?

c) How much the book value per share of common stock increases in the six years based on retained earnings? (PE Pa. revised)

16.18. A new corporation is being organized to produce a line of chemical products. The promoters have succeeded in raising $3,000,000, an adequate amount for initiating the enterprise. It is possible, however, to borrow as much as $1,200,000 with mortgage security, an amount that would increase plant capacity by 40%. The lending institution requires interest at 5% and fixed annual installments for 15 years to cover interest and amortization. Before the plant is constructed, a decision must be made regarding the extent of borrowing. To facilitate this decision, an economy study is to be made comparing the results of maximum borrowing against debt-free operation. Pertinent financial data are as follows:

	Without Debt	With Borrowed Capital
Shareholders' equity	$3,000,000	$3,000,000
Long-term debt	—	1,200,000
Capacity in sales	6,000,000	8,400,000
Fixed yearly operating cost excluding interest	— 1,500,000	2,100,000
Variable cost per dollar sales	55¢	55¢

The federal income tax is at 30% on taxable profit plus 22% on the profit increment above $25,000. There is a state income tax of 6% on profit prior to computation of federal tax. The promoters consider that a net yield of 10% on shareholders' equity is the minimum necessary to justify investment.

Assume that you are to present a report on the forementioned economy study. The following items are to be included in your report:

a) The break-even points for each proposal, both at no-gain no-loss (including interest on debt) and at required return on shareholders' equity. State in terms of sales dollars and per cent of capacity. *Compute* these break-even points.

b) The net profit at 100%-capacity operation for each proposal. From this information and that above (a), prepare a pair of graphs on one set of coordinates, profit versus sales dollars. What amount of sales is required from the larger plant to exceed the profit potential of the smaller plant?

In this analysis, you are to assume the first year of plant operations, excluding the starting period and that of construction and disregarding any changes in the financial condition during those periods.

16.19. Continue your analysis of the situation described in Problem 16.18. A tentative decision has been made to plan on the larger establishment with the $1,200,000 of borrowed capital. Assume that the ownership is to be represented by 7,500 shares of 6%, $100 par value preferred stock, and 22,500 shares of common stock. Your report should provide answers to the following questions:

a) What is the debt obligation at the end of the first year in amounts of interest and amortization?

b) At what rate of operations would it be possible to meet the debt
   obligations (including amortization) and preferred stock dividends?
   This is the point at which there would be no earnings available for
   dividends to common stockholders.

c) In event of sales at the level of breaking even at required return,
   and assuming that common stock dividends must be restricted to
   half of the earnings that would be available for that purpose:
   (1) What is the dividend rate per share of common?
   (2) What are the actual earnings per share of common?
   (3) What is the year-end book value per share of common after
       payment of dividends?

d) Based on the above computations and the results obtained in problem 16.18, make a brief summary of the advantages and risks in the
   borrowing situation.

CHAPTER 17

Analysis of Intangibles

NTANGIBLES have been mentioned in several chapters. The purpose of this chapter is to describe the character of intangibles and to discuss procedures for evaluating them.

Intangibles have been defined as factors that can not be readily evaluated in quantitative terms. Some authors use the term *irreducibles* for intangibles that can not be approximated in dollars, distinguishing these items from those listed as intangible in the financial statement. But intangibles that have been considered irreducible by some analysts have been converted to quantitative terms by others. Quantitative measurement of intangibles has been among the significant advances in management science.

In economy studies, the fact that some intangibles may not be measurable in money does not lessen their importance in influencing management decisions. Ordinarily, no project in private enterprise would be considered acceptable without a satisfactory cost or profit prediction. On the other hand, many proposals that appear profitable in tangible analysis must be rejected because of intangible considerations. Intangibles may stimulate a decision favoring an alternative that is less attractive than another in the tangible comparison. Intangibles often control decisions. Some intangible factors may have a mandatory effect. Others, of little importance individually, may have the combined weight of a critical factor.

TYPES OF INTANGIBLES

Intangibles may be classified in a general way as *financial* and *nonfinancial*. The distinction is not significant except as a convenience in the listing of items and their analysis. In fact, a nonfinancial factor, such as esthetic considerations, may have an ultimate effect on dollars of profit or loss.

Financial Intangibles

Financial intangibles are the intangibles directly affecting the problems of financing, cost, income, and profit. Consider the following:

> Availability of capital and competing demands for it.
> Safety of investment.
> Future marketability of investment.
> Value as collateral (security for future borrowing).
> Intangibles affecting profit and yield:
>> Risk or potential in demand for product or service.
>> Uncertainty of operating costs.
>> Uncertainty of tax obligations.
>> Uncertainty in life of project.
> Intangibles affecting *required* yield.
> Risk to financial control of enterprise.
> Financial liabilities as to:
>> Business obligations.
>> Damage claims for property or personal injuries.
> Effects on financial reputation among customers, creditors, and financial contributors.
> Risk or potential as to personal fortunes (e.g., job security).

These items require little explanation. Most of them are *risk* factors.

The objective of an economy study is to forecast future results. *Risk* is inherent in forecasting. There can be immediate uncertainties, such as processing time and quality variations—items that may be accounted for by allowances for contingencies. But the most conspicuous risks are those of time changes in conditions. Predictions must be discounted according to the remoteness of anticipated events. The extent of such risks depends also on the character of the projects. The effective life of a patent is much less certain than that of a well-constructed building.

Forecasting problems were discussed in Chapter 10. An appraisal of risk or uncertainty in forecasts should be included in the reports of economists, market researchers, and others who contribute to an important economy study. Almost all the financial intangibles may be involved. The forecasts may be long range or short range, nation-wide or local, for the state of general business or of a particular type of product or service. Consider the following examples: What is the uncertainty or variability in market growth for a new type of product, such as color television? In a new industrial community, what is the likelihood of an increase in wage levels or in local taxation? After the introduction of a new antibiotic, how soon will some competitor equal or better that product? Such intangible considerations are indeed numerous. The items that should be considered in a particular study need individual listings and appraisals for each type of project and situation.

Perhaps we have overemphasized the risk factors. Risk taking is essential to progress. The potential rewards of a venture counterbalance the risks. Appraisal of these favorable potentials is also a study of intangibles. The point that we should emphasize is this: The intangibles of potential rewards and risks should be identified and analyzed, and, to the maximum practical extent, the risks should be *calculated*. The weighing of intangible advantages and disadvantages will be discussed presently.

The Yield Requirement

Required yield, which has been so prominent a factor in our study techniques, is an amount that depends largely on intangibles. The specification of required yield was discussed at length in Chapter 8; and at that time, several factors contributing to the yield specification were mentioned. Hardly any of these bases for yield requirement can be forecasted with certainty. There are changes in the customary interest rates on borrowed money. Witness the increase in rates on federal bonds during the 1950's, from less than 3% to more than 4.5%. The market for investments is up and down with the supply of and demand for capital, and with business prospects in general, all of which affect the yields demanded by investors.

Competition with other demands for capital within an enterprise is one of the most important factors affecting a yield requirement. In some industries during recent years, the payoff period required of new ventures has been set as low as two years, because other projects demanding attention have appeared so attractive.

In commercial ventures, perhaps the most conspicuous factor in required yield is allowance for risk. The most inexperienced investor sets up a higher hurdle, a demand for greater profit potential, when greater risk is recognized. "Venture" capital deserves a higher goal for yield than the conservative safe investment. Although this element in required yield is usually established by business judgment, it may be practical to adjust the yield or return requirement by quantitative appraisal of intangibles, as will be described later.

Nonfinancial Intangibles

Classified here as *nonfinancial* are the factors that do not seem to bear directly on investment and profit potentials. Such intangibles do, with few exceptions, have an ultimate effect on financing and profit; but the quantitative result is more remote and difficult to estimate.

The possible nonfinancial intangibles are exceedingly numerous and varied. Such intangibles may relate to:

Character of product or service rendered.
Character of physical plant and operations.
Personnel factors.
Esthetic considerations.
Ethical considerations.
Social factors.
External relations.
Personal attitudes of management.
Personal attitudes of owners or those in financial control.

The significance of intangible considerations in most of these areas may be apparent to most readers; but a few comments regarding them may be of interest.

Intangibles relating to product, service, plant, and operations include possible details such as: specialization versus diversity, level of quality desired, whether to make and sell or to buy and sell, whether to centralize or decentralize, hazards to people and property, plant site conditions, quality of transportation service, and similar factors.

Personnel factors may include the following:

Availability of personnel and requisite skills.
Adaptability of personnel to change.
Relations with labor unions.
Personnel relations within organization.

Labor turnover.
Quality of available leadership.
Living conditions for personnel.

These considerations apply not only to rank-and-file employees but to staffs and executives. One of the brakes on automation is the limited knowledge of people who would be called upon to facilitate changes and new operations. Such difficulties have been experienced in conversion to war production. Personnel factors are important in any drastic change of program or change in location of activities.

Esthetic considerations have a bearing on internal morale and impressions conveyed to outsiders. People react to surroundings. The intangible aspect of the problem is to relate the advantages of attractive working conditions and good-looking property to the tangible success of the enterprise.

Ethical and social factors are concerned with the moral standards of the people involved and with human welfare. Certain ethical standards are mandatory in effect. But there are borderline situations where opininons may differ within the organization and when the pros and cons may have to be weighed. The social factors are broader in scope. They involve problems that range in importance from contributions to local charities to the effects of withdrawing a plant from a community where the industry is the major employer. Both of these categories of intangibles may well be classed with the problems of internal and external relations.

The intangibles concerned with external relations may have both immediate and long-range effects on the fortunes of the enterprise. Consider the importance of reputation with customers, community, financial interests, competitors, government agencies, and public at large. These factors have conspicuous effects on financing, attraction of personnel, sales, and government regulations. Most large companies have public relations staffs to gage public opinions and to promote company reputations.

Personal attitudes of owners and management may have exceedingly important bearings on decisions. All of us have likes and dislikes that may be difficult to support by argument. A certain type of enterprise or activity may attract us by its nature. Desires for security or stability and the attractions of adventure or risk pull in opposite directions. The prospect of extra work and worry may stimulate some and repel others.

Even more than with financial intangibles, it is impossible to prescribe a list of nonfinancial intangibles that apply to all projects. Each situation merits individual treatment. The case problem to be demonstrated later will illustrate this.

EVALUATING INTANGIBLES

Listing Intangibles

As in other types of investigation, a *complete check list* of pertinent factors is an almost essential beginning for intangible analysis. The list should be detailed. Minor factors may have combined weight that is important. The initial list should be as complete as possible, although additional items may come to light during the course of investigation. Although this list of factors is necessarily peculiar to the individual type of project—few intangibles or many—all of the alternatives in the study should be compared against the same list.

If the project is relatively simple, classification of items is unimportant. For machine replacement studies, the following list of intangibles may be sufficient for checking:

Availability of capital and competing demands for it.
Reliability of supplier.
Reliability of machine performance.
Reliability of maintenance estimate.
Availability of personnel.
Risk of premature machine obsolescence.
Risk of premature reduction or termination of need.
Operating safety.
Visual attractiveness.

An important, complex study may require a long list of intangible factors that should be classified to facilitate analysis. Such a list is illustrated in Table 17–1, to be described later.

The importance of an adequate check list is exampled by the experience of an executive known to the author. This man was the manager of a new branch factory established in a large city. The company had not investigated living conditions for potential employees. The oversight was a severe handicap. Employees had to be induced to travel too long a distance to the plant site. In another case, with which the author is familiar, the introduction and pricing of an improved product failed to consider the reactions of competitors.

The latter reduced their prices to levels which could not be competed against successfully. The amount of proposed investment and the critical nature of results dictate the extent and limit the cost of intangible analysis.

Qualitative Appraisal of Intangibles

It is now assumed that complete descriptions will have been obtained concerning all the pertinent intangibles. After accumulation of these data, the comparison and weighing of the pros and cons as they apply to the competing alternatives can be the most difficult stage of the decision process. For this purpose, a column-beside-column comparison of factors (as in tangible analysis) is often effective.

The simplest kinds of summarized appraisals are descriptive adjectives. Let us bear in mind that, in comparing alternatives, the descriptions should be comparable. A similar situation exists in job evaluation and merit rating, as in the appraisals of factors such as skill, cooperation, leadership, personality, job hazards, and the like. Therefore, it is useful to adopt some uniform set of adjectives or symbols. For example:

Excellent, Good, Adequate, Poor, Very Poor, NG

In this terminology, *Adequate* is intended to signify that the needs of the project will be met without apparent advantage or detriment; *NG* (no good) means a situation that would bar the project unless that condition could be corrected at a cost that should be indicated in the tangible analysis.

Whether or not the intangibles are to be reduced to quantitative measurement, the fundamental bases for their appraisals are matters of judgment. Therefore, the best available experience and recognized good judgment should be made available for these studies. The most critical appraisal should be the combined opinion of several qualified people.

Quantitative Appraisals

Important decisions are always complicated by the weighing of pros and cons. The weighing of intangibles involves some degree of *quantitative* measurement, even if that is done subconsciously. To the job seeker, how important are living conditions compared with professional prospects or with immediate salary? To the selector of a plant site, how important is the visual attractiveness of a location compared with convenience of access?

When it is possible to estimate the probability of an occurrence that has a tangible consequence (a machine breakdown, for example), that situation could be appraised in terms of dollars. Combinations of intangibles may be analyzed in this manner. The mathematical tools are those of probability, statistical analysis, game theory, and the like. Examples were given in Chapters 10 and 14. Even if such techniques can be applied, the elements of judgment in the basic assumptions (possibility of an occurrence, for example) limit the precision of these quantitative findings. If, as described above, any intangible items can be evaluated in dollars and incorporated in the tangible estimates, that fact should be noted in the summarized listings so that those items will not be given additional weight in the intangible analysis.

Let us now consider the possibility of weighing intangibles by the assignment of numerical values in place of descriptive terms. This type of numerical rating provides a means for the comparison of competing proposals by the totals of their scores. Many types of numerical scales have been used for comparisons of this type. The problem is to select values for each factor that will reflect the relative importance or weight of that factor. This assignment of weight is always the controversial issue in the adoption of such scales. The plan described below has the advantage that any desired *penalty* or *bonus* may be assigned to the intangible factor, depending, of course, on the relative importance of the condition evaluated.

It is suggested that potential ratings be assigned first to the least important factors. Then the scale values used for more important items can be multiples of the less important. The appropriateness of these scales can be checked by comparing the totals for groups of items. Before final adoption of rating scales, there should be considerable cut and try and comparisons of possible outcomes. Each scale must be tailor-made for each type of economy study.

Now consider numbers that could be assigned to the descriptive ratings previously mentioned. For a particular item of relatively minor importance, the potential ratings may be:

Excellent = 2	Poor = −3
Good = 1	Very Poor = −10
Adequate = 0	NG = disqualification

Note that the scale values need not have straight-line relationship. If such scales were used for rating all factors, a zero average would indicate that the sum of the intangibles would neither enhance nor penalize the prospects of the subject. On the other hand, a single *NG* would disqualify or require revision of the proposal. These types of ratings will be used later in our demonstration (Table 17–1).

Conversion to Dollar Values

The ultimate in quantitative appraisal of intangibles is to convert their ratings into dollar values that can be combined with the tangible findings of the study. Some conversion of intangible pros and cons into dollar equivalents is attempted by every decision maker in business, a process that is rarely precise or consistent. When alternatives are being compared, there is no problem if both the tangibles and the intangibles clearly favor one of the proposals. Often, however, the tangibles may favor one alternative, and the intangibles may score better for another.

Following is a suggested procedure for combining a dollar appraisal of intangibles with a conventional tangible analysis. The procedure starts with the use of numerical rating scales such as the one described above. The succeeding steps are:

1. Adopt a study period (e.g., 5 years) for the appraisal of the effects of intangibles.
2. Make an estimate of the profit improvement (or cost reduction) that will result from some ideal condition, such as an over-all total for *Good* or *Excellent,* by the end of the study period.
3. Reduce the above estimate to an annual average. This may be modified by time value according to the length of the study period and the uncertainty of the forecast (the annual equivalent of a present-worth determination).
4. Derive from the above result a dollar value for each advantage (plus) point of intangible rating; and apply this to the total plus points earned by the proposal in its appraisal.
5. Repeat Steps 2 to 4 with respect to the negative (disadvantage) points. A good basis for the unit dollar value is the number of potential negative points (disadvantageous conditions) that would reduce the profit estimate to zero by the end of the study period.
6. Combine the plus and minus dollars for each proposal to obtain a net value of the intangibles.
7. If the net value of the intangibles is plus (indicating that intangibles enhance the prospects of the project), subtract that amount

from the required return (or add it to the estimated profit). Treat
net disadvantage in reverse fashion. Required yields can be similarly adjusted by the intangible ratings.

An Example of Quantitative Evaluation of Intangibles

Let us consider a hypothetical case to demonstrate a dollar evaluation of intangibles by the method described above. The John Jones
Company has narrowed down a choice of plant location to two sites,
proposals A and B. The tangible analysis provides the following comparison:

Item	Proposal A	Proposal B
Net investment (owners' equity)	$2,550,000	$2,950,000
Required net yield	10%	10%
Required net return	$255,000	$295,000
Estimated yearly net profit	$331,000	$354,000
Estimated net yield	13%	12%
Yield on increment investment		5.75%

This comparison favors Proposal A with regard to yield on investment. But the results are similar enough to indicate that intangible
factors could easily influence a decision.

Table 17–1 is a tabulation of the intangible factors, rating scales,
and the plus or minus ratings for the two proposals. The point ratings' results are as follows:

	Proposal A	Proposal B
Advantage (plus) points	+65	+122
Disadvantage (minus) points	−119	−79

Since the intangibles seem to favor Proposal B, the over-all advantage of one or the other now depends on a dollar appraisal of the intangibles.

Let us assume that the company executives have agreed on the
following bases for dollar value of intangibles. In the ideal situation,
in which all intangibles are rated *Good* (+159), the estimated
profit would be doubled in 5 years. A study of several combinations
of *Poor* ratings has also led to the conclusion that a net of −110
would reduce profit to zero in 5 years. It is assumed that these
changes in the profit would take place in uniform annual increments,
so that the annual average would be half the total change. Time
value and forecasting uncertainty are neglected in the annual equivalents. Following is the summarized derivation of the dollar equivalents and their effects on the over-all appraisals of the two proposals.

Item	Proposal A	Proposal B
Potential increase or loss in annual profit in 5 years..............................	$ 331,000	$ 354,000
Annual average profit increase or loss......	165,500	177,000
Value of each plus rating point............	1,041	1,113
Value of each minus rating point..........	1,505	1,609
Value of advantage points................	+67,665	+135,786
Value of negative points.................	−179,095	−127,111
Net value intangibles (rounded)............	$−111,400	$ +8,700
Adjusted estimate of profit...............	$219,600	$362,700
Adjusted estimate of yield...............	8.6%	12.3%
or		
Adjusted required return................	$366,400	$286,300
Profit estimate in excess of required return..	$−35,400	$+76,400

According to this appraisal, it is now evident that Proposal B has considerable advantage over Proposal A.

SUMMARY

There are intangible aspects (uncertainties and contingencies) in the tangible estimates of most economy studies. There are additional intangible considerations that are distinctly separate from the tangible estimates, conditions associated with the project, that are difficult to resolve in quantitative terms. The analyst and decision maker must recognize and weigh the importance of these intangibles. Any project that deserves acceptance must have favorable cost or profit prospects indicated by tangible analysis; but it is also essential that intangible considerations indicate satisfactory outcome.

This chapter has been concerned with systematic appraisal of intangible factors. It is argued that systematic appraisal, in quantitative terms if practicable, will improve the reliability of conclusions, although the basic elements in such measurements must remain dependent on experience and judgment.

Procedures for the systematic analysis of intangibles may be summed up as follows:

1. Careful check-listing and investigation of the intangible factors must be made.
2. When the probability of outcome of certain intangibles can be estimated quantitatively, it may be practical to determine the best of alternatives by the mathematical procedures of probability, game theory, statistics, and the like—procedures that are described in the literature on operations research. Some of these intangibles in terms of dollars may be included directly in the tangible estimates.

TABLE 17–1

INTANGIBLE ANALYSIS OF ALTERNATIVE PLANT LOCATIONS (A AND B)
(A hypothetical case)

No.	Items Evaluated	Rating Scale					Point Ratings			
		Very Poor	Poor	Ade-quate	Good	Excel-lent	Proposal A		Proposal B	
							Minus	Plus	Minus	Plus
	Financing Intangibles									
100	Adequacy of present resources	NG	−20	0	5	10		0		0
	Potential for future borrowing									
101	Local sources	−20	−10	0	3	6		0		6
102	State assistance	−6	−3	0	3	6	6			6
103	Other sources	−20	−10	0	3	6	10		10	
104	Terms of proposed financing (except interest) and risk to ownership and control	NG	−20	0	5	10		0		0
105	Accessibility and capacity	−20	−10	0	5	10		10		5
106	Attitude of local banks	−20	−10	0	5	10		0		10
107	Marketability of fixed assets in event of move or change	NG	−20	0	5	10		0		0
108	Government restrictions on organization and finance	NG	−15	0	5	10		0		0
	Market and Labor Conditions									
109	Adaptability for product and process changes	−20	−10	0	3	6	10			6
110	Nearness to best potential markets	−6	−3	0	2	4		2	3	
111	Nearness to potential sources of material	−2	−1	0	1	2		1		2
112	Availability, supervisory and technical personnel	NG	−10	0	4	8		4	10	
113	Availability of wage labor	NG	−20	0	5	10		0		10
114	Productivity of labor	NG	−20	0	10	20		10		20
115	Stability of labor	−20	−10	0	4	8	10			8
116	Training requirements	−10	−5	0	5	10		0		10
117	Availability of training facilities	−6	−2	0	2	4		4	6	
	Labor relations									
118	Attitude of workers toward industry and management	NG	−10	0	5	10	10			5
119	Attitude of workers toward union affiliation (mgm't.) viewpoint	−10	−5	0	3	6	5			3
	Reputation of unions as to:									
120	Strikes and work stoppages	NG	−20	0	5	10		0		0
121	Interference with management	−20	−10	0	4	8	10			0
	Conditions at Proposed Site									
122	Visual attractiveness	−2	−1	0	1	2	1			2
123	Drainage conditions	NG	−10	0	3	6		0		3
124	Susceptibility to flood and erosion	NG	−50	0	3	6		6		0
125	Facilities for disposal of sewage and waste	NG	−20	0	2	4		4		0
126	Room for expansion	NG	−20	0	5	10	20			10
	Power and fuel supply									
127	Reliability for present needs	NG	−10	0	3	6		6		3
128	Capacity for expansion	NG	−10	0	3	6		0		6

TABLE 17–1 *Continued*

No.	Items Evaluated	Very Poor	Poor	Ade-quate	Good	Excel-lent	Proposal A Minus	Proposal A Plus	Proposal B Minus	Proposal B Plus
	Water supply									
129	Reliability of supply......	NG	−10	0	1	2		0		2
130	Quality................	NG	−10	0	1	2	10			1
131	Transportation facilities									
	Adequacy of carriers, connections..........	NG	−10	0	2	4		4		0
132	Highway conditions.......	NG	−10	0	2	4		2		0
133	Traffic density..........	−2	−1	0	1	2	2			2
134	Accessibility for business travel..............	−4	−2	0	1	2		2	2	
135	Accessibility for personnel	NG	−4	0	2	4		0		0
136	Adequacy of nearby eating places................	−2	−1	0	1	2		1	2	
	Community and Living Conditions									
137	Attitude of community toward proposed industry	NG	−10	0	5	10	10			10
138	Physical attractiveness of area.................	−4	−2	0	1	2	2			2
139	Adequacy of schools........	−10	−3	0	1	2		0		0
140	Adequacy of shopping facilities..............	−6	−3	0	1	2		0		0
141	Adequacy of religious facilities..............	−8	−4	0	1	2		0		0
142	Adequacy of recreation facilities..............	−6	−3	0	1	2	3		6	
143	Availability of housing......	NG	−10	0	2	4		0		0
144	Rating as to slums, clip joints, crime................	NG	−10	0	2	4	10			4
145	Comparative cost of living...	−20	−10	0	4	8	10			8
	Climate									
146	Desirability for operations...	NG	−10	0	4	8		0		0
147	Desirability for personnel....	−20	−5	0	1	2		0		2
	Local Business Aids (nonfinancial)									
148	Nearness to vendors of miscellaneous supplies and services..............	−10	−3	0	2	4			4	10
149	Availability of local trade and professional organizations................	−2	−1	0	1	2			2	2
150	Nearness to testing and consulting services........	−4	−1	0	1	2			2	4
151	Adequacy of facilities for visitors (hotels, restaurants, etc.)............	−6	−2	0	1	2			1	2
	Government Regulations (nonfinancial)									
152	Local restrictions affecting operations............	NG	−15	0	4	8		0		8
153	State regulations affecting operations............	NG	−15	0	4	8		0		0
	Miscellaneous									
154	Factors of Concern to Enterprise................	..	..	..	..	..	..	..	..	..
160	Totals..................		−525		159		−119	65	−79	122

Source: "The Textile Industry in Pennsylvania," *Engineering Research Bulletin* B-74, College of Engineering and Architecture, The Pennsylvania State University, May, 1958.

3. Intangible comparison of alternatives is also facilitated by column-beside-column tabulation of ratings.

4. Ratings of intangible factors may be summarized in descriptive terms and perhaps in numerical values that provide means for quantitative comparison of alternatives.

5. The ultimate in the quantitative analysis of intangibles is to convert ratings into dollars that can be combined with the tangibles for over-all appraisal of the project.

As in other industrial and business activities, the justifiable extent of an analysis of intangibles depends on the economic importance of the study. When the risks or potentials in a project are substantial, highly qualified personnel and systematic procedures are needed to reduce the uncertainties inherent in intangibles and to give them appropriate weight in arriving at decisions.

PROBLEMS

17.1.   Assume you have an automobile, for personal and family use, that is now eight years old. For several years, you have kept a record of expenditures on this car. Although it now costs more to operate and keep in good condition than estimated for a new car, an economy study shows that it is still more economical to keep the old car on account of the depreciation penalty on a new one.

The old car has a trade-in value of $500, and it will decline in value no more than 20% per year on a declining balance basis. A new car of the same class would cost $3,000. It would depreciate at least $700 the first year and 20% per year thereafter on a declining balance basis. Operational and maintenance savings would have to be exceptional indeed to offset the depreciation penalty.

Assuming that you contemplate no unusual demand, such as a transcontinental tour, and that the old car satisfies your present needs for transportation, make a list of the intangible considerations that would support the economy study or would encourage the purchase of the new car.

17.2.   A serious business depression makes it necessary for management to order a drastic reduction in the rate of plant operations. The trend indicates that it is unsafe to accumulate more inventory of finished goods, and the firm's financial condition does not permit it. In order to reduce operations, there are two alternatives (neglecting combinations of them for the present). Full-time operation may be continued with a reduced working force. Or, it is possible to maintain the present working force on a reduced schedule. Either of these alternatives is practical from the operating viewpoint.

Prior to computation of financial details, the intangible aspects of the situation are being considered. Assume that you are to contribute an opinion. What are the typical intangible factors, and how should they affect the decision?

17.3. An appliance manufacturer is considering the formulation of policy regarding specification changes in its principal product, a household vacuum cleaner. The industry is highly competitive. The cleaner is manufactured by typical production-line techniques appropriate for large-quantity, substantially continuous operations. Several of the processes are automatic; but the term "automation" hardly applies because there are no automatic assemblies, handlings, and inspections.

The present problem deals with design developments and changes in specifications. From various sources, particularly the research and development staff, there are frequent proposals for changes in design and process. Whenever a design proposal looks exceptionally attractive, there is considerable pressure from sales executives to introduce the improvement at once to enlarge the competitive advantage. Of course, there are several pros and cons to such action. Other executives argue that developments should be frozen until a number of such changes can be incorporated in a new model. Such new models could be spaced two or three years apart, depending on market conditions and economic factors.

With regard to changes that can be incorporated, one by one, into an existing model and to assist in policy formulation:

a) Enumerate the tangible economic factors, in essential detail, that that should be evaluated.

b) Enumerate the intangible factors that could be pertinent, and state how each factor should influence decision.

c) Under what unusual conditions (tangible or intangible) would it be advisable to deviate from general policy by immediate introduction of a new development?

17.4. Automation is a conspicuous trend of the times in American industry and is becoming increasingly practical in establishments of modest size. This comment applies to a manufacturer of electronic devices, the principal industry in a town of 2,000 population. The plant employs 400 people who live in town or within a ten-mile radius. The firm enjoys a good reputation in the community. The present labor turnover is about 20%. (Labor turnover is the annual average of employee replacements related to the average total of employees.) Management has had some difficulty with the Electrical Workers Union, which is directed from outside the region. For this reason and others, labor costs are increasing; and there is, at the same time, need for cost reduction. The business is growing, however, and the company's market is expected to increase at the rate of 25% per year for the next three or four years.

Management has been keeping track of possibilities for automation. A recent study shows that the labor force at the present demand for output could be reduced 50% by an investment of $2,000,000. It is possible to obtain the required capital. The annual saving in operating cost is estimated at $800,000. It is possible to convert the plant all at once, or in stages of not less than 25% of operations in any one year.

Make an intangible analysis of the situation described above. You may introduce additional considerations, if you wish, but they should be so stated. Assign any weight that seems appropriate to the various factors. Based on your analysis, what decision do you recommend?

17.5.   Assume that you are a recent college graduate whose job prospects have narrowed down to two interesting offers (A and B). You have no financial resources except those necessary to get started promptly in a new location. You have a wife and baby to consider.

Job A offers $425 per month. The firm is old and well-established, with a record of growth averaging about 5% per year. It now employs more than 40,000 in several plants nationally distributed. You would engage in a two-year training program that is generally well regarded. There would be a semiannual pay increase of 5% for the two years if you prove competent. After that, your future would depend on openings in the organization and your ability. Retirement plans and other fringe benefits are good. In this industry, most of the high executives have risen from the ranks in continuous employment with the firm. Many college graduates, however, do reach a plateau of advancement within five to ten years.

As to location, your training would start in a rather grimy industrial city. The cost-of-living index is 110. Rent to meet your needs would be at least $90 per month; and you would have to live at least five miles from the plant. Cultural and other living facilities are fairly good. You are advised that you would continue in this location for at least a year, after which you might be transferred to any of the plants. Most of the executives have worked at several plants.

Job B offers $475 per month. This concern, located in a small town, employs 200 people. The outfit has grown from a small beginning (20 employees) ten years ago. After two months of informal training by association with several of the key personnel, you would be on your own at a permanent job. There is no program for early pay increases, although there appears to be a good opportunity to grow with the firm. It depends, of course, on your demonstrated ability and experience. There are no fringe benefits other than the legal requirements (e.g., social security).

Concern B is located in a pleasant small town. No cost-of-living index is published, but inquiry reveals rental possibilities at about $75 per month. You could surely locate within one mile of the plant. The town is rather isolated—no city within 40 miles. Elementary schools are adequate. There are no cultural advantages other than the offerings of school, churches, and a motion-picture theater.

Assume that both of these alternatives are equally attractive as to character of work and types of people to whom you were introduced. Make a comparative listing of the intangible considerations. Introduce additional personal considerations if you wish. As a result of your analysis, which job do you prefer and why?

17.6. Replacement of an old, special-purpose automatic lathe is under consideration. The new machine would be of a similar type but with 20% greater capacity on account of improvements. It would be used continuously for a combination of operations on a spindle for aircraft landing gear. The old machine is just adequate for present demand operating one shift. Under this operating condition, tangible analysis favors deferment of replacement. Pertinent data follow:

	Old	New
Investment	$20,000	$65,000
Expected life	3 years	10 years
Ultimate salvage value	$5,000	$5,000
Annual costs:		
Depreciation	$ 5,000	$ 6,000
Required return	2,500	7,000
Other fixed charges	2,000	1,300
Variable operating cost	14,050	10,800
Operating cost + return	$23,550	$25,100

Considering the possibility of working more than one shift with no change in the rates for variable cost, the two machines would break even at 148% of present demand.

The production executive is urging the replacement for two reasons. The old machine is turning out too much scrap. The defectives average 5% (included in the estimate of variable cost). Rejects should not exceed .5% with the new machine. Scrap is expected to increase; how much is unknown. But, aside from computable cost, one effect of irregular quality is the tendency to upset planning and worker morale. Another risk in the old machine is the increasing possibility of complete breakdown. In that event, the machine would be out of commission for at least two weeks (more if parts can not be obtained promptly), and the job would cost at least $2,500. The timing of such a happening is variously predicted at three months to three years.

Future demand is uncertain. There has been an upward trend for the past five years; but predictions for the next three years vary from 50% to

300% of present demand. In an industry as uncertain as aircraft, there is the possibility of changes that would make present facilities obsolete; but no such development is foreseen at present.

Continue with this replacement study, using *quantitative* comparisons where practicable. Assign weight to intangibles according to your best judgment. Conclude with a recommendation, whether to replace or not, and when.

17.7. The most economical lot size has been computed for a steel drawer that is required, in various combinations, for a line of steel cabinets. The lot-size computation followed the formula method described on page 228 with these results:

a = average estimate of demand for year = 20,000
w = working days per year = 250
d = daily demand, average estimated = 80
r = rate of output during production = 260 per day
p = production cost = \$2 each
h = starting cost per lot = \$30
s = annual storage cost = 40¢ each, based on average inventory
i = interest rate (required yield) on average inventory, including insurance = 25%
B = factor in formula = $a(s + ip)(1 - d/r)/2$
n = number of lots per year
q = lot size = a/n for steady demand
C = annual cost plus required return on working capital
N = optimum lots per year corresponding with lot size Q
N = $\sqrt{B/h}$ = 14.4 in this case, and $Q = a/N = 1,390$
C = $ap + hn + B/n$ = \$40,864 at the optimum schedule

Planning is affected by several considerations, in addition to the results summarized above, for example: convenience in scheduling, deviations from predicted demand, risk of shortages, changes in cost, possibilities of change in specifications, and other demands for capital.

Although the basis for computation was a demand of 20,000 units per year, the predictions range from 15,000 to 25,000. The monthly demand can vary still more ±35%. The estimates of unit cost seem fairly reliable, but the trend in costs of labor and material has been upward. The cost of interrupted production due to shortages is a serious consideration, an amount estimated roughly at \$300 per day. With a tight schedule, delays as much as five days have occurred in the past. Although the optimum schedule would not be significantly affected by planning a minimum inventory for contingencies, the carrying charges on such an inventory must be balanced against the risk.

There are a good many demands for working capital (e.g., advertising) and long-term investment (e.g., equipment). Although there is some allowance for this in the specified yield requirement, management policy is to sacrifice slight operating cost advantage for conservation of capital.

The possibility of design changes would preclude any planned carry-over of inventory beyond the current year. At present, there are no labor disputes or material shortages in prospect.

Assume that you are the production executive responsible for planning. The annual cost of the item under consideration is enough to warrant serious attention. What instructions would you give for the scheduling, and why? Support your decision by tangible comparisons where practicable.

17.8. John Merck inherited half interest in his deceased father's business, a sole proprietorship known as Welware Company. John had been acting as manager at $10,000 annual salary. In the settlement of the estate, John acquired complete ownership of the business by borrowing funds to settle the claims of the other heirs. The latter accepted $100,-000 in cash, the equivalent of half the net worth of the business. At this point, the essential facts regarding the business were as follows:

John's investment.................................$100,000	
Long-term debt(terminates in 10 years).............. 100,000	
Anticipated annual profit before deduction of interest and income tax............................ 32,000	

The profit estimate was based on the average of the last five years and *includes the amount of John's salary.* The loan from the bank is secured by a mortgage on the business property. Interest is at 5%. Interest and amortization is to be cared for by a fixed annual payment with the provision that the loan may be retired more rapidly or in full at any time.

John's personal income tax obligation on taxable income will start at 20% plus the following rates on each increment of $4,000 above an initial $4,000: 22%, 26%, 30%, 34%, 38%, 43%, 47%, and 50%. Any capital gain realized by the sale of property will be subject to 25% tax, but no deduction from income will be allowed for net capital loss.

John is keenly interested in the enterprise and wents to keep it going. But he is not certain that he should continue to operate with the heavy debt and personal risk. Two additional alternatives have developed—incorporation and sale to a competitor.

The corporation would be capitalized at $200,000 as follows:

1,200 shares of common stock at $100 each..........$120,000	
800 shares of 6% cumulative preferred stock at $100 par value.................................... 80,000	

In the transfer of the business, John is to receive 700 shares of common stock, 240 shares of preferred, and $106,000 in cash. With the cash, John will retire his debt and will pay for promotion (sale of stock) and fees of incorporation. The transaction, therefore, involves a capital loss of

$6,000 for John; but his shares of common stock give him control of the corporation. He plans to become chairman of the board and president at a salary of $12,000 per year. The net earnings of the business in excess of preferred dividends are to be divided 40% to surplus (for growth and contingencies) and 60% for dividends on common stock. The proposed charter also provides for sale of additional common stock if desired. There is a federal income tax of 30% plus 22% on the increment of profit exceeding $25,000.

A large competitor offers to buy the business for $220,000. John will receive $120,000 in preferred stock that yields 5% and $100,000 in cash, with which his mortgage can be retired. The firm will continue operations at the Welware plant and offers John the managership at $12,000 per year for three years as part of the sale contract. This competitor is a stable, well-established concern. Its preferred stock is now quoted at par at the stock exchange.

Assume that you are John Merck. You are to make a prompt decision between the three alternatives: proprietorship, incorporation and sale of business. Make a tabulated comparison of tangibles and intangibles. Assume that the first year's results of the firm's operations will be as originally predicted, making appropriate allowance for John's salary. Your intangible analysis is to consider the future, however. As a result of your study, which alternative do you prefer? Your decision may be influenced by personal considerations (age, etc.) which should be mentioned in defending your decision.

17.9. A manufacturing firm is considering the location of a new plant. The company's products have nation-wide distribution. The size and character of the new plant have been decided upon, and location possibilities have been reduced to two alternatives that seem the most attractive. The tangible factors for the two sites are approximately equal. Pertinent data are:

```
Investment:
  First cost....................................$1,800,000
  Working capital.............................. 1,100,000
      Total....................................$2,900,000
Estimated annual income from sales................ 7,000,000
Annual operating cost:
  Direct labor................................$1,800,000
  Direct material............................. 1,300,000
  Indirect labor and salaries.....................  650,000
  Indirect material and supplies..................  170,000
  Depreciation................................  130,000
  Other overhead............................. 2,150,000
      Total....................................$6,200,000
Interest on debt...............................   40,000
Income taxes...................................  408,000
Net profit.....................................$  352,000
```

The estimate was based on operation at 85% capacity. The no-gain no-loss break-even point is approximately 53%. To break even on a net yield of 10% requires operation at approximately 80% of capacity. The two sites, however, differ in a number of characteristics that may be classed as intangible.

As to Location A: the site is an attractive lot in the outskirts of a small town, with plenty of room for expansion. The road to the site is in fair enough condition to handle auto traffic and light trucking. Heavy trucks may have difficulty in the winter. Promotion for highway improvement is anticipated. Power and water sources are now adequate, but capacity will have to be increased for industrial growth. The construction estimate provides for drainage, but some observers express concern about results from very unusual rains or spring thaws.

The village is attractive in appearance. Its elementary schools, churches, and retail stores are all right; but many residents go to a city 30 miles away for important purchases and entertainment. There is no good hotel, two adequate motels, and a fair restaurant for entertaining guests. A main-line railroad serves the forementioned city, and bus service from the town connects with the important trains. The city has a good airport, and an excellent highway connects the city and the town.

The town wants industry and intends to grow. The local bank is very cooperative. It can handle the payroll and miscellaneous small transactions. An out-of-town banking connection is necessary for borrowing and important financial transactions.

Rank-and-file employees can be obtained in the area. Some will commute from out of town. Some skilled people and key personnel must be imported. The population is 90% American of two or more generations. There have been no labor union difficulties as yet in the region.

Now assume that Location B is in your own community or metropolitan area. You may also assume a type of manufacture that you know something about and that seems appropriate for the region. Then, select a plant site, and make a list of the intangibles similar to those described above for Location A.

Compare the two locations, item by item. Weigh these factors in any way that seems reasonable to you. Make a definite recommendation as to location and explain your decision.

Compound Interest Formulas

Notation

I = nominal (annual) interest rate expressed as a decimal

N = time in years

t = number of times per year that interest is paid and proceeds are invested

i = periodic interest rate = I/t

i' = effective annual interest rate

n = number of interest periods = Nt

P = principal or present worth of an investment

F = future worth of an investment

D = periodic financial event in a series

S = future worth of a series of uniform periodic events

R = present worth of a series of uniform periodic events

Basic Compound Interest Factor $(1 + i)^n$—See Table B–1.

$$(1 + i)^n = 1 + in + k_1(n - 1)\, i/2 + k_2(n - 2)i/3 + k_3(n - 3)i/4 \text{ etc.,}$$

in which $k_1 = in$, $k_2 = k_1(n - 1)i/2$, $k_3 = k_2(n - 2)i/3$, etc.

$(1 + i)^n \rightarrow e^{in}$ or e^{IN} as n or $N \rightarrow \infty$, continuous compounding—a good approximation for $(1 + i)^n$ for small values of i. (Table B–4.)

Effective annual rate $(i') = (1 + I/t)^t - 1 = (1 + i)^t - 1$

For a Single Investment

$$F = P(1 + i)^n \text{ and } P = F/(1 + i)^n$$

Future Worth of a Uniform Periodic Series—See Table B–2.

Events (D) at the end of periods:

$$S = D\left[\frac{(1 + i)^n - 1}{i}\right] \text{ and } D = S\left[\frac{i}{(1 + i)^n - 1}\right]$$

Events (D) at the beginning of periods:

$$S = D\left[\frac{(1+i)^{n+1} - 1}{i} - 1\right] \text{ and } D = S\Big/\left[\frac{(1+i)^{n+1} - 1}{i} - 1\right]$$

Present Worth of a Uniform Periodic Series—See Table B–3.

Events (D) at the end of periods:

$$R = D\left[\frac{(1+i)^n - 1}{i(1+i)^n}\right] = D\left[\frac{1 - (1+i)^{-n}}{i}\right]$$

$$D = R\left[\frac{i(1+i)^n}{(1+i)^n - 1}\right] = R\left[\frac{i}{1 - (1+i)^{-n}}\right]$$

as $n \to \infty$, $R \to D/i$ and $D \to Ri$, for capitalized cost and perpetual endowment.

Events (D) at the beginning of periods:

$$R = D\left[\frac{(1+i)^{n-1} - 1}{i(1+i)^{n-1}} + 1\right] = D\left[\frac{1 - (1+i)^{1-n}}{i} + 1\right]$$

$$D = R\Big/\left[\frac{(1+i)^{n-1} - 1}{i(1+i)^{n-1}} + 1\right] = R\Big/\left[\frac{1 - (1+i)^{1-n}}{i} + 1\right]$$

as $n \to \infty$, $R \to D/i + D$, and $D \to Ri/(1+i)$

APPENDIX **B**

Compound Interest Tables

TABLE B-1

Compound amount factor $(1 + i)^n$, to determine *future worth* of a single amount. For *present worth*, use reciprocal factor.

n	.5%	1.0%	1.5%	2.0%	2.5%	3.0%	3.5%	4.0%	4.5%	5.0%	5.5%	6.0%
1	1.005	1.010	1.015	1.020	1.025	1.030	1.035	1.040	1.045	1.050	1.055	1.060
2	1.010	1.020	1.030	1.040	1.051	1.061	1.071	1.082	1.092	1.102	1.113	1.124
3	1.015	1.030	1.046	1.061	1.077	1.093	1.109	1.125	1.141	1.158	1.174	1.191
4	1.020	1.041	1.061	1.082	1.104	1.126	1.148	1.170	1.193	1.216	1.239	1.262
5	1.025	1.051	1.077	1.104	1.131	1.159	1.188	1.217	1.246	1.276	1.307	1.338
6	1.030	1.062	1.093	1.126	1.160	1.194	1.229	1.265	1.302	1.340	1.379	1.419
7	1.036	1.072	1.110	1.149	1.189	1.230	1.272	1.316	1.361	1.407	1.455	1.504
8	1.041	1.083	1.126	1.172	1.218	1.267	1.317	1.369	1.422	1.477	1.535	1.594
9	1.046	1.094	1.143	1.195	1.249	1.305	1.363	1.423	1.486	1.551	1.619	1.689
10	1.051	1.105	1.161	1.219	1.280	1.344	1.411	1.480	1.553	1.629	1.708	1.791
11	1.056	1.116	1.178	1.243	1.312	1.384	1.460	1.539	1.623	1.710	1.802	1.898
12	1.062	1.127	1.196	1.268	1.345	1.426	1.511	1.601	1.696	1.796	1.901	2.012
13	1.067	1.138	1.214	1.294	1.379	1.469	1.564	1.665	1.772	1.886	2.006	2.133
14	1.072	1.149	1.232	1.319	1.413	1.513	1.619	1.732	1.852	1.980	2.116	2.261
15	1.078	1.161	1.250	1.346	1.448	1.558	1.675	1.801	1.935	2.079	2.232	2.397
16	1.083	1.173	1.269	1.373	1.485	1.605	1.734	1.873	2.022	2.183	2.355	2.540
17	1.088	1.184	1.288	1.400	1.522	1.653	1.795	1.948	2.113	2.292	2.485	2.693
18	1.094	1.196	1.307	1.428	1.560	1.702	1.857	2.026	2.208	2.407	2.621	2.854
19	1.099	1.208	1.327	1.457	1.599	1.754	1.923	2.107	2.308	2.527	2.766	3.026
20	1.105	1.220	1.347	1.486	1.639	1.806	1.990	2.191	2.412	2.653	2.918	3.207
21	1.110	1.232	1.367	1.516	1.680	1.860	2.059	2.279	2.520	2.786	3.078	3.400
22	1.116	1.245	1.388	1.546	1.722	1.916	2.132	2.370	2.634	2.925	3.248	3.604
23	1.122	1.257	1.408	1.577	1.765	1.974	2.206	2.465	2.752	3.072	3.426	3.820
24	1.127	1.270	1.430	1.608	1.809	2.033	2.283	2.563	2.876	3.225	3.615	4.049
25	1.133	1.282	1.451	1.641	1.854	2.094	2.363	2.666	3.005	3.386	3.813	4.292
26	1.138	1.295	1.473	1.673	1.900	2.157	2.446	2.772	3.141	3.556	4.023	4.549
27	1.144	1.308	1.495	1.707	1.948	2.221	2.532	2.883	3.282	3.733	4.244	4.822
28	1.150	1.321	1.517	1.741	1.996	2.288	2.620	2.999	3.430	3.920	4.478	5.112
29	1.156	1.335	1.540	1.776	2.046	2.357	2.712	3.119	3.584	4.116	4.724	5.418
30	1.161	1.348	1.563	1.811	2.098	2.427	2.807	3.243	3.745	4.322	4.984	5.743
31	1.167	1.361	1.587	1.848	2.150	2.500	2.905	3.373	3.914	4.538	5.258	6.088
32	1.173	1.375	1.610	1.885	2.204	2.575	3.007	3.508	4.090	4.765	5.547	6.453
33	1.179	1.389	1.634	1.922	2.259	2.652	3.112	3.648	4.274	5.003	5.852	6.841
34	1.185	1.403	1.659	1.961	2.315	2.732	3.221	3.794	4.466	5.253	6.174	7.251
35	1.191	1.417	1.684	2.000	2.373	2.814	3.334	3.946	4.667	5.516	6.514	7.686
36	1.197	1.431	1.709	2.040	2.433	2.898	3.450	4.104	4.877	5.792	6.872	8.147
37	1.203	1.445	1.735	2.081	2.493	2.985	3.571	4.268	5.097	6.081	7.250	8.636
38	1.209	1.460	1.761	2.122	2.556	3.075	3.696	4.439	5.326	6.385	7.649	9.154
39	1.215	1.474	1.787	2.165	2.620	3.167	3.825	4.616	5.566	6.705	8.069	9.704
40	1.221	1.489	1.814	2.208	2.685	3.262	3.959	4.801	5.816	7.040	8.513	10.29
42	1.233	1.519	1.869	2.297	2.821	3.461	4.241	5.193	6.352	7.762	9.476	11.56
44	1.245	1.549	1.925	2.390	2.964	3.671	4.543	5.617	6.936	8.557	10.55	12.99
46	1.258	1.580	1.984	2.487	3.114	3.895	4.867	6.075	7.574	9.434	11.74	14.59
48	1.270	1.612	2.043	2.587	3.271	4.132	5.214	6.571	8.271	10.40	13.07	16.39
50	1.283	1.645	2.105	2.692	3.437	4.384	5.585	7.107	9.033	11.47	14.54	18.42
52	1.296	1.678	2.169	2.800	3.611	4.651	5.983	7.687	9.864	12.64	16.19	20.70
54	1.309	1.711	2.234	2.913	3.794	4.934	6.409	8.314	10.77	13.94	18.01	23.26
56	1.322	1.746	2.302	3.031	3.986	5.235	6.865	8.992	11.76	15.37	20.05	26.13
58	1.335	1.781	2.372	3.154	4.188	5.553	7.354	9.726	12.85	16.94	22.32	29.36
60	1.349	1.817	2.443	3.281	4.400	5.892	7.878	10.52	14.03	18.68	24.84	32.99
65	1.383	1.909	2.632	3.623	4.978	6.830	9.357	12.80	17.48	23.84	32.46	44.14
70	1.418	2.007	2.835	4.000	5.632	7.918	11.11	15.57	21.78	30.43	42.43	59.08
75	1.454	2.109	3.055	4.416	6.372	9.179	13.20	18.95	27.15	38.83	55.45	79.06
80	1.490	2.217	3.291	4.875	7.210	10.64	15.68	23.05	33.83	49.56	72.48	105.8
85	1.528	2.330	3.545	5.383	8.157	12.34	18.62	28.04	42.16	63.25	94.72	141.6
90	1.567	2.449	3.819	5.943	9.229	14.30	22.11	34.12	52.54	80.73	123.8	189.5
95	1.606	2.574	4.114	6.562	10.44	16.58	26.26	41.51	65.47	103.0	161.8	253.5
100	1.647	2.705	4.432	7.245	11.81	19.22	31.19	50.50	81.59	131.5	211.5	339.3

TABLE B-1—*Continued*

n	7%	8%	9%	10%	11%	12%	13%	14%	15%	16%	17%	18%
1	1.070	1.080	1.090	1.100	1.110	1.120	1.130	1.140	1.150	1.160	1.170	1.180
2	1.145	1.166	1.188	1.210	1.232	1.254	1.277	1.300	1.322	1.346	1.369	1.392
3	1.225	1.260	1.295	1.331	1.368	1.405	1.443	1.482	1.521	1.561	1.602	1.643
4	1.311	1.360	1.412	1.464	1.518	1.574	1.630	1.689	1.749	1.811	1.874	1.939
5	1.403	1.469	1.539	1.611	1.685	1.762	1.842	1.925	2.011	2.100	2.192	2.288
6	1.501	1.587	1.677	1.772	1.870	1.974	2.082	2.195	2.313	2.436	2.565	2.700
7	1.606	1.714	1.828	1.949	2.076	2.211	2.353	2.502	2.660	2.826	3.001	3.185
8	1.718	1.851	1.993	2.144	2.305	2.476	2.658	2.853	3.059	3.278	3.511	3.759
9	1.838	1.999	2.172	2.358	2.558	2.773	3.004	3.252	3.518	3.803	4.108	4.435
10	1.967	2.159	2.367	2.594	2.839	3.106	3.395	3.707	4.046	4.411	4.807	5.234
11	2.105	2.332	2.580	2.853	3.152	3.479	3.836	4.226	4.652	5.117	5.624	6.176
12	2.252	2.518	2.813	3.138	3.498	3.896	4.335	4.818	5.350	5.936	6.580	7.288
13	2.410	2.720	3.066	3.452	3.883	4.363	4.898	5.492	6.153	6.886	7.699	8.599
14	2.579	2.937	3.342	3.797	4.310	4.887	5.535	6.261	7.076	7.988	9.007	10.15
15	2.759	3.172	3.642	4.177	4.785	5.474	6.254	7.138	8.137	9.266	10.54	11.97
16	2.952	3.426	3.970	4.595	5.311	6.130	7.067	8.137	9.358	10.75	12.33	14.13
17	3.159	3.700	4.328	5.054	5.895	6.866	7.986	9.276	10.76	12.47	14.43	16.67
18	3.380	3.996	4.717	5.560	6.544	7.690	9.024	10.58	12.38	14.46	16.88	19.67
19	3.617	4.316	5.142	6.116	7.263	8.613	10.20	12.06	14.23	16.78	19.75	23.21
20	3.870	4.661	5.604	6.727	8.062	9.646	11.52	13.74	16.37	19.46	23.11	27.39
22	4.430	5.437	6.659	8.140	9.934	12.10	14.71	17.86	21.64	26.19	31.63	38.14
24	5.072	6.341	7.911	9.850	12.24	15.18	18.79	23.21	28.63	35.24	43.30	53.11
26	5.807	7.396	9.399	11.92	15.08	19.04	23.99	30.17	37.86	47.41	59.27	73.95
28	6.649	8.627	11.17	14.42	18.58	23.88	30.63	39.20	50.07	63.80	81.13	103.0
30	7.612	10.06	13.27	17.45	22.89	29.96	39.12	50.95	66.21	85.85	111.1	143.4
32	8.715	11.74	15.76	21.11	28.21	37.58	49.95	66.21	87.57	115.5	152.0	199.6
34	9.978	13.69	18.73	25.55	34.75	47.14	63.78	86.05	115.8	155.4	208.1	278.0
36	11.42	15.97	22.25	30.91	42.82	59.14	81.44	111.8	153.2	209.2	284.9	387.0
38	13.08	18.63	26.44	37.40	52.76	74.18	104.0	145.3	202.5	281.5	390.0	538.9
40	14.97	21.72	31.41	45.26	65.00	93.05	132.8	188.9	267.9	378.7	533.9	750.4
45	21.00	31.92	48.33	72.89	109.5	164.0	244.6	363.7	538.8	795.4	1170.	1717.
50	29.46	46.90	74.36	117.4	184.6	289.0	450.7	700.2	1084.	1671.	2566.	3927.
55	41.31	68.91	114.4	189.1	311.0	509.3	830.5	1348.	2180.	3509.	5626.	8985.
60	57.95	101.3	176.0	304.5	524.1	897.6	1530.	2596.	4384.	7370.		

n	20%	22%	24%	26%	28%	30%	32%	34%	36%	38%	40%	42%
1	1.200	1.220	1.240	1.260	1.280	1.300	1.320	1.340	1.360	1.380	1.400	1.420
2	1.440	1.488	1.538	1.588	1.638	1.690	1.742	1.796	1.850	1.904	1.960	2.016
3	1.728	1.816	1.907	2.000	2.097	2.197	2.300	2.406	2.515	2.628	2.744	2.863
4	2.074	2.215	2.364	2.520	2.684	2.856	3.036	3.224	3.421	3.627	3.842	4.066
5	2.488	2.703	2.932	3.176	3.436	3.713	4.007	4.320	4.653	5.005	5.378	5.774
6	2.986	3.297	3.635	4.002	4.398	4.827	5.290	5.789	6.328	6.907	7.530	8.198
7	3.583	4.023	4.508	5.042	5.629	6.275	6.983	7.758	8.605	9.531	10.54	11.64
8	4.300	4.908	5.590	6.353	7.206	8.157	9.217	10.40	11.70	13.15	14.76	16.53
9	5.160	5.987	6.931	8.005	9.223	10.60	12.17	13.93	15.92	18.15	20.66	23.47
10	6.192	7.305	8.594	10.09	11.81	13.79	16.06	18.67	21.65	25.05	28.93	33.33
11	7.430	8.912	10.66	12.71	15.11	17.92	21.20	25.01	29.44	34.57	40.50	47.33
12	8.916	10.87	13.21	16.01	19.34	23.30	27.98	33.52	40.04	47.70	56.69	67.21
13	10.70	13.26	16.39	20.18	24.76	30.29	36.94	44.91	54.45	65.83	79.37	95.44
14	12.84	16.18	20.32	25.42	31.69	39.37	48.76	60.18	74.05	90.85	111.1	135.5
15	15.41	19.74	25.20	32.03	40.56	51.19	64.36	80.64	100.7	125.4	155.6	192.5
16	18.49	24.09	31.24	40.36	51.92	66.54	84.95	108.1	137.0	173.0	217.8	273.3
18	26.62	35.85	48.04	64.07	85.07	112.5	148.0	194.0	253.3	329.5	426.9	551.0
20	38.34	53.36	73.86	101.7	139.4	190.0	257.9	348.4	468.6	627.5	836.7	1111
22	55.21	79.42	113.6	161.5	228.4	321.2	449.4	625.6	866.7	1195.	1640.	2240.
24	79.50	118.2	174.6	256.4	374.1	542.8	783.0	1123.	1603.	2276.	3214.	4518.
26	114.5	175.9	268.5	407.0	613.0	917.3	1364.	2017.	2965.	4334.	6300.	9110
28	164.8	261.9	412.9	646.2	1004.	1550.	2377.	3622.	5484.	8253.		
30	237.4	389.8	634.8	1026.	1646.	2620.	4142.	6503.				

TABLE B-2

Sinking fund amount factor, $\dfrac{(1+i)^n - 1}{i}$, *to determine future worth* of a uniform series of periodic amounts. To determine periodic amount equivalent to a future sum, use reciprocal factor.

n	.5%	1.0%	1.5%	2.0%	2.5%	3.0%	3.5%	4.0%	4.5%	5.0%	5.5%	6.0%
1	1.000	1.000	1.000	1.000	1.000	1.000	1.000	1.000	1.000	1.000	1.000	1.000
2	2.005	2.010	2.015	2.020	2.025	2.030	2.035	2.040	2.045	2.050	2.055	2.060
3	3.015	3.030	3.045	3.060	3.076	3.091	3.106	3.122	3.137	3.152	3.168	3.184
4	4.030	4.060	4.091	4.122	4.153	4.184	4.215	4.246	4.278	4.310	4.342	4.375
5	5.050	5.101	5.152	5.204	5.256	5.309	5.362	5.416	5.471	5.526	5.581	5.637
6	6.075	6.152	6.230	6.308	6.388	6.468	6.550	6.633	6.717	6.802	6.888	6.975
7	7.106	7.214	7.323	7.434	7.547	7.662	7.779	7.898	8.019	8.142	8.267	8.394
8	8.141	8.286	8.433	8.583	8.736	8.892	9.052	9.214	9.380	9.549	9.722	9.897
9	9.182	9.369	9.559	9.755	9.955	10.16	10.37	10.58	10.80	11.03	11.26	11.49
10	10.23	10.46	10.70	10.95	11.20	11.46	11.73	12.01	12.29	12.58	12.88	13.18
11	11.28	11.57	11.86	12.17	12.48	12.81	13.14	13.49	13.84	14.21	14.58	14.97
12	12.34	12.68	13.04	13.41	13.80	14.19	14.60	15.03	15.46	15.92	16.39	16.87
13	13.40	13.81	14.24	14.68	15.14	15.62	16.11	16.63	17.16	17.71	18.29	18.88
14	14.46	14.95	15.45	15.97	16.52	17.09	17.68	18.29	18.93	19.60	20.29	21.02
15	15.54	16.10	16.68	17.29	17.93	18.60	19.30	20.02	20.78	21.58	22.41	23.28
16	16.61	17.26	17.93	18.64	19.38	20.16	20.97	21.82	22.72	23.66	24.64	25.67
17	17.70	18.43	19.20	20.01	20.86	21.76	22.71	23.70	24.74	25.84	27.00	28.21
18	18.79	19.61	20.49	21.41	22.39	23.41	24.50	25.65	26.86	28.13	29.48	30.91
19	19.88	20.81	21.80	22.84	23.95	25.12	26.36	27.67	29.06	30.54	32.10	33.76
20	20.98	22.02	23.12	24.30	25.54	26.87	28.28	29.78	31.37	33.07	34.87	36.79
21	22.08	23.24	24.47	25.78	27.18	28.68	30.27	31.97	33.78	35.72	37.79	39.99
22	23.19	24.47	25.84	27.30	28.86	30.54	32.33	34.25	36.30	38.51	40.86	43.39
23	24.31	25.72	27.23	28.84	30.58	32.45	34.46	36.62	38.94	41.43	44.11	47.00
24	25.43	26.97	28.63	30.42	32.35	34.43	36.67	39.08	41.69	44.50	47.54	50.82
25	26.56	28.24	30.06	32.03	34.16	36.46	38.95	41.65	44.57	47.73	51.15	54.86
26	27.69	29.53	31.51	33.67	36.01	38.55	41.31	44.31	47.57	51.11	54.97	59.16
27	28.83	30.82	32.99	35.34	37.91	40.71	43.76	47.08	50.71	54.67	58.99	63.71
28	29.97	32.13	34.48	37.05	39.86	42.93	46.29	49.97	53.99	58.40	63.23	68.53
29	31.12	33.45	36.00	38.79	41.86	45.22	48.91	52.97	57.42	62.32	67.71	73.64
30	32.28	34.78	37.54	40.57	43.90	47.58	51.62	56.08	61.01	66.44	72.44	79.06
31	33.44	36.13	39.10	42.38	46.00	50.00	54.43	59.33	64.75	70.76	77.42	84.80
32	34.61	37.49	40.69	44.23	48.15	52.50	57.33	62.70	68.67	75.30	82.68	90.89
33	35.78	38.87	42.30	46.11	50.35	55.08	60.34	66.21	72.76	80.06	88.22	97.34
34	36.96	40.26	43.93	48.03	52.61	57.73	63.45	69.86	77.03	85.07	94.08	104.2
35	38.15	41.66	45.59	49.99	54.93	60.46	66.67	73.65	81.50	90.32	100.3	111.4
36	39.34	43.08	47.28	51.99	57.30	63.28	70.01	77.60	86.16	95.84	106.8	119.1
37	40.53	44.51	48.99	54.03	59.73	66.17	73.46	81.70	91.04	101.6	113.6	127.3
38	41.74	45.95	50.72	56.11	62.23	69.16	77.03	85.97	96.14	107.7	120.9	135.9
39	42.94	47.41	52.48	58.24	64.78	72.23	80.72	90.41	101.5	114.1	128.5	145.1
40	44.16	48.89	54.27	60.40	67.40	75.40	84.55	95.03	107.0	120.8	136.6	154.8
42	46.61	51.88	57.92	64.86	72.84	82.02	92.61	104.8	118.9	135.2	154.1	176.0
44	49.08	54.93	61.69	69.50	78.55	89.05	101.2	115.4	131.9	151.1	173.6	199.8
46	51.58	58.05	65.57	74.33	84.55	96.50	110.5	126.9	146.1	168.7	195.2	226.5
48	54.10	61.22	69.57	79.35	90.86	104.4	120.4	139.3	161.6	188.0	219.4	256.6
50	56.65	64.46	73.68	84.58	97.48	112.8	131.0	152.7	178.5	209.3	246.2	290.3
52	59.22	67.77	77.92	90.02	104.4	121.7	142.4	167.2	197.0	232.9	276.1	328.3
54	61.82	71.14	82.30	95.67	111.8	131.1	154.5	182.8	217.1	258.8	309.4	370.9
56	64.44	74.58	86.80	101.6	119.4	141.2	167.6	199.8	239.2	287.3	346.4	418.8
58	67.09	78.09	91.44	107.7	127.5	151.8	181.6	218.1	263.2	318.9	387.6	472.6
60	69.77	81.67	96.21	114.1	136.0	163.1	196.5	238.0	289.5	353.6	433.4	533.1
65	76.58	90.94	108.8	131.1	159.1	194.3	238.8	295.0	366.2	456.8	572.1	719.1
70	83.57	100.7	122.4	150.0	185.3	230.6	288.9	364.3	461.9	588.5	753.3	967.9
75	90.73	110.9	137.0	170.8	214.9	272.6	348.5	448.6	581.0	756.7	990.1	1301.
80	98.07	121.7	152.7	193.8	248.4	321.4	419.3	551.2	729.6	971.2	1300.	1747.
85	105.6	133.0	169.7	219.1	286.3	377.9	503.4	676.1	914.6	1245.	1704.	2343.
90	113.3	144.9	187.9	247.2	329.2	443.3	603.2	828.0	1145.	1595.	2233.	3141.
95	121.2	157.4	207.6	278.1	377.7	519.3	721.8	1013.	1433.	2041.	2924.	4209.
100	129.3	170.5	228.8	312.2	432.5	607.3	862.6	1238.	1791.	2610.	3827.	5638.

TABLE B-2—*Continued*

n	7%	8%	9%	10%	11%	12%	13%	14%	15%	16%	17%	18%
1	1.000	1.000	1.000	1.000	1.000	1.000	1.000	1.000	1.000	1.000	1.000	1.000
2	2.070	2.080	2.090	2.100	2.110	2.120	2.130	2.140	2.150	2.160	2.170	2.180
3	3.215	3.246	3.278	3.310	3.342	3.374	3.407	3.440	3.472	3.506	3.539	3.572
4	4.440	4.506	4.573	4.641	4.710	4.779	4.850	4.921	4.993	5.066	5.141	5.215
5	5.751	5.867	5.985	6.105	6.228	6.353	6.480	6.610	6.742	6.877	7.014	7.154
6	7.153	7.336	7.523	7.716	7.913	8.115	8.323	8.536	8.754	8.977	9.207	9.442
7	8.654	8.923	9.200	9.487	9.783	10.09	10.40	10.73	11.07	11.41	11.77	12.14
8	10.26	10.64	11.03	11.44	11.86	12.30	12.76	13.23	13.73	14.24	14.77	15.33
9	11.98	12.49	13.02	13.58	14.16	14.78	15.42	16.09	16.79	17.52	18.28	19.09
10	13.82	14.49	15.19	15.94	16.72	17.55	18.42	19.34	20.30	21.32	22.39	23.52
11	15.78	16.65	17.56	18.53	19.56	20.65	21.81	23.04	24.35	25.73	27.20	28.76
12	17.89	18.98	20.14	21.38	22.71	24.13	25.65	27.27	29.00	30.85	32.82	34.93
13	20.14	21.50	22.95	24.52	26.21	28.03	29.98	32.09	34.35	36.79	39.40	42.22
14	22.55	24.21	26.02	27.97	30.09	32.39	34.88	37.58	40.50	43.67	47.10	50.82
15	25.13	27.15	29.36	31.77	34.41	37.28	40.42	43.84	47.58	51.66	56.11	60.97
16	27.89	30.32	33.00	35.95	39.19	42.75	46.67	50.98	55.72	60.93	66.65	72.94
17	30.84	33.75	36.97	40.54	44.50	48.88	53.74	59.12	65.08	71.67	78.98	87.07
18	34.00	37.45	41.30	45.60	50.40	55.75	61.73	68.39	75.84	84.14	93.41	103.7
19	37.38	41.45	46.02	51.16	56.94	63.44	70.75	78.97	88.21	98.60	110.3	123.4
20	41.00	45.76	51.16	57.27	64.20	72.05	80.95	91.02	102.4	115.4	130.0	146.6
22	49.01	55.46	62.87	71.40	81.21	92.50	105.5	120.4	137.6	157.4	180.2	206.3
24	58.18	66.76	76.79	88.50	102.2	118.2	136.8	158.7	184.2	214.0	248.8	289.5
26	68.68	79.95	93.32	109.2	128.0	150.3	176.9	208.3	245.7	290.1	342.8	405.3
28	80.70	95.34	113.0	134.2	159.8	190.7	227.9	272.9	327.1	392.5	471.4	566.5
30	94.46	113.3	136.3	164.5	199.0	241.3	293.2	356.8	434.7	530.3	647.4	790.9
32	110.2	134.2	164.0	201.1	247.3	304.8	376.5	465.8	577.1	715.7	888.4	1103.
34	128.3	158.6	197.0	245.5	306.8	384.5	482.9	607.5	765.4	965.3	1218.	1539.
36	148.9	187.1	236.1	299.1	380.2	484.5	618.7	791.7	1014.	1301.	1670.	2145.
38	172.6	220.3	282.6	364.0	470.5	609.8	792.2	1031.	1344.	1753.	2288.	2988.
40	199.6	259.1	337.9	442.6	581.8	767.1	1014.	1342.	1779.	2361.	3135.	4163.
45	285.7	386.5	525.9	718.9	986.6	1358.	1874.	2591.	3585.	4965.	6879.	9532.
50	406.5	573.8	815.1	1164.	1669.	2400.	3460.	4995.	7218.			
55	575.9	848.9	1260.	1881.	2818.	4236.	6380.	9623.				
60	813.5	1253.	1945.	3035.	4755.	7472.						

n	20%	22%	24%	26%	28%	30%	32%	34%	36%	38%	40%	42%
1	1.000	1.000	1.000	1.000	1.000	1.000	1.000	1.000	1.000	1.000	1.000	1.000
2	2.200	2.220	2.240	2.260	2.280	2.300	2.320	2.340	2.360	2.380	2.400	2.420
3	3.640	3.708	3.778	3.848	3.918	3.990	4.062	4.136	4.210	4.284	4.360	4.436
4	5.368	5.524	5.684	5.848	6.016	6.187	6.362	6.542	6.725	6.912	7.104	7.300
5	7.442	7 740	8.048	8.368	8.700	9.043	9.398	9.766	10.15	10.54	10.95	11.37
6	9.930	10.44	10.98	11.54	12.14	12.76	13.41	14.09	14.80	15.54	16.32	17.14
7	12.92	13.74	14.62	15.55	16.53	17.58	18.70	19.88	21.13	22.45	23.85	25.34
8	16.50	17.76	19.12	20.59	22.16	23.86	25.68	27.63	29.73	31.98	34.39	36.98
9	20.80	22.67	24.71	26.94	29.37	32.01	34.90	38.03	41.43	45.14	49.15	53.51
10	25.96	28.66	31.64	34.94	38.59	42.62	47.06	51.96	57.35	63.29	69.81	76.98
11	32.15	35.96	40.24	45.03	50.40	56.41	63.12	70.62	79.00	88.34	98.74	110.3
12	39.58	44.87	50.89	57.74	65.51	74.33	84.32	95.64	108.4	122.9	139.2	157.7
13	48.50	55.75	64.11	73.75	84.85	97.63	112.3	129.2	148.5	170.6	195.9	224.9
14	59.20	69.01	80.50	93.93	109.6	127.9	149.2	174.1	202.9	236.4	275.3	320.3
15	72.04	85.19	100.8	119.3	141.3	167.3	198.0	234.2	277.0	327.3	386.4	455.8
16	87.44	104.9	126.0	151.4	181.9	218.5	262.4	314.9	377.7	452.7	542.0	648.3
18	128.1	158.4	196.0	242.6	300.3	371.5	459.4	567.8	700.9	864.4	1065.	1310.
20	186.7	238.0	303.6	387.4	494.2	630.2	802.9	1022.	1299.	1649.	2089.	2643.
22	271.0	356.4	469.1	617.3	812.0	1067.	1401.	1837.	2405.	3142.	4097.	5332.
24	392.5	532.7	723.5	982.3	1333.	1806.	2444.	3301.	4450.	5986.	8033.	
26	567.4	795.2	1115.	1562.	2186.	3054.	4260.	5930.	8233.			
28	819.2	1186.	1716.	2482.	3583.	5164.	7426.					
30	1182.	1767.	2641.	3942.	5873.	8730.						

TABLE B–3

Annuity fund factor, $\dfrac{(1+i)^n - 1}{i(1+i)^n}$, to determine *present worth* of a uniform series of periodic amounts. To determine periodic amount equivalent to an initial sum, use reciprocal factor (*capital recovery factor*).

n	.5%	1.0%	1.5%	2.0%	2.5%	3.0%	3.5%	4.0%	4.5%	5.0%	5.5%	6.0%
1	.9950	.9901	.9852	.9804	.9756	.9709	.9662	.9615	.9569	.9524	.9479	.9434
2	1.985	1.970	1.956	1.942	1.927	1.913	1.900	1.886	1.873	1.859	1.846	1.833
3	2.970	2.941	2.912	2.884	2.856	2.829	2.802	2.775	2.749	2.723	2.698	2.673
4	3.950	3.902	3.854	3.808	3.762	3.717	3.673	3.630	3.588	3.546	3.505	3.465
5	4.926	4.853	4.783	4.713	4.646	4.580	4.515	4.452	4.390	4.329	4.270	4.212
6	5.896	5.795	5.697	5.601	5.508	5.417	5.329	5.242	5.158	5.076	4.996	4.917
7	6.862	6.728	6.598	6.472	6.349	6.230	6.115	6.002	5.893	5.786	5.683	5.582
8	7.823	7.652	7.486	7.325	7.170	7.020	6.874	6.733	6.596	6.463	6.335	6.210
9	8.779	8.566	8.361	8.162	7.971	7.786	7.608	7.435	7.269	7.108	6.952	6.802
10	9.730	9.471	9.222	8.983	8.752	8.530	8.317	8.111	7.913	7.722	7.538	7.360
11	10.68	10.37	10.07	9.787	9.514	9.253	9.002	8.760	8.529	8.306	8.093	7.887
12	11.62	11.26	10.91	10.58	10.26	9.954	9.663	9.385	9.119	8.863	8.619	8.384
13	12.56	12.13	11.73	11.35	10.98	10.63	10.30	9.986	9.683	9.394	9.117	8.853
14	13.49	13.00	12.54	12.11	11.69	11.30	10.92	10.56	10.22	9.899	9.590	9.295
15	14.42	13.87	13.34	12.85	12.38	11.94	11.52	11.12	10.74	10.38	10.04	9.712
16	15.34	14.72	14.13	13.58	13.05	12.56	12.09	11.65	11.23	10.84	10.46	10.11
17	16.26	15.56	14.91	14.29	13.71	13.17	12.65	12.17	11.71	11.27	10.86	10.48
18	17.17	16.40	15.67	14.99	14.35	13.75	13.19	12.66	12.16	11.69	11.25	10.83
19	18.08	17.23	16.43	15.68	14.98	14.32	13.71	13.13	12.59	12.09	11.61	11.16
20	18.99	18.05	17.17	16.35	15.59	14.88	14.21	13.59	13.01	12.46	11.95	11.47
21	19.89	18.86	17.90	17.01	16.18	15.42	14.70	14.03	13.40	12.82	12.28	11.76
22	20.78	19.66	18.62	17.66	16.77	15.94	15.17	14.45	13.78	13.16	12.58	12.04
23	21.68	20.46	19.33	18.29	17.33	16.44	15.62	14.86	14.15	13.49	12.88	12.30
24	22.56	21.24	20.03	18.91	17.88	16.94	16.06	15.25	14.50	13.80	13.15	12.55
25	23.45	22.02	20.72	19.52	18.42	17.41	16.48	15.62	14.83	14.09	13.41	12.78
26	24.32	22.80	21.40	20.12	18.95	17.88	16.89	15.98	15.15	14.38	13.66	13.00
27	25.20	23.56	22.07	20.71	19.46	18.33	17.29	16.33	15.45	14.64	13.90	13.21
28	26.07	24.32	22.73	21.28	19.96	18.76	17.67	16.66	15.74	14.90	14.12	13.41
29	26.93	25.07	23.38	21.84	20.45	19.19	18.04	16.98	16.02	15.14	14.33	13.59
30	27.79	25.81	24.02	22.40	20.93	19.60	18.39	17.29	16.29	15.37	14.53	13.76
31	28.65	26.54	24.65	22.94	21.40	20.00	18.74	17.59	16.54	15.59	14.72	13.93
32	29.50	27.27	25.27	23.47	21.85	20.39	19.07	17.87	16.79	15.80	14.90	14.08
33	30.35	27.99	25.88	23.99	22.29	20.77	19.39	18.15	17.02	16.00	15.08	14.23
34	31.20	28.70	26.48	24.50	22.72	21.13	19.70	18.41	17.25	16.19	15.24	14.37
35	32.04	29.41	27.08	25.00	23.15	21.49	20.00	18.66	17.46	16.37	15.39	14.50
36	32.87	30.11	27.66	25.49	23.56	21.83	20.29	18.91	17.67	16.55	15.54	14.62
37	33.70	30.80	28.24	25.97	23.96	22.17	20.57	19.14	17.86	16.71	15.67	14.74
38	34.53	31.48	28.81	26.44	24.35	22.49	20.84	19.37	18.05	16.87	15.80	14.85
39	35.35	32.16	29.36	26.90	24.73	22.81	21.10	19.58	18.23	17.02	15.93	14.95
40	36.17	32.83	29.92	27.36	25.10	23.11	21.36	19.79	18.40	17.16	16.05	15.05
42	37.80	34.16	30.99	28.23	25.82	23.70	21.83	20.19	18.72	17.42	16.26	15.22
44	39.41	35.46	32.04	29.08	26.50	24.25	22.28	20.55	19.02	17.66	16.46	15.38
46	41.00	36.73	33.06	29.89	27.15	24.78	22.70	20.88	19.29	17.88	16.63	15.52
48	42.58	37.97	34.04	30.67	27.77	25.27	23.09	21.20	19.54	18.08	16.79	15.65
50	44.14	39.20	35.00	31.42	28.36	25.73	23.46	21.48	19.76	18.26	16.93	15.76
52	45.69	40.39	35.93	32.14	28.92	26.17	23.80	21.75	19.97	18.42	17.06	15.86
54	47.22	41.57	36.83	32.84	29.46	26.58	24.11	21.99	20.16	18.57	17.17	15.95
56	48.74	42.72	37.71	33.50	29.96	26.97	24.41	22.22	20.33	18.70	17.28	16.03
58	50.24	43.85	38.56	34.15	30.45	27.33	24.69	22.43	20.49	18.82	17.37	16.10
60	51.73	44.96	39.38	34.76	30.91	27.68	24.94	22.62	20.64	18.93	17.45	16.16
65	55.38	47.63	41.34	36.20	31.96	28.45	25.52	23.05	20.95	19.16	17.62	16.29
70	58.94	50.17	43.15	37.50	32.90	29.12	26.00	23.39	21.20	19.34	17.75	16.38
75	62.41	52.59	44.84	38.68	33.72	29.70	26.41	23.68	21.40	19.48	17.85	16.46
80	65.80	54.89	46.41	39.74	34.45	30.20	26.75	23.92	21.57	19.60	17.93	16.51
85	69.11	57.08	47.86	40.71	35.10	30.63	27.04	24.11	21.70	19.68	17.99	16.55
90	72.33	59.16	49.21	41.59	35.67	31.00	27.28	24.27	21.80	19.75	18.03	16.58
95	75.48	61.14	50.46	42.38	36.17	31.32	27.48	24.40	21.88	19.81	18.07	16.60
100	78.54	63.03	51.62	43.10	36.61	31.60	27.66	24.50	21.95	19.85	18.10	16.62

TABLE B–3—*Continued*

n	7%	8%	9%	10%	11%	12%	13%	14%	15%	16%	17%	18%
1	.9346	.9259	.9174	.9091	.9009	.8929	.8850	.8772	.8696	.8621	.8547	.8475
2	1.808	1.783	1.759	1.736	1.713	1.690	1.668	1.647	1.626	1.605	1.585	1.566
3	2.624	2.577	2.531	2.487	2.444	2.402	2.361	2.322	2.283	2.246	2.210	2.174
4	3.387	3.312	3.240	3.170	3.102	3.037	2.974	2.914	2.855	2.798	2.743	2.690
5	4.100	3.993	3.890	3.791	3.696	3.605	3.517	3.433	3.352	3.274	3.199	3.127
6	4.767	4.623	4.486	4.355	4.231	4.111	3.998	3.889	3.784	3.685	3.589	3.498
7	5.389	5.206	5.033	4.868	4.712	4.564	4.423	4.288	4.160	4.039	3.922	3.812
8	5.971	5.747	5.535	5.335	5.146	4.968	4.799	4.639	4.487	4.344	4.207	4.078
9	6.515	6.247	5.995	5.759	5.537	5.328	5.132	4.946	4.772	4.607	4.451	4.303
10	7.024	6.710	6.418	6.145	5.889	5.650	5.426	5.216	5.019	4.833	4.659	4.494
11	7.499	7.139	6.805	6.495	6.207	5.938	5.687	5.453	5.234	5.029	4.836	4.656
12	7.943	7.536	7.161	6.814	6.492	6.194	5.918	5.660	5.421	5.197	4.988	4.793
13	8.358	7.904	7.487	7.103	6.750	6.424	6.122	5.842	5.583	5.342	5.118	4.910
14	8.745	8.244	7.786	7.367	6.982	6.628	6.302	6.002	5.724	5.468	5.229	5.008
15	9.108	8.559	8.061	7.606	7.191	6.811	6.462	6.142	5.847	5.575	5.324	5.092
16	9.447	8.851	8.313	7.824	7.379	6.974	6.604	6.265	5.954	5.668	5.405	5.162
17	9.763	9.122	8.544	8.022	7.549	7.120	6.729	6.373	6.047	5.749	5.475	5.222
18	10.06	9.372	8.756	8.201	7.702	7.250	6.840	6.467	6.128	5.818	5.534	5.273
19	10.34	9.604	8.950	8.365	7.839	7.366	6.938	6.550	6.198	5.877	5.584	5.316
20	10.59	9.818	9.129	8.514	7.963	7.469	7.025	6.623	6.259	5.929	5.628	5.353
22	11.06	10.20	9.442	8.772	8.176	7.645	7.170	6.743	6.359	6.011	5.696	5.410
24	11.47	10.53	9.707	8.985	8.348	7.784	7.283	6.835	6.434	6.073	5.746	5.451
26	11.83	10.81	9.929	9.161	8.488	7.896	7.372	6.906	6.491	6.118	5.783	5.480
28	12.14	11.05	10.12	9.307	8.602	7.984	7.441	6.961	6.534	6.152	5.810	5.502
30	12.41	11.26	10.27	9.427	8.694	8.055	7.496	7.003	6.566	6.177	5.829	5.517
32	12.65	11.43	10.41	9.526	8.769	8.112	7.538	7.035	6.591	6.196	5.844	5.528
34	12.85	11.59	10.52	9.609	8.829	8.157	7.572	7.060	6.609	6.210	5.854	5.536
36	13.04	11.72	10.61	9.677	8.879	8.192	7.598	7.079	6.623	6.220	5.862	5.541
38	13.19	11.83	10.69	9.733	8.919	8.221	7.618	7.094	6.634	6.228	5.867	5.545
40	13.33	11.92	10.76	9.779	8.951	8.244	7.634	7.105	6.642	6.233	5.871	5.548
45	13.61	12.11	10.88	9.863	9.008	8.283	7.661	7.123	6.654	6.242	5.877	5.552
50	13.80	12.23	10.96	9.915	9.042	8.304	7.675	7.133	6.661	6.246	5.880	5.554
55	13.94	12.32	11.01	9.947	9.062	8.317	7.683	7.138	6.664	6.248	5.881	5.555
60	14.04	12.38	11.05	9.967	9.074	8.324	7.687	7.140	6.665	6.249	5.882	5.555

n	20%	22%	24%	26%	28%	30%	32%	34%	36%	38%	40%	42%
1	.8333	.8197	.8065	.7937	.7812	.7692	.7576	.7463	.7353	.7246	.7143	.7042
2	1.528	1.492	1.457	1.424	1.392	1.361	1.331	1.303	1.276	1.250	1.224	1.200
3	2.106	2.042	1.981	1.923	1.868	1.816	1.766	1.719	1.673	1.630	1.589	1.549
4	2.589	2.494	2.404	2.320	2.241	2.166	2.096	2.029	1.966	1.906	1.849	1.795
5	2.991	2.864	2.745	2.635	2.532	2.436	2.345	2.260	2.181	2.106	2.035	1.969
6	3.326	3.167	3.020	2.885	2.759	2.643	2.534	2.433	2.339	2.251	2.168	2.091
7	3.605	3.416	3.242	3.083	2.937	2.802	2.677	2.562	2.455	2.355	2.263	2.176
8	3.837	3.619	3.421	3.241	3.076	2.925	2.786	2.658	2.540	2.432	2.331	2.237
9	4.031	3.786	3.566	3.366	3.184	3.019	2.868	2.730	2.603	2.487	2.379	2.280
10	4.192	3.923	3.682	3.465	3.269	3.092	2.930	2.784	2.649	2.527	2.414	2.310
11	4.327	4.035	3.776	3.543	3.335	3.147	2.978	2.824	2.683	2.555	2.438	2.331
12	4.439	4.127	3.851	3.606	3.387	3.190	3.013	2.853	2.708	2.576	2.456	2.346
13	4.533	4.203	3.912	3.656	3.427	3.223	3.040	2.876	2.727	2.592	2.469	2.356
14	4.611	4.265	3.962	3.695	3.459	3.249	3.061	2.892	2.740	2.603	2.478	2.363
15	4.675	4.315	4.001	3.726	3.483	3.268	3.076	2.905	2.750	2.611	2.484	2.369
16	4.730	4.357	4.033	3.751	3.503	3.283	3.088	2.914	2.757	2.616	2.489	2.372
18	4.812	4.419	4.080	3.786	3.529	3.304	3.104	2.926	2.767	2.624	2.494	2.377
20	4.870	4.460	4.110	3.808	3.546	3.316	3.113	2.933	2.772	2.627	2.497	2.379
22	4.909	4.488	4.130	3.822	3.556	3.323	3.118	2.936	2.775	2.629	2.498	2.380
24	4.937	4.507	4.143	3.831	3.562	3.327	3.121	2.939	2.776	2.630	2.499	2.380
26	4.956	4.520	4.151	3.837	3.566	3.330	3.123	2.940	2.777	2.631	2.500	2.381
28	4.970	4.528	4.157	3.840	3.568	3.331	3.124	2.940	2.777	2.631	2.500	2.381
30	4.979	4.534	4.160	3.842	3.569	3.332	3.124	2.941	2.778	2.631	2.500	2.381

TABLE B–4

Continuous compounding factor, e^{in}. An approximation of $(1+i)^n$ for small values of i.

in	e^{in}	in	e^{in}	in	e^{in}	in	e^{in}	in	e^{in}	in	e^{in}
0.00	1.000	0.50	1.649	1.00	2.718	1.50	4.482	2.00	7.389	3.00	20.09
0.01	1.010	0.51	1.665	1.01	2.746	1.51	4.527	2.02	7.538	3.02	20.49
0.02	1.020	0.52	1.682	1.02	2.773	1.52	4.572	2.04	7.691	3.04	20.91
0.03	1.031	0.53	1.699	1.03	2.801	1.53	4.618	2.06	7.846	3.06	21.33
0.04	1.041	0.54	1.716	1.04	2.829	1.54	4.665	2.08	8.005	3.08	21.76
0.05	1.051	0.55	1.733	1.05	2.858	1.55	4.712	2.10	8.166	3.10	22.20
0.06	1.062	0.56	1.751	1.06	2.886	1.56	4.759	2.12	8.331	3.12	22.65
0.07	1.073	0.57	1.768	1.07	2.915	1.57	4.807	2.14	8.499	3.14	23.10
0.08	1.083	0.58	1.786	1.08	2.945	1.58	4.855	2.16	8.671	3.16	23.57
0.09	1.094	0.59	1.804	1.09	2.974	1.59	4.904	2.18	8.846	3.18	24.05
0.10	1.105	0.60	1.822	1.10	3.004	1.60	4.953	2.20	9.025	3.20	24.53
0.11	1.116	0.61	1.840	1.11	3.034	1.61	5.003	2.22	9.207	3.22	25.03
0.12	1.128	0.62	1.859	1.12	3.065	1.62	5.053	2.24	9.393	3.24	25.53
0.13	1.139	0.63	1.878	1.13	3.096	1.63	5.104	2.26	9.583	3.26	26.05
0.14	1.150	0.64	1.897	1.14	3.127	1.64	5.155	2.28	9.777	3.28	26.58
0.15	1.162	0.65	1.916	1.15	3.158	1.65	5.207	2.30	9.974	3.30	27.11
0.16	1.174	0.66	1.935	1.16	3.190	1.66	5.259	2.32	10.18	3.32	27.66
0.17	1.185	0.67	1.954	1.17	3.222	1.67	5.312	2.34	10.38	3.34	28.22
0.18	1.197	0.68	1.974	1.18	3.254	1.68	5.366	2.36	10.59	3.36	28.79
0.19	1.209	0.69	1.994	1.19	3.287	1.69	5.420	2.38	10.81	3.38	29.37
0.20	1.221	0.70	2.014	1.20	3.320	1.70	5.474	2.40	11.02	3.40	29.96
0.21	1.234	0.71	2.034	1.21	3.354	1.71	5.529	2.42	11.25	3.42	30.57
0.22	1.246	0.72	2.054	1.22	3.387	1.72	5.585	2.44	11.47	3.44	31.19
0.23	1.259	0.73	2.075	1.23	3.421	1.73	5.641	2.46	11.71	3.46	31.82
0.24	1.271	0.74	2.096	1.24	3.456	1.74	5.697	2.48	11.94	3.48	32.46
0.25	1.284	0.75	2.117	1.25	3.490	1.75	5.755	2.50	12.18	3.50	33.12
0.26	1.297	0.76	2.138	1.26	3.525	1.76	5.812	2.52	12.43	3.52	33.78
0.27	1.310	0.77	2.160	1.27	3.561	1.77	5.871	2.54	12.68	3.54	34.47
0.28	1.323	0.78	2.182	1.28	3.597	1.78	5.930	2.56	12.94	3.56	35.16
0.29	1.336	0.79	2.203	1.29	3.633	1.79	5.990	2.58	13.20	3.58	35.87
0.30	1.350	0.80	2.226	1.30	3.670	1.80	6.050	2.60	13.46	3.60	36.60
0.31	1.363	0.81	2.248	1.31	3.706	1.81	6.110	2.62	13.74	3.62	37.34
0.32	1.377	0.82	2.271	1.32	3.743	1.82	6.172	2.64	14.01	3.64	38.09
0.33	1.391	0.83	2.293	1.33	3.781	1.83	6.234	2.66	14.30	3.66	38.86
0.34	1.405	0.84	2.316	1.34	3.819	1.84	6.297	2.68	14.59	3.68	39.65
0.35	1.419	0.85	2.340	1.35	3.857	1.85	6.360	2.70	14.88	3.70	40.48
0.36	1.433	0.86	2.363	1.36	3.896	1.86	6.424	2.72	15.18	3.72	41.26
0.37	1.448	0.87	2.387	1.37	3.935	1.87	6.488	2.74	15.49	3.74	42.10
0.38	1.462	0.88	2.411	1.38	3.975	1.88	6.554	2.76	15.80	3.76	42.95
0.39	1.477	0.89	2.435	1.39	4.015	1.89	6.619	2.78	16.12	3.78	43.82
0.40	1.492	0.90	2.460	1.40	4.055	1.90	6.686	2.80	16.45	3.80	44.70
0.41	1.507	0.91	2.484	1.41	4.096	1.91	6.753	2.82	16.78	3.82	45.60
0.42	1.522	0.92	2.509	1.42	4.137	1.92	6.821	2.84	17.12	3.84	46.53
0.43	1.537	0.93	2.535	1.43	4.179	1.93	6.890	2.86	17.46	3.86	47.47
0.44	1.553	0.94	2.560	1.44	4.221	1.94	6.959	2.88	17.81	3.88	48.42
0.45	1.568	0.95	2.586	1.45	4.263	1.95	7.029	2.90	18.17	3.90	49.40
0.46	1.584	0.96	2.612	1.46	4.306	1.96	7.099	2.92	18.54	3.92	50.40
0.47	1.600	0.97	2.638	1.47	4.349	1.97	7.171	2.94	18.92	3.94	51.42
0.48	1.616	0.98	2.665	1.48	4.393	1.98	7.243	2.96	19.30	3.96	52.46
0.49	1.632	0.99	2.691	1.49	4.437	1.99	7.316	2.98	19.69	3.98	53.52
0.50	1.649	1.00	2.718	1.50	4.482	2.00	7.389	3.00	20.09	4.00	54.60

APPENDIX **C**

Common Logarithms

TABLE C-1

MANTISSAS OF COMMON LOGARITHMS

N	0	1	2	3	4	5	6	7	8	9
10	0000	0043	0086	0128	0170	0212	0253	0294	0334	0374
11	0414	0453	0492	0531	0569	0607	0645	0682	0719	0755
12	0792	0828	0864	0899	0934	0969	1004	1038	1072	1106
13	1139	1173	1206	1239	1271	1303	1335	1367	1399	1430
14	1461	1492	1523	1553	1584	1614	1644	1673	1703	1732
15	1761	1790	1818	1847	1875	1903	1931	1959	1987	2014
16	2041	2068	2095	2122	2148	2175	2201	2227	2253	2279
17	2304	2330	2355	2380	2405	2430	2455	2480	2504	2529
18	2553	2577	2601	2625	2648	2672	2695	2718	2742	2765
19	2788	2810	2833	2856	2878	2900	2923	2945	2967	2989
20	3010	3032	3054	3075	3096	3118	3139	3160	3181	3201
21	3222	3243	3263	3284	3304	3324	3345	3365	3385	3404
22	3424	3444	3464	3483	3502	3522	3541	3560	3579	3598
23	3617	3636	3655	3674	3692	3711	3729	3747	3766	3784
24	3802	3820	3838	3856	3874	3892	3909	3927	3945	3962
25	3979	3997	4014	4031	4048	4065	4082	4099	4116	4133
26	4150	4166	4183	4200	4216	4232	4249	4265	4281	4298
27	4314	4330	4346	4362	4378	4393	4409	4425	4440	4456
28	4472	4487	4502	4518	4533	4548	4564	4579	4594	4609
29	4624	4639	4654	4669	4683	4698	4713	4728	4742	4757
30	4771	4786	4800	4814	4829	4843	4857	4871	4866	4900
31	4914	4928	4942	4955	4969	4983	4997	5011	5024	5038
32	5051	5065	5079	5092	5105	5119	5132	5145	5159	5172
33	5185	5198	5211	5224	5237	5250	5263	5276	5289	5302
34	5315	5328	5340	5353	5366	5378	5391	5403	5416	5428
35	5441	5453	5465	5478	5490	5502	5514	5527	5539	5551
36	5563	5575	5587	5599	5611	5623	5635	5647	5658	5670
37	5682	5694	5705	5717	5729	5740	5752	5763	5775	5786
38	5798	5809	5821	5832	5843	5855	5866	5877	5888	5899
39	5911	5922	5933	5944	5955	5966	5977	5988	5999	6010
40	6021	6031	6042	6053	6064	6075	6085	6096	6107	6117
41	6128	6138	6149	6160	6170	6180	6191	6201	6212	6222
42	6232	6243	6253	6263	6274	6284	6294	6304	6314	6325
43	6335	6345	6355	6365	6375	6385	6395	6405	6415	6425
44	6435	6444	6454	6464	6474	6484	6493	6503	6513	6522
45	6532	6542	6551	6561	6571	6580	6590	5699	6609	6618
46	6628	6637	6646	6656	6665	6675	6684	6693	6702	6712
47	6721	6730	6739	6749	6758	6767	6776	6785	6794	6803
48	6812	6821	6830	6839	6848	6857	6886	6875	6884	6893
49	6902	6911	6920	6928	6937	6946	6955	6964	6972	6981
50	6990	6998	7007	7016	7024	7033	7042	7050	7059	7067
51	7076	7084	7093	7101	7110	7118	7126	7135	7143	7152
52	7160	7168	7177	7185	7193	7202	7210	7218	7226	7235
53	7243	7251	7259	7267	7275	7284	7292	7300	7308	7316
54	7324	7332	7340	7348	7356	7364	7372	7380	7388	7396

TABLE C–1—*Continued*

N	0	1	2	3	4	5	6	7	8	9
55	7404	7412	7419	7427	7435	7443	7451	7459	7466	7474
56	7482	7490	7497	7505	7513	7520	7528	7536	7543	7551
57	7559	7566	7574	7582	7589	7597	7604	7612	7619	7627
58	7634	7642	7649	7657	7664	7672	7679	7686	7694	7701
59	7709	7716	7723	7731	7738	7745	7752	7760	7767	7774
60	7782	7789	7796	7803	7810	7818	7825	7832	7839	7846
61	7853	7860	7868	7875	7882	7889	7896	7903	7910	7917
62	7924	7931	7938	7945	7952	7959	7966	7973	7980	7987
63	7993	8000	8007	8014	8021	8028	8035	8041	8048	8055
64	8062	8069	8075	8082	8089	8096	8102	8109	8116	8122
65	8129	8136	8142	8149	8156	8162	8169	8176	8182	8189
66	8195	8202	8209	8215	8222	8228	8235	8241	8248	8254
67	8261	8267	8274	8280	8287	8293	8299	8306	8312	8319
68	8325	8331	8338	8344	8351	8357	8363	8370	8376	8382
69	8388	8395	8401	8407	8414	8420	8426	8432	8439	8445
70	8451	8457	8463	8470	8476	8482	8488	8494	8500	8506
71	8513	8519	8525	8531	8537	8543	8549	8555	8561	8567
72	8573	8579	8585	8591	8597	8603	8609	8615	8621	8627
73	8633	8639	8645	8651	8657	8663	8669	8675	8681	8686
74	8692	8698	8704	8710	8716	8722	8727	8733	8739	8745
75	8751	8756	8762	8768	8774	8779	8785	8791	8797	8802
76	8808	8814	8820	8825	8831	8837	8842	8848	8854	8859
77	8865	8871	8876	8882	8887	8893	8899	8904	8910	8915
78	8921	8927	8932	8938	8943	8949	8954	8960	8965	8971
79	8976	8982	8987	8993	8998	9004	9009	9015	9020	9025
80	9031	9036	9042	9047	9053	9058	9063	9069	9074	9079
81	9085	9090	9096	9101	9106	9112	9117	9122	9128	9133
82	9138	9143	9149	9154	9159	9165	9170	9175	9180	9186
83	9191	9196	9201	9206	9212	9217	9222	9227	9232	9238
84	9243	9248	9253	9258	9263	9269	9274	9279	9284	9289
85	9294	9299	9304	9309	9315	9320	9325	9330	9335	9340
86	9345	9350	9355	9360	9365	9370	9375	9380	9385	9390
87	9395	9400	9405	9410	9415	9420	9425	9430	9435	9440
88	9445	9450	9455	9460	9465	9469	9474	9479	9484	9489
89	9494	9499	9504	9509	9513	9518	9523	9528	9533	9538
90	9542	9547	9552	9557	9562	9566	9571	9576	9581	9586
91	9590	9595	9600	9605	9609	9614	9619	9624	9628	9633
92	9638	9643	9647	9652	9657	9661	9666	9671	9675	9680
93	9685	9689	9694	9699	9703	9708	9713	9717	9722	9727
94	9731	9736	9741	9745	9750	9754	9759	9763	9768	9773
95	9777	9782	9786	9791	9795	9800	9805	8909	9814	9818
96	9823	9827	9832	9836	9841	9845	9850	9854	9859	9663
97	9868	8772	9877	9881	9886	9890	9894	9899	9903	9908
98	9912	9917	9921	9926	9930	9934	9939	9943	9948	9952
99	9956	9961	9965	9969	9974	9978	9983	9987	9991	9996

Engineering Data

The following data are intended for readers outside the engineering professions. The professional handbooks are recommended for the greater detail and precision required in specialized estimating.

ENERGY AND POWER

Energy, in economy studies, is customarily measured in terms of heat (British thermal units), mechanical units (horsepower hours), or electricity (kilowatt hours). *Power* is a *rate* at which energy in some form is produced or consumed (foot-pounds, inch-tons, horsepower, B.T.U.'s per hour, watts, kilowatts). In common language, the term *power* is often used (incorrectly) for energy, as in the electrical industry. Units of energy, other than those mentioned here, are employed in basic sciences, laboratory work, chemical engineering, and nuclear engineering.

Formulas and conversion factors that may be useful in economy problems accompanying this book are given below.

Mechanical Units

1 foot-pound (ft.-lb.) = energy required to lift a load or move a resistance of 1 lb. a distance of 1 ft.

1 ft.-lb. in fluid mechanics = energy required to move 1 lb. of fluid against 1 ft. of head or its equivalent in pressure.

1 horsepower (H.P.) = 550 ft.-lbs./sec = 33,000 ft.-lbs./min. Horsepower hours (H.P.H.) is the practical measure of mechanical energy.

Mechanical machines, electric motors, and boilers are rated in horsepower *output.*

Electrical Units

1 watt (basic practical unit of electrical power) = power combination equivalent to 1 ampere of current at 1 volt potential. Watts = (volts)(amperes) = (amperes)^2(ohmic resistance) = volts/ohmic resistance.

1 kilowatt (kw.) = 1,000 watts

For alternating current devices:

Apparent power = kilovolt-amperes (kva) = (volts)(amps)/1,000
Effective power = kw. = (volts)(amps)(power factor)/1,000

The practical unit of energy is kilowatt-hour (K.W.H.). Electrical devices (except motors) are usually rated in watts, kw., or kva.

Heat

1 British thermal unit (B.T.U.) = energy required to heat 1 lb. of water 1°F, in the liquid state.

Corresponding units of power are B.T.U./sec, B.T.U./min, and B.T.U./hour. B.T.U. is the common practical unit for energy in fuel (per lb., gal., ton, cu. ft., etc.).

Conversion Factors

1 H.P. = .746 k.w. = .707 B.T.U./sec
1 H.P.H. = .746 K.W.H. = 2,544 B.T.U.
1 kw. = 1.341 H.P. = .948 B.T.U./sec
1 K.W.H. = 1.341 H.P.H. = 3,412 B.T.U.
1 B.T.U. = .000393 H.P.H. = .000293 K.W.H.

Efficiency and Energy Loss

The term *efficiency* as applied to energy-producing or -consuming devices is the ratio of energy output to energy input. *Energy loss* is the difference between input and output.

Efficiency = output/input
Input required for a stated output = output/efficiency
Output from a stated input = (efficiency)(input)
Energy loss = input − output = (output)(1/efficiency − 1) = (input)(1 − efficiency)

Income Taxes—Effects on Yield Requirement

Notation

I = investment

i = net required yield (after taxes)

i' = required yield before income taxes

P = net required return (net profit after income taxes)

P' = profit before income taxes

P_s = profit base for state income tax

P_f = profit base for federal income tax

C = portion of P_f exempt from federal surtax ($25,000 in 1960)

r_1 = basic federal tax rate (30% in 1960)

r_2 = federal surtax rate (22% in 1960)

r_3 = state tax rate

T_s = state income tax

T_f = federal income tax

Basic Formulas

$i = P/I$, and $i' = P'/I$

$P = P' - T_s - T_f$

P_s varies with state, as does the rate r_3

$T_s = r_3 P_s$

$P_f = P' - T_s$

When $P_f \leq C$,

$$T_f = r_1 P_f$$

When $P_f > C$,

$$T_f = (r_1 + r_2)P_f - r_2C = .52P_f - 5{,}500 \text{ in } 1960$$

When There Is No State Income Tax

$$P_f = P'$$

335

When $P_f \leq C$,

$$P = iI = P_f - r_1P_f = (1 - r_1)P_f = (1 - r_1)i'I$$

Then,

$$i' = i/(1 - r_1)$$

When $P_f > C$,

$$P = P_f - (r_1 + r_2)P_f + r_2C$$

Substituting iI for P, and $i'I$ for P_f,

$$iI = i'I(1 - r_1 - r_2) + r_2C$$
$$i' = (i - r_2C/I)/(1 - r_1 - r_2)$$

When the State Tax Is Based on P′ (as in New York, 1957):

$$T_s = r_3P', \text{ and } P_f = P' - T_s = (1 - r_3)P'$$

When $P_f \leq C$,

$$P = P' - T_s - T_f$$
$$P = P' - r_3P' - r_1(1 - r_3)P' = (1 - r_1 - r_3 + r_1r_3)P'$$

Substituting iI and $i'I$ for P and P' respectively,

$$i' = i/(1 - r_1 - r_3 + r_1r_3)$$

When $P_f > C$,

$$P = P' - r_3P' - (r_1 + r_2)(P' - r_3P') + r_2C$$

Substituting for P and P' as above,

$$i' = (i + r_2C/I)/(1 - r_1 - r_2 - r_3 + r_1r_3 + r_2r_3)$$

When the State Tax Is Based on P_f (as in Pennsylvania, 1960):

$$T_s = r_3(P' - T_s), \text{ and } T_s + r_3T_s = r_3P'$$

Then,

$$T_s = r_3P'/(1 + r_3),$$

which means that the effective state tax rate on profit P' before tax is $r_3/(1 + r_3)$. This value will be substituted for r_3 in the preceding formulas, thus:

When $P_f \leq C$,

$$i' = i/[1 - r_1 - r_3/(1 + r_3) + r_1r_3/(1 + r_3)]$$

When $P_f > C$,

$$i' = \frac{i - r_2 C/I}{(1 - r_1 - r_2)[1 - r_3/(1 + r_3)]}$$

When the State Tax Is Based on P' — T$_f$ (as in Alabama, 1957):

$$T_s = r_3(P' - T_f) = r_3 P' - r_3 T_f$$

When $P_f \leq C$,

$$T_f = r_1(P' - T_s) = r_1(P' - r_3 P' + r_3 T_f)$$

Then,

$$T_f = r_1(1 - r_3)P'/(1 - r_1 r_3)$$

Substituting this in the above formula for T_s,

$$T_s = r_3(1 - r_1)P'/(1 - r_1 r_3)$$

$$P = P' - T_s - T_f = P' - \frac{r_3(1 - r_1)P'}{(1 - r_1 r_3)} - \frac{r_1(1 - r_3)P'}{(1 - r_1 r_3)}$$

Substituting iI and $i'I$ for P and P' respectively and transposing,

$$i' = i(1 - r_1 r_3)/(1 - r_1 - r_3 + r_1 r_3)$$

When $P_f > C$,

$$T_f = (r_1 + r_2)P_f - r_2 C$$

Since

$$P_f = P' - r_3(P' - T_f),$$

$$T_f = \frac{(r_1 + r_2 - r_1 r_3 - r_2 r_3)P' - r_2 C}{1 - r_1 r_3 - r_2 r_3}$$

Substituting this in the formula for T_s, the result is

$$T_s = \frac{r_3(1 - r_1 - r_2)P' + r_2 r_3 C}{1 - r_1 r_3 - r_2 r_3}$$

$$P = P' - T_s - T_f = \frac{(1 - r_1 - r_2 - r_3 + r_1 r_3 + r_2 r_3)P' + r_2 C - r_2 r_3 C}{1 - r_1 r_3 - r_2 r_3}$$

Substituting iI for P and $i'I$ for P', and transposing,

$$i' = \frac{(1 - r_1 r_3 - r_2 r_3)i - r_2(1 - r_3)C/I}{1 - r_1 - r_2 - r_3 + r_1 r_3 + r_2 r_3}$$

Increment Tax

When the study involves a project within an enterprise that is operating already in the surtax bracket, the required yield (i') before income tax, can be computed by substituting zero for C in the above formulas (those that apply for $P_f > C$). Then the federal tax rate is, in effect, $r_1 + r_2$ (52% in 1960):

Effective Tax Rate at Required Return

It may be of interest to know about the effective income tax rate (r). Because of the federal surtax, the over-all rate depends on the level of profit. When i' has been computed, the corresponding effective income tax rate is as follows:

$$r = (P' - P)/P' = (i'I - iI)/(i'I) = 1 - i/i'$$

An Example

To illustrate the situation where the state tax is based on the federal tax base (P_f), assume a Pennsylvania firm in 1960. The net worth was $2,000,000. Required net yield was 10% (after taxes). Tax rates were as follows: $r_1 = .30$, $r_2 = .22$, $r_3 = .06$, and $C = 25,000$.

$$i' = \frac{.10 - (.22)(25,000)/2,000,000}{(1 - .30 - .22)(1 - .06/1.06)} = .215$$

required return before taxes $= i'P' = .215(2,000,000) = \$430,000$.

Now assume that a $100,000 project was being studied and that the federal tax had already exceeded $5,500 (the surtax level). Then,

$$i' = \frac{.10}{(1 - .30 - .22)(1 - .06/1.06)} = .221$$

Required return on the project $= .221(100,000) = \$22,100$.

In the two cases, the effective income tax rates are 53.5% and 54.7% respectively at the level of required return.

Glossary of Technical Terms

Accounting. The accumulation and analysis of records of financial transactions, including receipts, expenditures, assets, and liabilities.

Accounts payable. In accounting, the amounts currently due creditors of the enterprise. A *current liability*. Does not include long-term financial obligations that are not due for payment during the current accounting period.

Accounts receivable. In accounting, the amounts of current obligations to the enterprise by those indebted to it. A *current asset*. Does not include long-term financial properties such as bonds and mortgages.

Administrative overhead (expense). That part of operating cost attributed to the general office organization and to matters of concern to the organization as a whole as distinguished from primary functions such as production and sales.

Allowances. In operation standardization, the time allowed for normally expected work interruptions and fatigue.

Allowances factor. A factor to be multiplied by *normal time* to arrive at the time standard. (See *Normal time.*)

Amortization. (1) As applied to a capitalized asset, the distribution of the initial cost by periodic charges to operations as in depreciation. Most properly applies to assets with indefinite life. (2) The reduction of a debt by either periodic or irregular payments.

Annual equivalent. In time value of money, a uniform annual amount for a prescribed number of years that is equivalent in value to the present worth of any sequence of financial events.

Annuity. An amount of money payable to a beneficiary at regular intervals for a prescribed period of time out of a fund reserved for that purpose.

Annuity factor. The function of interest rate and time that determines the amount of periodic annuity that may be paid out of a given fund. Same as *Capital recovery factor.* Reciprocal of *Annuity fund factor.*

Annuity fund. A fund that is reserved for payment of annuities. The present worth of funds required to support future annuity payments.

Annuity fund factor. The function of interest rate and time that determines the present worth of funds required to support a specified program of annuity payments. (See Table B–3.)

Apportion. In accounting or budgeting, to assign a cost responsibility to a specific individual, organization unit, product, project, or order. (See *Distribution of cost.*)

Asset. In accounting, any physical or financial property, or other possession of value to which the enterprise has title.

Atomic energy. See *Nuclear energy.*

Automation. An integrated combination of several automatic machines or other automatic devices performing a coordinated sequence of operations.

Average-interest method. A method of computing required return on investment based on the average book value of the asset during its life or during a specified study period. As usually practiced, depreciation is assumed to be straight line in discrete annual increments. A simplified formula is based on continuous straight-line depreciation.

Balance sheet. In accounting, a financial statement that gives a classified listing of assets and liabilities as of a stated date.

Board of directors. In a corporation, a board elected by the stockholders to act for them as the governing body of the organization.

Bond. In financing, a document representing a loan by the holder to a business, institution, or government, said loan being a share in a large borrowing program known as a *bond issue.*

Bonus. Extra compensation in addition to a regular wage, commission, or salary.

Book value. In accounting, the recorded current value of an asset. First cost less accumulated depreciation, amortization, or depletion. Also, *depreciated book value.*

Break-even point. (1) In business operations, the rate of operations, output, or sales at which income is sufficient to equal operating cost, or operating cost plus additional obligations that may be specified. (2) The operating condition, such as output, at which two alternatives are equal in economy.

British thermal unit (B.T.U.). The commonly used industrial unit for measurement of thermal energy. The amount of heat required to raise one pound of liquid water one degree Fahrenheit.

Burden. See *Overhead.*

Callable bonds. Bonds that include a specification that enables the borrower to redeem any portion of the issue prior to the normal date of retirement.

Capital. The financial resources involved in establishing and sustaining an enterprise or project. See *Investment* and *Working capital.*

Capital gain. In accounting, the gain realized from the sale or salvage disposal of an asset previously classified as long term (e.g., capitalized). The excess of actual sale or salvage value over book value. A form of profit.

Capital loss. Negative capital gain.

Capital recovery. In accounting, charging periodically to operations amounts that will ultimately equal the amount of capital expenditure. (See *Amortization, Depletion,* and *Depreciation.*)

Capital recovery factor. In economy study, the function of interest rate and time that determines the sum of periodic depreciation and required return for a specified investment. (See *Exact method.*)

Capital turnover. The ratio: annual amount of sales or output over average capital employed. (See *Inventory turnover.*)

Capitalize. In accounting, classifying a cost as a *long-term investment* rather than as a charge to current operations.

Capitalized cost. The present worth of a uniform series of periodic costs that continue for an indefinitely long time (hypothetically infinite). Not to be confused with a *capitalized* expenditure.

Chattel mortgage. A mortgage on movable property. (See *Mortgage.*)

Commission. A form of compensation for the sale of products or services, usually based on the amount of the transactions.

Common stock. A type of stock that represents share in the primary ownership of a corporation. Usually characterized by voting privilege and rights to profit and equity after all other obligations are met. (See *Stock.*)

Compound amount. The future worth of a sum invested (or loaned) at compound interest.

Compound amount factor. The function of interest rate and time that determines the compound amount from a stated initial sum. The primary factor in time-value-of-money computation. (See Tables B–1 and B–4.)

Compound interest. The type of interest that is periodically added to the amount of investment (or loan) so that subsequent interest is based on the cumulative amount. The economic basis for time value of money.

Compounding, continuous. A compound interest situation in which the compounding period is zero and the number of periods infinitely great. A mathematical concept that is practical for dealing with frequent compounding and small interest rates. (See *Compounding period.*)

Compounding period. Time interval between dates at which interest is paid and added to the amount of an investment or loan. Designates frequency of compounding.

Contingencies, allowance for. The estimated cost of unexpected conditions not otherwise accounted for in a detailed cost estimate.

Control. In management, the function of seeing that policies and plans are carried out. Can be a specialized activity concerned with a particular area of interest (e.g., *production, inventory,* and *cost*).

Controller. Executive responsible for control of operating expenditures and accounting activity.

Coypright. Applying to published material (including art work and musical compositions), a government grant of exclusive right to subject material by a designated owner. Owners of copyrights may grant privilege of use to others or may transfer ownership.

Corporation. A business or institution that is legally constituted as an entity apart from the individuals who participate in its ownership, financing, and management. It exists by charter from a government, is owned by stockholders, and is subject to control by those who possess the majority of voting shares.

Cost accounting. A branch of accounting that relates particularly to the cost of projects, orders, products, and activities of individuals and departments.

Cost index. See *Index.*

Cost of goods sold. In accounting practice, the manufacturing cost of goods sold, a cost that does not include sales and administrative expenses and deferred charges such as depreciation.

Credit. (1) In accounting, an amount entered in the books in favor of an account, individual, or order. Equivalent to a plus factor or item of income. Opposed to *debit.* (2) Permission by a creditor to a debtor to defer a financial obligation. (E.g., a *seller* gives credit to a *buyer,* so that the latter need not pay immediately for goods received or services rendered.)

Creditor. The party to whom financial obligations are owed by the debtor.

Current assets. In accounting, the assets which constantly fluctuate in value or which are not *capitalized* (e.g., cash, inventory, and accounts receivable).

Current liabilities. In accounting, the value of obligations that are due for settlement within the current accounting period. Excludes long-term debt.

Debenture. In corporation finance, a type of bond with no special security other than the rights of creditors in general. (See *Bond.*)

Debit. In accounting, a charge in the books against an account, individual, department, or order. Opposed to *credit.*

Debt, long-term. The amount of a debt that is not due for settlement during the current accounting period. (Excludes amounts for interest and payments on principal due within the period.)

Declining balance depreciation. Also known as *per cent on diminishing value.* A method of computing depreciation in which the annual charge is a fixed percentage of the depreciated book value at the beginning of the year to which the depreciation applies.

Deflation. A general decrease in costs and property values. A trend of increasing purchasing power of money.

Departmentized cost. In accounting, cost broken down or distributed into individual departments for cost finding and administrative purposes.

Depletion. A form of capital recovery applicable to extractive property (e.g., mines). Can be on a unit-of-output basis the same as straight-line depreciation related to original or current appraisal of extent and value of deposit. (Known as cost *depletion.*) Can also be a percentage of income received from extractions. (Known as *percentage* depletion.)

Depreciated book value. See *Book value.*

Depreciation. (1) Decline in value of a property. (2) A form of capital recovery applicable to a property with two or more years' life span, in which an appropriate portion of the asset's value is periodically charged to current operations. In accounting practice, is based on initial cost and life estimate. For economy study, can be based on current appraisal of decline in value for desired time interval (e.g., a year). (See *Amortization* and *Depletion.*)

Diminishing returns, law of. An economic law concerning the comparative decline in advantage from a useful practice as that practice is extended. The incremental gain is greatest at first and becomes less and less, perhaps negative as the practice is increased.

Direct costs. Items of cost that can be exclusively associated with and conveniently charged to a particular product, project, or order.

Direct labor. A direct cost usually applied to production workers, but may include wages and salaries of others whose time can be appropriately charged to the product, project, or order under consideration.

Direct material. The cost of material that goes into a particular product, project, or order including that which is lost in the processing. Excludes materials that can not be conveniently classified as direct.

Distribution of cost. In accounting, the apportionment of costs to individual projects, orders, departments, etc. Particularly applies to costs that may not be direct or charged exclusively to individual departments or divisions, but which should be shared by them.

Dividend. As applied to stock in a corporation, an amount that may be periodically or irregularly distributed to stockholders in proportion to the number of shares held by each, and usually paid out of accumulated earnings. A *stock dividend* is one that is paid in the form of additional shares of stock.

Economic return. The profit derived from a project or business enterprise without consideration of obligations to financial contributors and claims of others based on profit. Profit before interest, profit-sharing bonuses, and profit taxes.

Economics. The social science concerned with the material wealth of a society. A study of conditions relating to money, production, trade, and distribution of wealth.

Economy. As the term is used here, the cost or profit situation regarding a practical enterprise or project, as in *economy study, engineering economy, project economy.*

Efficiency. (1) Of an energy-consuming device or process, the ratio, output/input, expressed as a percentage or a decimal. (2) A ratio which compares actual performance with a standard, as in time-study *performance rating.*

Endowment. A fund established for the support of some project or succession of donations or financial obligations.

Endowment method. As applied to economy study, a comparison of alternatives based on the present worths of the anticipated financial events.

Energy. In physical sciences, a basic quality of matter that measures capacity for doing work.

Engineering economy. A subject devoted to economy studies of engineering projects. (See *Economy.*)

Equity. As applied to ownership of a business or a property, the portion out of the total value or total assets that belongs to a specified participant after prior claims are accounted for (e.g., *net worth* or *shareholders' equity*).

Exact method. A method of computing required return combined with depreciation, based on the assumption that the present worth of these plus that of salvage value during the prescribed study period is equivalent to the first cost.

Expected return. (1) See *Required return.* (2) The profit anticipated from a venture. (The term *expected* must be interpreted according to context or author's usage.)

Expected yield. The ratio expected return/investment, usually expressed as a percentage on an annual basis.

Expense. In accounting, the operating costs attributed to general administration or sales. To some accountants, the term also applies to factory burden or overhead. (See *Overhead.*)

Face value. As applied to a bond, note, or similar financial document, a designated amount on which periodic interest is based and which usually (not always) is the intended redemption value at a stated maturity date.

Facility. In industrial economy, an aggregation of equipment, plant, and organization for the operation of a project or enterprise. (See *Plant.*)

Factory. (1) In general, a manufacturing establishment in which congregated labor is organized for a common enterprise. (2) In the accounting sense, the *manufacturing division* of an enterprise.

Factory cost. In accounting, all cost incurred by or apportioned to the manufacturing division. The sum of direct labor, direct material, and factory overhead.

Factory overhead (burden or expense). In accounting, all *indirect costs* incurred by or apportioned to the manufacturing division.

First cost. The initial cost of a capitalized property, including transportation, installation, preparation for service, and other related initial expenditures.

Fixed assets. In accounting, the physical properties that are capitalized on account of relatively long life and substantial value (e.g., land, buildings, and equipment).

Fixed cost. In economy studies, cost that is fixed with relation to some variable factor such as output or rate of operations. Unless otherwise designated, the annual operating costs that are fixed in amount (e.g., taxes on real estate and annual depreciation).

Franchise. As applied to business operations, a formal grant by a higher authority (e.g., a government) to do business. Usually involves compliance with prescribed regulations, and may require payment of initial or periodic fees.

Fringe benefits. That portion of compensation to employees which is not paid currently in the form of wages, salaries, commissions, or bonuses. Restricted to benefits *paid for by the employer* and excluding contributions by the employees (e.g., employer's contribution to social security, insurance, retirement funds, social activities, and the like).

Future worth. Of an event valued in money, or a sequence of financial events, the equivalent value at a designated future date based on *time value of money.*

Game theory. Mathematical probability applied to situations in which two or more alternatives are available for adoption by two or more competitors.

General expense. Ordinarily synonymous with *administrative expense.* Sometimes includes sales expense.

Goodwill. In accounting and economy study, the dollar value assigned to represent the excess of net worth or purchase price over the tangible net assets—a value presumed to result from business reputation and earning power.

Gross profit. (1) In the usual accounting sense, the difference between *cost of goods sold* (manufacturing cost or purchase price) and income received from sales. (2) In economy study, may be used in the sense of *economic return.*

Head. In fluid mechanics (hydraulics), the elevation of a source of pressure above the point of use. Comparable with voltage in electricity. Loss of head results from fluid friction, turbulence, and velocity of flow.

Horsepower (H.P.). The practical unit of mechanical power. Used in measuring or rating the *rate* at which energy can be delivered by mechanical machinery and electrical motors. (See *Power.*)

Horsepower hours (H.P.H.). The practical unit of mechanical energy. The product of horsepower and time.

Income. (1) In economy studies, the receipts from operations that affect profit or loss. Excludes certain financial transactions such as payments received from debtors, receipts for deposit into funds, and the like. (2) Often refers to profit as in *income* tax regulations and certain accounting practices.

Income tax. Tax imposed by federal, state, or local government based on income. Usually applies to profit after deduction of various costs and prior taxes as specified by law. May apply to gross income (receipts) or to gross profit.

Increment. In economy study, the amount of change (increase or decrease) in some economic factor such as cost, profit, yield, output, or sales.

Index. As applied to economic conditions such as costs, cost of living, prices, productivity, and the like, a yardstick for comparing the current situation with that of some reference date. Usually expressed as a decimal or a percentage. The reference date should be stated so that the significance of such an index can be judged.

Indirect material. Materials or supplies consumed in construction, factory, and other operations, and which can not be reasonably classified as *direct.* (See *Direct material.*)

Inflation. A trend of generally rising costs and decreasing purchasing power of money.

Intangibles. (1) In economy studies, conditions or economy factors that cannot be readily evaluated in *quantitative* terms as in money. (2) In accounting, the assets that can not be reliably evaluated (e.g., *goodwill*).

Inplace value. A value of a physical property—market value plus costs of transportation to site and installation.

Interest. (1) Financial share in a project or enterprise. (2) Periodic compensation for the lending of money. (3) In economy study, synonymous with *required return, expected profit,* or *charge for the use of capital.*

Interest rate. Interest expressed as a percentage of the principal (loan or investment) to which it applies. In economy study, synonymous with *required yield* or *expected yield.*

Interest rate, effective. An interest rate for a stated period (per year unless otherwise specified) that is the equivalent of a smaller rate of interest that is more frequently compounded.

Interest rate, nominal. The customary type of interest rate designation on an annual basis without consideration of compounding periods. The usual basis for computing periodic interest payments.

Inventory. In industrial operations the aggregation of supplies, raw materials, parts, work in process, and finished goods. May apply to single items, to groups, and to individual locations. Not to be confused with *fixed assets,* such as buildings and equipment. Inventories are *current assets.*

Inventory control. The control of the quantity or value of inventory between desired maximum and minimum limits.

Inventory turnover. A ratio: (cost of goods sold or consumed)/(cost of average inventory), usually on an annual basis. Used by management to appraise efficiency of inventory control and utilization of working capital.

Investment. (1) As applied to an enterprise as a whole, the cost (or present value) of all the properties and funds necessary to establish and maintain the enterprise as a going concern. The *capital* tied up in the enterprise or project. (2) Any expenditure which has substantial and enduring value (at least two years' anticipated life), and which is therefore capitalized.

Irreducibles. A term that may be used for the class of intangible conditions or economy factors that can only be *qualitatively* appraised (e.g., ethical considerations).

Job lot. In industry, a separate discontinuous lot or order for a product or service.

Kilovolt-amperes (kva). Electrical unit of capacity for power used for alternating current devices.

Kilowatt (kw.). The practical industrial unit of electrical power consumed or delivered.

Kilowatt hours (K.W.H.). The practical industrial unit of electrical energy. The product of kilowatts and time.

Labor. As applied to employees in an enterprise, usually refers to the rank-and-file wage earners. Can also apply to salaried employees below the ranks of management and professions.

Labor turnover. A ratio that may apply strictly to labor in an organization, but may apply to all employees: (the number of replacements)/ (the average number employed), usually expressed as a percentage and for a year. A measure of stability of the working force.

Liability. (1) In accounting, the dollar value of an obligation to a creditor of the enterprise. (2) In the legal sense, a potential or real obligation to some party as a result of a business transaction, service, injury sustained, property damage, or the like.

Limited partnership. See *Partnership.*

Linear programming. A complex mathematical procedure for developing an operating program involving linearly variable factors, and for obtaining maximum profit (or minimum loss).

Liquidation. The sale of assets, or conversion of assets into cash. Usually applies to an entire enterprise or to a group of properties.

Load factor. A ratio that applies to physical plant or equipment: average load/maximum demand, usually expressed as a percentage. Equivalent to per cent of capacity operation if facilities just accommodate the maximum demand.

Log-log slide rule. A type of slide rule with scales for computation of a wide range of powers and roots, and based on *natural logarithms.*

Long-term debt. See *Debt, long term.*

Lot interval. Time interval between starting dates of successive purchase or production lots that are intermittently scheduled.

Lot size. The quantity of an item purchased or produced in one *lot* at regular or irregular intervals. Usually distinguished from *batches,* which are quantities produced at successive, short intervals as in bakeries.

Lumen. The practical unit of energy rate in the form of light. Can be used for comparing economy of illuminating devices.

Maintenance. As applied to physical plant or equipment, the function of keeping the property in effective operating or stand-by condition.

Manufacturing cost. In economy study, synonymous with *factory cost.* In accounting, may involve year-end adjustments for inventory status.

MAPI Method. A procedure for replacement analysis sponsored by the Machinery and Allied Products Institute.

Market research. The area of research concerned with product acceptance, desires and demands of potential customers, sales and price potentials, competition, and other aspects of market conditions.

Matheson Formula. A title for the formula used for *declining balance* depreciation.

Methods-Time-Measurement (MTM). A procedure for synthetic motion and time study developed by Maynard, Stegemerten, and Schwab.

Mortgage. A form of security for a loan in which the lender may claim settlement (if borrower fails to meet interest and amortization payments as specified) out of proceeds from forced sale or by physical recovery of the borrower's *mortgaged* property. Ordinary mortgage applies to fixed property such as land and buildings. *Chattel mortgage* applies to movable property such as furnishings and equipment. *First mortgage* has prior right to proceeds from disposal of mortgaged property (*foreclosure*). *Second mortgage* has right to settlement after claim of first mortgage is satisfied.

Net. As applied to income, cost, or profit, the amount remaining after all necessary deductions or obligations are accounted for.

Net worth. The net dollar value of the owners' interest in a business. Owners' or shareholders' equity.

Nominal interest rate. See *Interest rate, nominal.*

Normal time. In operation standardization, the time required for an operation by equipment or by an average, experienced operator working at normal pace under standard conditions and according to standard procedure, but without allowance for work interruptions and fatigue. Termed *standard time* by some; but, for economy study and wage payments, standard should include *allowances.*

Nuclear (atomic) energy. The energy within the atom, energy that may be released by thermonuclear reaction or by radiation.

Obsolescence. The condition of being out of date. A loss of value occasioned by new developments which place the older property at a competitive disadvantage. A factor in depreciation.

Operating cost. As used in this book, the current cost of operating an enterprise or a part of it, including direct labor, direct material, and overhead. Includes depreciation (unless otherwise specified); but excludes financing charges and other deductions from economic return, and capital expenditures.

Operations research. In general, scientific research method applied to operating problems in business and other enterprises. In analyses of problems in strategy and economy, usually associated with advanced mathematical procedures and computing devices.

Overhead. Operating costs which can not be conveniently identified as direct. Often termed *burden* or *expense.* Subclassification identified by appropriate adjective (e.g., *factory* overhead).

Overhead rate. The ratio of overhead charge to some base (e.g., direct labor cost) which measures the amount of work performed. Examples: 150% based on direct labor cost; $2 per direct labor hour, 10¢ per pound of direct material; and so on.

Partnership. The ownership of a business or property by two or more individuals who are personally responsible for operations and liabilities. In *limited partnership,* some (not all) partners may participate without personal liability for debts and operations of the enterprise.

Par value. The initial specified value or standard value of a financial property such as a bond or a share of stock. Usage similar to *face value*.

Payoff period. Regarding an investment, the number of years (or months) required for the related profit or savings in operating cost to equal the amount of said investment.

Perpetual endowment. An endowment with hypothetically infinite life. (See *Capitalized cost* and *Endowment*.)

Physical plant. Physical facilities of an establishment including grounds, buildings, equipment, tools, and accessories.

Plant. A term usually applied to a physically integrated industrial establishment, consisting of an aggregation of equipment, a single building, or a group of buildings within adjacent areas, and under centralized management. Synonymous with *works* (e.g., Fairless Works of United States Steel).

Policy. A code or guide for action that directs, in a general way, the preferred method of handling a situation or responsibility.

Power. In physical sciences, the *rate* capacity for doing work. (E.g, *horsepower* and *kilowatts*.) Often used inaccurately for *energy*, which is not a rate.

Power factor. In alternating current systems, the ratio: actual power (e.g., kilowatts) over apparent or potential power (e.g., kilovolt-amperes), expressed as a percentage or a decimal.

Preferred stock. A type of stock which is entitled to dividends prior to payments on common stock and at a specified percentage based on a par value. Usually without vote in affairs of corporation. In *cumulative* preferred, each year of unpaid dividends adds to succeeding years' obligations. In *participating* preferred, stockholder has right to additional dividends after amount paid on common stock has reached a stated minimum.

Present worth. Of a future financial event or sequence of events, the equivalent value at the present, based on *time value of money*.

Price index. See *Index*.

Prime cost. The sum of direct costs (direct labor and direct material). Usually considered the immediate "out-of-pocket" expenditures attributed to a project, product, or order.

Production control. The function of planning and controlling production operations. Closely related to controls of inventory, cost, and quality.

Production cost. Often used to designate the cost of a manufactured product up to the point of sales. *Factory cost* plus *administrative expense*.

Profit and loss statement. In accounting, a tabulation of income items, operating costs, and other costs showing the profit or loss for a stated time period.

Profit sharing. A method of compensation to employees (a type of bonus payments) based on the profit realized from the enterprise.

Profit tax. See *Income tax.*

Proprietorship. (More exactly, *single* or *sole* proprietorship). The ownership of a business or a property by a single individual who is personally responsible for operations and liabilities.

Public projects. Projects that are owned by the public or a public agency.

Public utilities. Services to the general public in transportation, power supply, water supply, and communications. May be owned and operated by governments or private agencies.

Queueing theory. In operations research or economy studies, a mathematical technique for determining the optimum compromise between waiting time and economical utilization of personnel and facilities.

Quick assets. Current assets that can be readily converted into cash at close to book value.

Required return. The *minimum* return or profit necessary to justify an investment. Often termed *interest, expected* return or profit, or *charge for the use of capital.*

Required yield. The ratio of required return over amount of investment, usually expressed as a percentage on an annual basis.

Retirement of debt. The termination of a debt obligation by appropriate settlement with lender—understood to be in full amount unless partial settlement is specified.

Royalty. A type of periodic compensation to the owner of certain kinds of properties (e.g., patents, copyrights, mineral deposits) for the right to use said property. Includes periodic payments to author or composer by publisher. Royalties are usually on a unit basis—per unit of output, per copy sold, etc.

Salary. Compensation paid to employees in regular periodic amounts based on elapsed time (e.g., weekly or monthly), not on short periods or on output as are wages.

Sales expense (overhead). That portion of operating cost that is appropriately charged to selling and related activity. In accounting summaries, usually understood to include advertising, warehousing, and other items related to distribution of product.

Sales tax. A state or local tax to be paid by the buyer on purchases within the jurisdiction of the government. Uusually a fixed percentage of the price charged for specified classes of goods or services purchased.

Salvage value. In economy study, the cost recovered or which could be recovered from a used property when removed, sold, or scrapped. A factor in appraisal of property value and in computing depreciation.

Secular trend. A business trend which typifies the course of a new type of product or service from its inception to the ultimate saturation or decline of the market. Usually a gradual beginning accelerating to rapid rise, followed by a leveling-off, and possibly an ultimate decline.

Share. See *Stock*.

Shareholder. See *Stockholder*.

Simple interest. Interest that is not compounded—is not added to the income-producing investment or loan. (See *Compound interest*.)

Sinking fund. A fund accumulated by periodic deposits and reserved exclusively for a specific purpose, such as retirement of a debt or replacement of a property.

Sinking fund deposit factor. The function of interest rate and time that determines the periodic deposit required to accumulate a specified future amount. Reciprocal of *sinking fund factor*.

Sinking fund depreciation. A method of computing depreciation in which the periodic amount is presumed to be deposited in a *sinking fund* that earns interest at a specified rate. Sinking fund may be real but is usually hypothetical.

Sinking fund factor. The function of interest rate and time that determines the cumulative amount of a sinking fund resulting from specified periodic deposits. Future worth per unit of uniform periodic amounts. (See Table B-2).

Standard cost. A periodically established standard of cost for an item or an operation, used in accounting for cost determination and for appraisal of operating efficiency.

Standard time. In operation standardization, the performance that the average experienced worker or machine is expected to maintain working at a normal pace under standard conditions and according to a standard procedure. Also known as *allowed time*. A basis for wage payment, standard cost, and estimating new work.

Statistics, science of. The mathematical science for analyses of statistical information and interpretation or prediction of results, based on laws of probability.

Stock. (1) Stored finished goods ready for sale. Often loosely applied to any stored materials more appropriately termed *stores* or *supplies*. (2) In corporation financing, the form in which the owners' interests are represented. Distributed in units known as *shares*. Principal kinds of stock are known as *common* and *preferred*. (See *Common stock* and *Preferred stock*.)

Stores. In industrial operations, that class of stored goods which is to be used in making products or otherwise consumed in the operations of the enterprise.

Straight-line depreciation. Method of depreciation whereby the amount to be recovered (written off) is spread uniformly over the estimated life of the asset in terms of time periods or units of output. May be designated *per cent of initial value.*

Study period. In economy study, the length of time that is presumed to be covered in the schedule of events and appraisal of results. Often the anticipated life of the project under consideration, but a shorter time may be more appropriate for decision making.

Sum-of-digits method. Also known as *sum-of-the-years-digits* method. A method of computing depreciation in which the amount for any year is based on the ratio: (years of remaining life)$/(1 + 2 + 3 \cdots + n)$, n being the total anticipated life. Effect similar to *declining balance.*

Supplies. Also known as *indirect materials.* Materials that are accessory to industrial operations but that are not incorporated in the finished product (e.g., paper for correspondence and cleaning materials).

Supply and demand, law of. An economic law expressing the natural relationship between availability of a commodity, price, and demand. Increased demand or shortage of supply tends to increase price. Decreased demand or oversupply tends to reduce price.

Surplus. In corporation accounting, that portion of stockholders' equity in excess of the par or nominal value of the issued stock. (See *Equity.*)

Surtax. That portion of a tax on income or profit which is in addition to the basic tax. In federal corporation income tax, applies to the increment of taxable profit exceeding a specified amount.

Synthetic time study. Time study in which machines or operators are not actually observed at work, but which is derived from various other sources of time data (e.g., Methods-Time-Measurement).

Tangibles. Things that can be *quantitatively* measured or valued, such as items of cost and physical assets.

Time value of money. The cumulative effect of elapsed time on the money value of an event, based on the earning power of equivalent invested funds. (See *Future worth* and *Present worth.*)

Treasurer. Officer of company or institution responsible for external financial relations—financing, banking, disbursements. Responsibilities may include records of and payments to holders of stocks and bonds issued by the organization.

Use tax. A state or local tax imposed on items purchased outside the region controlled by the government but used by the purchaser within said region. Often parallels a *sales* tax to discourage avoidance of that tax. (See *Sales tax.*)

Utilities. See *Public utilities.*

Variable cost. In economy study, a cost that varies as a function of

some independent variable such as rate of operations, output, amount
of sales, schedule, or detail of specifications. Usually a class of operating costs, and on a time basis.

Wages. Compensation for labor based on hours or days worked, or
quantity of output, or both.

Watt. The practical unit of power for smaller electrical devices. (See
Kilowatt.)

Watt hour. The practical unit of energy for smaller electrical devices,
usually converted to *kilowatt hours* in cost estimates.

Wear and tear. The accumulation of wear resulting from use of a
physical property, part of which may be corrected by maintenance and
part of which is a factor in estimation of depreciation.

Working capital. That portion of investment represented by *current*
assets (assets that are not capitalized) less the *current* liabilities. The
capital necessary to *sustain* operations.

Yield. Customary usage in engineering economy: the ratio of return or
profit over the associated investment, expressed as a percentage or
decimal usually on an annual basis. In the securities market, often
refers to dividend rate based on market price of stock.

Selected Bibliography

ACCOUNTING AND DEPRECIATION

ANTHONY, R. N. *Management Accounting.* Rev. ed. Homewood, Ill.: Richard D. Irwin, Inc., 1960.

GRANT, E. L. *Basic Accounting and Cost Accounting.* New York: McGraw-Hill Book Co., Inc., 1956.

GRANT, E. L., and NORTON, P. T., Jr. *Depreciation.* Rev. ed. New York: Ronald Press Co., 1955.

HENRICI, S. B. *Standard Costs for Manufacturing.* 2d ed. New York: McGraw-Hill Book Co., Inc., 1953.

J. K. LASSER TAX INSTITUTE (ed). *Standard Handbook for Accountants.* New York: McGraw-Hill Book Co., Inc., 1956.

NEUNER, J. J. W. *Cost Accounting.* 5th ed. Homewood, Ill.: Richard D. Irwin, Inc., 1957.

TERBORGH, GEORGE. *Realistic Depreciation Policy.* Washington, D.C.: Machinery and Allied Products Institute, 1954.

* U.S. Treasury Department, Internal Revenue Service. *Depreciation Guidelines and Rules.* Publication No. 456. September, 1962.

ECONOMIC STATISTICS, GENERAL

* U.S. Department of Commerce.
Census of Manufactures. Biennial.
Statistical Abstract of the United States. Annual.
Survey of Current Business. Monthly.

* U.S. Department of Labor.
Monthly Labor Review. Monthly.
Occupational Wage Survey bulletins. Periodic by industry.
Wage Structure bulletins. Periodic by region.

---

* U.S. Government publications are printed and distributed by the U.S. Government Printing Office, Washington 25, D.C.

356

Project Economy

* U.S. Treasury Department, Internal Revenue Service. *Statistics of Income, Corporation Income Tax Returns.* Annual.

Wall Street Journal. New York. Weekly.

ECONOMY ANALYSIS, GENERAL

Engineering Economy

BULLINGER, C. E. *Engineering Economy.* 3d ed. New York: McGraw-Hill Book Co., Inc., 1959.

DEAN, JOEL. *Managerial Economics.* Englewood Cliffs, N.J.: Prentice-Hall, Inc., 1951.

DE GARMO, E. P. *Engineering Economy.* 3d ed. New York: The Macmillan Co., 1960.

GRANT, E. L., and IRESON, W. G. *Principles of Engineering Economy.* 4th ed. New York: Ronald Press Co., 1960.

KRUTILLA, J. V., and ECKSTEIN, O. *Multiple Purpose Development Studies in Applied Economic Analysis.* Baltimore: The Johns Hopkins Press, 1958.

MORRIS, W. T. *Engineering Economy.* Homewood, Ill.: Richard D. Irwin, Inc., 1960.

SCHWEYER, H. E. *Process Engineering Economics.* New York: McGraw-Hill Book Co., Inc., 1955.

TERBORGH, GEORGE. *Business Investment Policy.* Washington, D.C.: Machinery and Allied Products Institute, 1958.

TERBORGH, GEORGE. *Dynamic Equipment Policy.* Washington, D.C.: Machinery and Allied Products Institute, 1949.

THUESEN, H. G. *Engineering Economy.* 2d ed. Englewood Cliffs, N.J.: Prentice-Hall, Inc., 1957.

INVENTORY AND PRODUCTION CONTROLS

BETHEL, L. L.; TANN, W. L.; ATWATER, F. S.; and RUNG, E. E. *Production Control.* 2d ed. New York: McGraw-Hill Book Co., Inc., 1948.

BOWMAN, E. H., and FETTER, R. B. *Analysis for Production Management.* Homewood, Ill.: Richard D. Irwin, Inc., 1957.

BROWN, R. *Statistical Forecasting for Inventory Control.* New York: McGraw-Hill Book Co., Inc., 1959.

KOEPKE, C. A. *Plant Production Control.* New York: John Wiley & Sons, Inc., 1949.

MacNIECE, E. H. *Production Forecasting and Control.* New York: John Wiley & Sons, Inc., 1951.

MAGEE, J. F. *Production Planning and Inventory Control.* New York: McGraw-Hill Book Co., Inc., 1958.

MELNITSKY, B. *Management of Industrial Inventory.* New York: Conover-Mast Publications, 1951.

NATIONAL INDUSTRIAL CONFERENCE BOARD. *Inventory Management in Industry.* Studies in Business Policy No. 88. New York, 1958.

WHITIN, T. M. *The Theory of Inventory Management.* 2d ed. Princeton, N.J.: Princeton University Press, 1957.

INDUSTRIAL DIVISIONS—ECONOMY DATA

ARIES, R. S., and NEWTON, R. D. *Chemical Engineering Cost Estimation.* New York: McGraw-Hill Book Co., Inc., 1955.

BAUMEISTER, T. (ed.). *Marks' Mechanical Engineers' Handbook.* 6th ed. New York: McGraw-Hill Book Co., Inc., 1958.

BEEMAN, DONALD (ed.). *Industrial Power Systems Handbook.* 1st ed. New York: McGraw-Hill Book Co., Inc., 1955.

CARSON, G. B. (ed.). *Production Handbook.* New York: Ronald Press Co., 1958.

COOMBS, W. E. *Construction Accounting and Financial Management.* New York: F. W. Dodge Corporation, 1959.

DALLAVIA, LOUIS. *Estimating General Construction Costs.* 2d ed. New York: F. W. Dodge Corporation, 1957.

ENGINEERING NEWS-RECORD. *Construction Costs.* New York: McGraw-Hill Publishing Co. (Annual).

GAFFERT, G. A. *Steam Power Stations.* 4th ed. New York: McGraw-Hill Book Co., Inc., 1952.

HAPPEL, JOHN. *Chemical Process Economics.* New York: John Wiley & Sons, Inc., 1958.

HEWES, L. I., and OGLESBY, C. H. *Highway Engineering.* New York: John Wiley & Sons, Inc., 1954.

HUR, J. J. *Chemical Process Economics in Practice.* New York: Reinhold Publishing Corp., 1956.

IRESON, W. G., and GRANT, E. L. (eds.). *Handbook of Industrial Engineering and Management.* Englewood Cliffs, N.J.: Prentice-Hall, Inc., 1955.

KELLOGG, F. H. *Construction Methods and Machinery.* Englewood Cliffs, N.J.: Prentice-Hall, Inc., 1954.

KNOWLTON, A. E. *Standard Handbook for Electrical Engineers.* 9th ed. New York: McGraw-Hill Book Co., Inc., 1957.

LOVELL, A. H. *Generating Stations.* 4th ed. New York: McGraw-Hill Book Co., Inc., 1951.

MACINTIRE, H. J., and HUTCHISON, F. W. *Refrigeration Engineering.* 2d ed. New York: John Wiley & Sons, Inc., 1950.

MAYNARD, H. B. (ed.). *Industrial Engineering Handbook.* New York: McGraw-Hill Book Co., Inc., 1956.

OSBURN, J. O., and KAMMERMEYER, K. *Money and the Chemical Engineer.* Englewood Cliffs, N.J.: Prentice-Hall, Inc., 1958.

PETERS, M. S. *Plant Design and Economics for Chemical Engineers.* New York: McGraw-Hill Book Co., Inc., 1958.

PEURIFOY, R. L. *Estimating Construction Costs.* New York: McGraw-Hill Book Co., Inc., 1958.

STALEY, W. W. *Mine Plant Design.* 2d ed. New York: McGraw-Hill Book Co., Inc., 1949.

STEELE, E. W. *Water Supply and Sewerage.* 3d ed. New York: McGraw-Hill Book Co., Inc., 1953.

UREN, L. C. *Petroleum Production Engineering.* 4th ed. New York: McGraw-Hill Book Co., Inc., 1956.

URQUHART, L. C. (ed.). *Civil Engineering Handbook.* 4th ed. New York: McGraw-Hill Book Co., Inc., 1959.

WOODRUFF, E. B., and LAMMERS, H. B. *Steam Plant Operation.* 2d ed. New York: McGraw-Hill Book Co., Inc., 1950.

MARKET RESEARCH

HEIDINGSFIELD, M. S. *Market and Marketing Analysis.* New York: Henry Holt & Co., Inc., 1947.

SMITH, C. W. *Targeting Sales Effort.* New York: Columbia University Press, 1958.

OPERATIONS RESEARCH

BLACKWELL, D., and GINSHICK, M. A. *Theory of Games and Statistical Decision.* New York: John Wiley & Sons, Inc., 1954.

BROSS, IRWIN D. J. *Design for Decision.* New York: The Macmillan Co., 1953.

CHARNES, A.; COOPER, W. W.; and HENDERSON, A. *An Introduction to Linear Programming.* New York: John Wiley & Sons, Inc., 1953.

CHORAFAS, D. *Operations Research for Industrial Management.* New York: Reinhold Publishing Corp., 1958.

CHURCHMAN, C. W.; ACKOFF, R. L.; and ARNOFF, E. L. *Introduction to Operations Research.* New York: John Wiley & Sons, Inc., 1957.

GITZENDANNER, F. A. "Risk Analysis in Engineering Economy." *Journal of Engineering Education,* Vol. 46, No. 2 (October, 1955).

KURNOW, E.; GLASSER, G. J.; and OTTMAN, F. R. *Statistics for Business Decisions.* Homewood, Ill.: Richard D. Irwin, Inc., 1959.

McCLOSKEY, J. F., and FREFETHEN, F. N. *Operations Research for Management*. New York: McGraw-Hill Book Co., Inc., 1956.

MILLER, D. W., and STARR, M. K. *Executive Decisions and Operations Research*. Englewood Cliffs, N.J.: Prentice-Hall, Inc., 1960.

OPERATIONS RESEARCH GROUP, CASE INSTITUTE OF TECHNOLOGY. *Comprehensive Bibliography on Operations Research through 1956, with Supplement for 1957*. New York: John Wiley & Sons, Inc., 1958.

SCHLAIFER, ROBERT. *Probability and Statistics for Business Decisions*. New York: McGraw-Hill Book Co., Inc., 1959.

VAN NEUMANN, JOHN, and MORGENSTERN, OSKAR. *Theory of Games and Economic Behavior*. 3d ed. Princeton, N.J.: Princeton University Press, 1953.

OWNERSHIP AND FINANCE

DAUTEN, C. A. *Business Finance*. 2d ed. Englewood Cliffs, N.J.: Prentice-Hall, Inc., 1956.

DEWING, A. S. *Financial Policy of Corporations*. 5th ed. New York: Ronald Press Co., 1953.

GUTHMANN, H. G. *Corporate Financial Policy*. 3d ed. Englewood Cliffs, N.J.: Prentice-Hall, Inc., 1955.

HOWARD, B. B., and UPTON, M. *Introduction to Business Finance*. New York: McGraw-Hill Book Co., Inc., 1953.

JOHNSON, R. W. *Financial Management*. Boston: Allyn and Bacon, Inc., 1959.

SIMPSON, T. M.; PIRENIAN, Z. M.; and CRENSHAW, B. H. *Mathematics of Finance*. 3d ed. Englewood Cliffs, N.J.: Prentice-Hall, Inc., 1951.

PLANT LOCATION, LAYOUT, AND MAINTENANCE

APPLE, J. M. *Plant Layout and Materials Handling*. New York: Ronald Press Co., 1950.

BOLZ, H. A., and HAGEMANN, G. E. (eds.). *Materials Handling Handbook*. New York: Ronald Press Co., 1958.

IMMER, J. R. *Layout Planning Techniques*. New York: McGraw-Hill Book Co., Inc., 1950.

IRESON, W. G. *Factory Planning and Plant Layout*. Englewood Cliffs, N.J.: Prentice-Hall, Inc., 1952.

MALLICK, R. W., and GAUDREAU, A. T. *Plant Layout, Planning and Practice*. New York: John Wiley & Sons, Inc., 1951.

MORROW, L. C. (ed.). *Maintenance Engineering Handbook*. New York: McGraw-Hill Book Co., Inc., 1957.

ROSCOE, E. S., and THUERING, G. L. "Evaluation of Factory Locations," *Textile Industry in Pennsylvania, Engineering Research Bulletin,* No. B-74. University Park, Pa.: Pennsylvania State University, 1958, pp. 107–30, 195–204.

STANIAR, WILLIAM (ed.). *Plant Engineering Handbook.* 2d ed. New York: McGraw-Hill Book Co., Inc., 1959.

STOCKER, H. E. *Materials Handling.* 2d ed. Englewood Cliffs, N.J.: Prentice-Hall, Inc., 1951.

TAXES*

BARDES, P.; MAHON, J. J., Jr.; McCULLOUGH, J.; and RICHARDSON, M. E. (eds.). *Montgomery's Federal Taxes.* New York: Ronald Press Co. (Frequently revised.)

U.S. Master Tax Guide. Chicago: Commerce Clearing House, Inc. (Annual.)

VALUATION

MARSTON, A.; WINFREY, R.; and HEMPSTEAD, J. C. *Engineering Valuation and Depreciation.* New York: McGraw-Hill Book Co., Inc., 1953.

SCHMUTZ, G. L. *Condemnation Appraisal Handbook.* Englewood Cliffs, N.J.: Prentice-Hall, Inc., 1949.

---

* For taxes, state and local, refer to current publications of state and local governments and chambers of commerce.

Index

361

Index

Interest; *see also* Required return, Required yield, *and* Time value of money
compound, 11
concept of, 10
on debt, 91, 196–97, 279–90
effective rate, 15
nominal rate, 12, 284
simple, 10–11, 284

Inventory
in lot-size economy, 222–30
turnover, 33–34
valuation, 53–54

Investment
in aged property, 31–32; *see also* Valuation
characteristics of, 29–30
based on first cost, 30–31
intangible assets, 35–36
working capital, 32–35, 55

Irreducibles; *see* Intangibles

L

Labor cost
direct, 72–73
estimating, 150–52

Liabilities, in balance sheet, 54–55

Liability of owners, 272–74

Life, factor in depreciation, 41

Limited liability
in corporation ownership, 274
in partnership, 273

Limited partnership, 273

Linear programming
definition, 5, 234–35
example of, 235–37

Long-term debt; *see* Debt

Lot interval; *see* Lot-size economy

Lot-size economy, 221–30

M

Maintenance
economy of, 156
not to be included in depreciation, 40

Management, role of, 2

Manufacturing cost; *see* Factory cost

MAPI method of replacement analysis, 254–55

Market research, 4

Market value, 59–60

Matheson formula; *see* Declining balance depreciation

Maximum profit, 214–39

Minimum cost, 214–39

N

Net profit and yield, 95–96, 102, 107–8

Net worth, 55

Nominal interest rate, 12, 284

O

Objectives of economy study, 1–3, 143–45

Operating cost, 71–79
minimum, 218–30, 237–39
periodic costs and unit costs, 78–79
versus rate of operations, 121–35, 219–20
versus variable investment, 220–30

Operations research, relation to engineering economy, 5; *see also* Games, theory of, Linear programming, *and* Queueing theory

Organizing expense, amortization of, 47

Overhead, 73–78
budgets, 76–77
departmental rates, 77–78
distribution of, 74–78
estimates of, 153–54

Ownership
equity and earnings of, 279–80, 286–90
forms of, 270–79

P

Partnership, 272–73

Patent valuation, 63

Payoff period, 115, 248–49

Perpetual endowment, 20; *see also* Capitalized cost

Precision of estimates, 154–56

Preferred stock, 278

Present worth, 18–20
for comparing alternatives, 194–209
for replacement analysis, 255–57
of a uniform series, 18–20

Price index; *see* Index

Prices
of purchased items, 148–49
selling prices, 85–88, 230–32

Prime cost, 72; *see also* Direct costs

Profit
determination of, 88–97
distribution of, 288–90
intangibles, adjusted for, 306–7
maximum, 214–39
variable, 127–28, 214–39

Profit and loss statement, 95–97

Profit sharing, 91
in present worth analysis, 198–99

Profit tax; *see* Income tax

Project realization, 1–2